W9-CNY-016

PRENTICE-HALL INTERNATIONAL SERIES IN MANAGEMENT

PRENTICE-HALL, INC.
PRENTICE-HALL INTERNATIONAL, INC., UNITED KINGDOM AND EIRE
PRENTICE-HALL OF CANADA, LTD., CANADA
J. H. DE BUSSY, LTD., HOLLAND AND FLEMISH-SPEAKING BELGIUM
DUNOD PRESS, FRANCE
MARUZEN COMPANY, LTD., FAR EAST
C. BERTELSMANN VERLAG, WEST GERMANY AND AUSTRIA
HERRERO HERMANOS, SUCS., SPAIN AND LATIN AMERICA

PRENTICE-HALL INTERNATIONAL, INC., *LONDON*
PRENTICE-HALL OF AUSTRALIA, PTY., LTD., *SYDNEY*
PRENTICE-HALL OF CANADA, LTD., *TORONTO*
PRENTICE-HALL FRANCE, S.A.R.L., *PARIS*
PRENTICE-HALL OF JAPAN, INC., *TOKYO*
PRENTICE-HALL DE MEXICO, S.A., *MEXICO CITY*

Industrial Scheduling

Industrial Scheduling

edited by **John F. Muth** and **Gerald L. Thompson**
with the collaboration of **Peter R. Winters**

GRADUATE SCHOOL OF INDUSTRIAL ADMINISTRATION, CARNEGIE INSTITUTE OF TECHNOLOGY

Prentice-Hall, Inc., Englewood Cliffs, New Jersey

PRINTED IN THE UNITED STATES OF AMERICA

Preface

In recent years there has been a great increase in interest in industrial scheduling problems from the points of view of both practice and research. Of course, such problems have existed since the creation of the first factory consisting of more than one worker or machine. But the solution of these problems by hand is impossible. Hence the recent interest in their solution has centered on attempts to make use of electronic computers for solving them.

On May 10–12, 1961, a conference on "Factory Scheduling" was held at the Graduate School of Industrial Administration at Carnegie Institute of Technology. It was sponsored by the Graduate School of Industrial Administration, the Office of Naval Research, and the Bureau of Ships. About 50 participants from various industrial and academic centers heard the 14 papers presented.

Most of the papers presented at that conference are included in the present volume. We have included a number of additional papers on the topic that later came to our attention. Therefore, we feel that this volume contains papers typical of most of the current approaches to the problem, so that it serves as an introduction to the topic as well as a report on its current status. The bibliography at the end of the book will also serve as a guide to the literature for those interested in pursuing the subject further.

The editors would like to express their warmest thanks to the authors of the chapters in this volume for permitting us to include their work.

We would also like to thank the organizations listed above for supporting the work on the conference and the subsequent work on the preparation of this volume. We owe a great debt of gratitude to Professor Peter R. Winters who helped in the planning of the conference and in the preliminary planning for this book. Thanks are also due to B. Contini, G. K. Groff, F. K. Levy, and J. D. Wiest for their aid in refereeing the papers. We also would like to thank Mrs. Dorothy Goodheart for helping with the conference plans, and Miss Barbara Roper for assistance in the preparation of the manuscript.

                                                                                    J. F. MUTH
                                                                                    G. L. THOMPSON

Introduction

Control over the detailed operations of large industrial firms has recently become a subject for basic research. An important aspect of industrial control is deciding upon the precise use of manufacturing facilities at each instant of time. Several factors have to be taken into account in making these decisions such as, the availability of resources, costs of implementing the decisions, due dates, and so forth. It is this kind of decision making that we call "scheduling."

Industrial scheduling problems differ greatly from one firm to another. Sometimes the manufacturing process consists of a series of operations at one work station on only one physical part; sometimes operations require very different labor skills and equipment on each of many thousands of sub-assemblies. Sometimes inventories of finished goods must be maintained to satisfy customer demands; sometimes such inventories are impossible to keep under all conceivable circumstances. Unique features of the firm's organization, of the market, of plant capabilities are always present.

Because of the diversity and complexity of industrial scheduling problems, it is impractical to account for every factor in any single analysis. A few special simplifications have so far been studied. The papers in the present book examine mixtures of the following three:

Job-Shop Scheduling Problem. A plant is said to consist of several work centers, all with different capabilities. Sometimes duplication of facilities is allowed. There is a list of products to be completed. The routing for each product is a simple order: the first operation must be completed before the second may be started, and so on down the list. A specific machine is designated to carry out each of these operations, with dates for the completion of each of the products possibly having been assigned. How shall the products be scheduled to machines in such a way that (a) due dates are met whenever possible, or (b) the total time to complete all jobs is minimized, or (c) some other criterion function is optimized?

Finished-Goods Inventory Control. Individual products are assumed to be stored until they are sold to customers. Demand for the product, costs of making the product, and prices received for the product may or may not be known. Under what conditions should a new lot be manufactured, and how large should that lot be? Here again, the question is to be answered so that some criterion function is optimized.

Project Scheduling. A single project is to be undertaken, consisting of a large number of individual jobs. Every job has a set of immediate predecessors which must be completed before it can be started. Thus, some pairs of jobs can be worked on simultaneously, while other pairs of jobs must be done serially. How can we monitor the progress of the project so that the due date of the project shall be met, if it is possible to do so?

Part V of the present book is devoted to the project scheduling problem. Here the principal tool is the "critical path analysis" of the project graph. Most of the remaining papers in the book discuss the job-shop scheduling problem, although the papers in Part II emphasize certain aspects of the finished goods inventory control problem.

Because of the emphasis in this book on the job-shop scheduling problem, it is appropriate to discuss it in more detail.

THE JOB-SHOP SCHEDULING PROBLEM

Among the current methods being used to attack the job-shop scheduling problem are loading rules, heuristic rules, integer linear programming, complete enumeration, sampling methods, and learning techniques. We discuss each of these briefly.[1]

Loading Rules. As usually discussed, loading rules use only the information available to operators of machines to decide which of a large number of commodities waiting to be processed on the machine should be worked on next. The operator

[1] For a more comprehensive survey of research (up to about 1960), see R. L. Sisson [9].

may choose to work on the job that arrived first, the job that he can complete most quickly, or the job that has the maximum number of uncompleted operations still to be performed. He may even just choose a job at random from among those waiting. Some of these rules of thumb, such as the last, may be quite bad. Others, such as to choose the job with the shortest operation time, may have quite acceptable characteristics under most conditions. Many of these rules have been compared by simulating their performance on electronic computers. The papers in Part IV are primarily concerned with such comparisons.

Heuristic Rules. Another approach is to develop procedures which duplicate or exceed the performance of "skillful" schedulers. With heuristic rules, skill, or expertise, has the same connotation as the skill of a chess master, or a master of some other game. Loading rules can be regarded as heuristic rules which do not exhibit very much skill. Work along these lines offers, we believe, good prospects for future studies, but no practical applications to industrial scheduling have yet been completed. However, Chapter 16 represents a pilot study in this direction, and F. Tonge in reference [11] gives another such study on a related problem. In his thesis [3], W. Gere has developed a heuristic approach to the job-shop scheduling program.

Integer Linear Programming. There are three published formulations of the job-shop scheduling problem as an integer linear programming problem, those of E. H. Bowman [1], H. M. Wagner [12], and A. S. Manne [8], (see also Chapter 12). We shall not go into explicit descriptions of these formulations, but merely give estimates of the size of the resulting computational problem in each case. Bowman estimates that formulating a simple problem involving three jobs and four machines in his terms would require an integer programming problem containing 300 to 600 variables and many more constraints. The formulation by Wagner of the problem would be of the same order of magnitude. Manne's formulation, the most compact of the three, would apparently require 31 variables and 94 constraints. This last formulation could probably be solved by existing computing machines in a reasonable length of time. It should be emphasized, however, that in the solution of an integer linear programming problem, additional constraints are added during the course of its solution so that the ultimate number of constraints will be considerably larger. None of these authors claims that his formulation is computationally practical (Chapter 14 reports on computational experience with the Wagner formulation), but they are theoretical formulations suitable for further study. The properties of integer linear programming formulations are the subject of Part III of this volume.

Complete Enumeration. The other approach to the problem that is guaranteed to give an optimal answer is complete enumeration, which has been studied by B. Giffler and G. L. Thompson [5]. Their first effort was to devise an algorithm for the complete enumeration of all "active" schedules. (They define an active schedule to be a feasible schedule with the following properties: (a) no machine is idle for a length of time sufficient to process completely a commodity simultaneously idle, and (b) whenever an assignment of a commodity to a machine has been made, its processing is started at the earliest time that both the machine and the commodity are free.) For Bowman's simple example mentioned above, it is possible in a few minutes to enumerate all the five active feasible schedules with nine lines of computations. Larger problems yield many more active feasible schedules and take a proportionately longer time to evaluate. Further discussion of the enumeration problem is given in Chapter 3.

Another approach to complete enumeration of feasible schedules was taken by J. Heller [7]. He studies the problem from a graph-theoretic point of view, rather than that of the Gantt-chart.

Sampling Methods. A Monte Carlo version of the Giffler-Thompson program which samples from the population of active feasible schedules has also been tested. It does not guarantee the finding of an optimal schedule, but it does permit the rapid computation of a fairly large number of feasible schedules chosen at random, and the shortest one found can then be used. By continuing the process long enough, it is possible to make the probability of not having observed an optimal schedule be as small as desired—but, of course, the cost of computation must also be taken into account. The Monte Carlo program, if run for only a few choices of feasible schedules, qualifies merely as a skillful scheduler. It compares favorably with many of the commonly used loading rules—being better than they are for some classes of problems, and worse in other cases (see Chapter 3).

In [6], J. Heller and G. Logemann describe a Monte Carlo version of their complete enumeration approach. They also discuss its use with loading rules.

Learning Techniques. Since loading and heuristic rules have only modest success when used singly, and since their success varies from problem to problem, it seems desirable to try various rules on each given problem singly and in concert to see what combination works best. In Chapter 15, H. Fischer and G. L. Thompson discuss the probabalistic learning combination of loading rules. Results of simulations show that such a probabilistic combination does considerably better than any rule singly. They also demonstrate that learning is possible, but is time-consuming and not yet much better than a random combination of rules without learning.

CONCLUSION

It is clear that complete enumeration is impractical and also that no computationally feasible formulation of an integer linear programming model has yet been developed. With possible improvements in computational methods for integer programs there is some hope that progress will be made in that direction in the long run.

Progress being made toward approximate or skillful computational methods to solve scheduling problems by the use of heuristic, Monte Carlo, or learning methods, or combinations of these, seems very promising at this time. Early practical application of scheduling techniques will probably be made using these methods.

REFERENCES

1. Bowman, E. H., "The Schedule Sequence Problem," *Operations Research* **7** (1959), 621–624.

2. Fischer, H. and G. L. Thompson, "Probabilistic Learning Combinations of Local Job-Shop Scheduling Rules," Chapter 5 of this volume.

3. Gere, W., "A Heuristic Approach to Job-Shop Scheduling," Ph.D. Thesis, Carnegie Institute of Technology, 1962.

4. Giffler, B. and G. L. Thompson, "Algorithms for Solving Production Scheduling Problems," *Operations Research* **8** (1960), 487–503.

5. Giffler, B., G. L. Thompson, and V. Van Ness, "Numerical Experience with the Linear and Monte Carlo Algorithms for Solving Production Scheduling Problems," Chapter 3 of this volume.

6. Heller, J., and G. Logemann, "An Algorithm for the Construction and Evaluation of Feasible Schedules," *Management Science* **8** (1962), 168–183.

7. Heller, J., "Some Problems in Linear Graph Theory That Arise in the Analysis of the Sequence of Jobs Through Machines," AEC Research and Development Report NYO–9487 (1960).

8. Manne, A. S., "On the Job-Shop Scheduling Problem," *Operations Research* **8** (1960), 219–223.

9. Sisson, R. L., "Sequence Theory," Chapter 7 of R. L. Ackoff (Ed.), *Progress in Operations Research*, Vol. I, New York: John Wiley & Sons, Inc., 1961.

10. Thompson, G. L., "Recent Developments in the Job-Shop Scheduling Problem," *Naval Logistic Research Quarterly* **7** (1960), 585–589.

11. Tonge, F. M., "Summary of a Heuristic Line Balancing Procedure," *Management Science* **7** (1960), 21–39.

12. Wagner, H. M., "An Integer Linear-Programming Model for Machine Shop Scheduling," *Naval Logistics Research Quarterly* **6** (1959), 131–140.

Contents

xvi

xvii

Industrial Scheduling

I

Structures of
Scheduling Problems

The papers in this part of the book are concerned mainly with exploring certain ways of finding schedules which are in some sense optimal and with laying the groundwork for future developments. Although the papers are quite diverse in their approaches, they do show a common concern for characterizing the factory scheduling problem.

In the first chapter, "The Scheduling Environment," W. F. Pounds asks two kinds of questions: (1) In what sense is the scheduling of jobs through work centers a problem to plant management? (2) When a new scheduling system is installed in a firm, what steps must be taken to insure that its potential benefits will be realized? Pounds argues that the scheduling problem is not a visible one in many firms because other parts of the firm have absorbed much of the impact of poor scheduling, e. g., by quoting excessively long lead times for delivery of finished goods to the customer and by investing in too much production equipment. As a result, most of the improvements through different scheduling procedures will be seen in parts of the firm other than the scheduling department. Along with other specific recommendations, Pounds concludes that this interdependence must

1

be taken into account when one is attempting to install a new scheduling system in an industrial firm.

The next paper, "Optimal Two- and Three-Stage Production Schedules" (Chapter 2), by S. M. Johnson, has quite a different character. It is one of the earliest mathematical papers on job-shop scheduling, and its results are simple and elegant. The formal problem which Johnson is concerned with is the following: n jobs must go through one production stage (or machine) and then through a second one. There is only one machine for each stage; at most, one item can be processed by a machine at a given time. In what order should the jobs be performed on the machines in order to minimize the time to process all n jobs? After a series of theorems about the structure of an optimal solution, Johnson presents a "working rule" for calculating an optimal schedule for arbitrary job times. The results have been generalized to some extent (see Jackson [1], Mitten [3], and Johnson [2]).

A more general problem would involve scheduling n jobs on m machines, with the jobs not necessarily being run on the machines in the same order. Even for six jobs and six machines, the number of possible feasibles active schedules is a rather frightening statistic. Nevertheless, some complete populations of schedules have been enumerated by B. Giffler, G. L. Thompson, and V. Van Ness, and the results have been summarized in their paper, "Numerical Experience with the Linear and Monte Carlo Algorithms for Solving Production Scheduling Problems" (Chapter 3). The complete enumeration is also compared with a procedure for sampling from the entire population. The sampling procedure does not select each schedule with equal probability but, when all job times are equal, selects the short schedules more frequently. With different job times, this useful result, unfortunately, is no longer necessarily true.

As a possible aid to future developments in schedule analysis, B. Giffler in "Schedule Algebras and Their Use in Formulating General Systems Simulations" (Chapter 4), has constructed two algebras in terms of which certain scheduling problems might be stated. Order relations on the operation sequence for a job, together with the operation times, lead to the definition of variables on sets, on which are defined abstract "addition" and "multiplication." Certain sets of these variables may be taken as elements of matrices which have properties analogous to those of ordinary matrices. The algebras are then explored in relation to two basic types of problems: (1) those whose answers are implicit in the given data (e. g., to find the starting times for tasks when order relations and times are given) and (2) those for which the order of various tasks is not completely given in advance but must be determined by a scheduling rule.

Chapters 5 and 6 use results from waiting-line theory as a basis for scheduling the job which is to be performed next at a machine when one job is completed. (For a general description of waiting-line theory, see Morse [4] and Saaty [5.]) The paper, "On the Job-Shop Scheduling Problem," by Rudolph C. Reinitz, views the shop operations as a collection of separate machine centers, each of which processes the flow of jobs routed through it. The operation of an individual center and its queue of uncompleted jobs are represented by a Markov process. Two topics are studied at the level of an individual machine center: (1) the calculation of the average waiting time of a job for a given sequencing procedure and (2) the use of a dynamic programming procedure to obtain a sequencing procedure which is optimal in that it minimizes the expected value of the sum of inventory storage, set-up, and customers' delay costs. The question of estimating completion times and establishing delivery commitments for the shop as a whole is then examined.

A similar division of the scheduling problem is followed by Charles C. Holt in the paper, "Priority Rules for Minimizing the Cost of Queues in Machine Scheduling" (Chapter 6). The object of the first part of the analysis is to find starting times and expected queue delays for each product in order to minimize the sum of inventory holding costs and penalties for late delivery. A stable relation is assumed to exist between the average queue delay at a machine and the average loading of that machine. Three priority rules for sequencing the jobs at a machine are then suggested. The first rule is designed to be consistent with the analysis for the plant as a whole, whereas the latter two rules take account of the costs of delay at the machine as well.

REFERENCES

1. Jackson, James R., "An Extension of Johnson's Results on Job Lot Scheduling," Naval Research Logistics Quarterly 3 (1956), 201–203.

2. Johnson, S. M., "Discussion," Management Science 5 (1959), 299–303.

3. Mitten, L. G., "Sequencing n Jobs on Two Machines with Arbitrary Time Lags," Management Science 5 (1959), 293–298.

4. Morse, Philip M., Queues, Inventories and Maintenance, New York: John Wiley & Sons, Inc., 1958.

5. Saaty, Thomas L., Elements of Queuing Theory with Applications New York: McGraw-Hill Book Company, Inc., 1961.

1

The Scheduling Environment

William F. Pounds
MASSACHUSETTS INSTITUTE OF TECHNOLOGY

In a manufacturing organization the scheduling of production is a unifying problem which relates such diverse elements of the organization as sales, cost control, purchasing, capital budgeting, and many others. It seems worthwhile, therefore, in any discussion of the factory scheduling problem, to consider not only the complexities of the problem itself but also the environment within which it exists. When the discussion is directed toward the development of new factory scheduling systems, it seems especially important to consider the environment to which these new systems will have to adapt and the possible changes in that environment which they may cause and require.

1. THE PROBLEM

Most manufacturing processes involve several operations to transform relatively raw material into a relatively finished product. The

A paper presented at the Factory Scheduling Conference, Carnegie Institute of Technology, May 10–12, 1961.

problem of defining the transformation to be accomplished by each of these operations is a technological one. The problem of determining the sequence of these operations may, however, be only partially determined technologically; i. e., it may be possible to define a set of operations which, from a technological point of view, may equally well follow a given operation. In such cases it is sometimes possible to define a subset of the technologically feasible sequences that are preferred according to some (perhaps economic) criterion. We shall refer to the problem of discovering these preferred sequences as the sequencing problem.

In some manufacturing situations the sequencing problem can be solved once and for all. For example, a special-purpose machine can be designed to perform a series of operations in a preferred sequence to produce one item of a finished product. If this item is satisfactory, then this same solution to the sequencing problem can be applied again and again to the production of an indefinite number of identical items. In this case the preferred sequence on each item is independent of all other items.

In many other manufacturing situations, however, such a solution is not possible, for the preferred sequence of operations on one item may be a function of the sequence of operations chosen for another, or, perhaps, many other items. In such a case, in order to determine the preferred sequence for one items, it is usually necessary to determine the preferred sequence for all items simultaneously. As a result, the sequencing problem can become one of considerable size and complexity. For example, consider the following relatively simple sequencing problem:

Five items are to be produced, each of which requires one operation on each of five different machines. The time for each machine operation on each item is known with certainty and is independent of the machine-item sequence. The criterion to be applied to each possible sequence is that the sequence which requires the least overall time to complete all five items is preferred.

In this simple problem there are approximately 25 billion sequences of operations which could be evaluated before the preferred one would be discovered. And, if each sequence could be generated and evaluated in one second (a sizable job even for a high-speed computer), it would take almost eight centuries of 24-hour days to solve this problem by straightforward methods. The problem of discovering preferred sequences in the considerably larger and more complex setting of the typical factory is clearly even more difficult than this simple example, and it is these fantastically difficult sequencing problems which are currently attracting considerable theoretical attention.

Moreover, the problem of plant management is not simply one of determining a preferred sequence of operations to be performed on given facilities. It is also one of determining simultaneously which items to produce, which machines to purchase and install, how much labor to employ, etc. And each of these decisions is affected by and affects the optimum sequences of operations. Thus, the factory scheduling problem is far more difficult to solve than even the fantastically difficult sequencing problem.

Just as the sequencing problems can vary from relatively simple to highly complex, the scheduling problems are similarly variable. As might be expected, scheduling problems are relatively simple when demand is steady, items of production are identical, process times are constant, and sequences are independent. On the other hand, scheduling problems become complex as demand becomes uncertain, items exhibit variability in specification, process times are probabilistic, and preferred-item sequences are strongly interdependent. The name job-shop scheduling problem has been used to describe the complex end of the continuum of scheduling situations, and much of the current work to develop scheduling systems has been directed at the solution of this type of problem.

2. PRESENT METHODS OF SOLUTION

Our purpose here is not to comment on the details of these scheduling systems but rather to discuss certain attributes of the environment to which they will have to adapt themselves. My education in this aspect of the scheduling problem began a few years ago with journeys to various manufacturing plants. I had hoped, I suppose, that, by immersing myself in the factory situation, the real essence of the job-shop problem would present itself to me and that, given this insight, I could then proceed to solve the scheduling problem.

To say that I did not succeed in this effort would be something of an understatement. If these trips accomplished anything, they convinced me that there was something about this problem that I did not quite understand. Since I now believe this to be an important point, I shall attempt to describe the source of my confusion.

In all my plant visits, I arranged to spend most of my time with the man in the organization responsible for the detailed sequencing of production orders. This seemed sensible to me since this was the man who every day somehow dealt with the vast complexity of the job-shop problem—this was the man who should be able to tell me what I needed to know.

Upon meeting this gentleman, therefore, it was with considerable anticipation that I would say that I had come to discuss with him his very complicated job-shop scheduling problem. Without exception he would look somewhat perplexed and ask, "What job-shop scheduling problem?"

Despite my explanations—which varied from "The problem of scheduling N products through M machines in such a way as to minimize the total processing time" and "The sum of past due deliveries" to "The problem of getting your orders out on time or keeping your people busy"—he never could see my definition of his problem. He showed me records which indicated in great detail that he met virtually all his promised deliveries, and he showed me other records which revealed his precise control of costs, but. he never admitted any problem of scheduling.

Now, as I said, my inability to elicit any recognition of a scheduling problem from people who schedule discouraged me. But I can now report that I have found the explanation.

The job-shop scheduling problem is not recognized by most factory schedulers because *for them*, in most cases, no scheduling problem exists. That is there is no scheduling problem for them because the organization which surrounds the schedulers reacts to protect them from strongly interdependent sequencing problems.

Consider a plant which produces paint to meet the specifications of its customers, who are, in general, themselves producers of products for sale. It provides finishes to manufacturers of everything from toys and rubber balls to automobiles. In the language of the paint business, it produce industrial finishes. In the language of scheduling, it is a job shop.

Orders flow into its scheduling system through a number of channels: by phone, by wire, by letter, or by personal contact with any of a number of people. A standard lead time has been established for use in estimating and promising delivery. If the customer wants his product in more than the standard lead time in the futures, it is usually promised without question. If the customer occasionally wants his order in less than the standard lead time, the request normally is accepted. If, however, the customer *habitually* requests fast service, the plant becomes reluctant to make promises of delivery and, in some cases, may even refuse to make such a promise.

The plant has no precise estimate of the cost of fast service. In fact, this is clearly not a fixed figure but one which depends on the other work in process. It does cost something, however, and one of the components of this cost is the scheduling problems which arise because of high-priority orders. The sales department, therefore, is protecting the scheduling function from a scheduling problem when the department begins to resist requests for fast service. There are other ways by which the scheduling function is protected.

Every day a report is prepared on all orders which are rush (i.e., delivery as soon as possible) or late (i. e., delivery is past due). This report is circulated through both the sales and production departments.

As well as being a reminder of priority, this list is the basis for sets of decisions in both the sales and production departments, which stabilize and simplify the scheduling problem.

If the list gets long, say, greater than ten items, the sales depart· ment begins to resist promising rush orders. This tends to reduce the load on scheduling. Then, too, if the length of the list seems to be growing, the production department may begin to authorize over· time or even to consider adding to the work force. These moves, also, reduce the scheduling load and permit delivery dates to be met.

In extreme cases, when the addition of manpower raises certain variable costs, management suspects a shortage of production equip· ment and may begin either to add to the plant production facilities or to plan multiple-shift schedules.

Although the above system is not offered as a model of optimum plant operation, the plant may, by using this system maintain a good record of customer service, and its costs remain competitive.

In reviewing the basic elements of this system, consider the follow· ing. Average lead time is set by the market as interpreted by sales management. When there are deviations from this objective, cor· rective action is instituted by both the sales and the production de· partments. The scheduling activity is assumed to be constant and is expected only to behave consistently enough to make action by others have a predictable effect on delivery.

Computationally difficult scheduling problems do not arise, because those constraints that would create them are removed when they become active.

After some exposure to this organization, it occurred to me one day that perhaps all the schedulers with whom I talked earlier were right. For them, at least, there was no job-shop scheduling problem. A similar effect was observed at a plant which manufactures heavy machinery. Waiting lines of work in progress were found to be up to 30 working days long, yet all jobs were on or ahead of schedule. No scheduling problem was reported. By negotiating with customers, apparently, the management of this firm has been able to get delivery dates so far in the future that considerable smoothing of the work flow in the long queues of in-process inventory was possible. Here, low labor and capital costs were more important than prompt delivery.

This, then, seems to summarize the present state of the scheduling art. So long as the scheduling system can generate costs or deliveries consistent with the external controls on manpower and/or productive equipment, discriminating functions outside the scheduling system can gradually learn what to do to accomplish what is required to make a profit. The effects of the scheduling system tends to be taken as given in this response mechanism.

3. A LOOK INTO THE FUTURE

Up to this point, the discussion has attempted to establish that highly constrained job-shop problems do not exist in factories today because the problems cannot be handled by present scheduling methods. In fact, they are explicitly prevented from arising by stabilizing decisions made in various parts of the plant organization.

Suppose for a moment, however, that the current efforts to solve the scheduling problem have succeeded and that an optimum solution to this problem has been described. Let us suppose further that we take this solution and put it in the hands of a factory scheduling department. What can we predict as the effect of this solution?

If what I have said is true, there would be no effect at all. For if factory scheduling problems are now virtually trival, the solutions to them are problems already optimum or very close to optimum. Therefore, new and more powerful analytical methods would contribute little, if anything, to the firm which might attempt to use them.

This is not to say that these solutions are of no potential value, however. If those parts of the organization which now control the constraints in such a way as to avoid difficult scheduling problems could learn to react, not to present limits of scheduling ability, but to the new limits implied by the more powerful techniques—then and only then will progress have been made. This, I think is a crucial point, and one which is easy to overlook in our concern for abstract scheduling problems. The benefits to the firm of better scheduling algorithms will not result from changes in the scheduling activity alone. Unless policy is changed in the areas of capital budgeting, labor cost control, employment policy, sales policy, and policies on customer service, the new scheduling techniques might not only prevent any beneficial effect whatsoever, but they could also conceivably do more harm than good—despite their very real *potential* benefits.

The damage which can be done by an incomplete system installation was made very clear to me several years ago, when I had the opportunity to observe the effect of a scheduling system where little or no attempt was made to control or adapt the environment to the new system.

Rather than go into the details of the installation of this system, let me briefly recount some of the shortcomings I observed and their effects.

1. No control system was established to guarantee that the scheduling rule was being followed. As a result, three years after the rule was installed, I observed that, despite glowing reports about the effect of the system, no decisions in the factory were being based explicitly on the rule.

2. No attempt was made to incorporate the costs upon which the decisions of the rule were based into the factory budget. As a result, the budget and the rule became conflicting influences on the same decisions. This may partially account for the rule's having been ignored.

3. No attempt was made to establish a system of review and reevaluation of the assumptions of the system. As a result, this was offered as the reason for the rule's not being followed when, in fact, the assumptions were not inappropriate.

4. No system to evaluate the performance of the rule was established. As a result, three years after installation management was still wondering whether the rule had improved or damaged the performance of the plant.

If you will forgive a biological analogy, a new system will be like a mutation in an environment in which existing systems have evolved. It is highly unlikely that these mutants will survive unless the environment changes. There are several ways in which this mutant can die or be killed.

1. It might be ignored. Therefore, a system of follow-up and reporting will have to be installed along with any new scheduling system.

2. Other decisions may limit its effectiveness. Therefore, some rough guides and controls will have to be effected over those external variables such as sales policy, capital budgeting, and employment policy, in order that the benefits of the new system can be utilized. These controls will not be easy to devise.

3. Some means of evaluating the performance of the new systems must be established to justify its continued use.

4. A means to adjust, modify, and maintain the system must be established to sustain its validity.

These four steps are minimum requirements to insure the survival of any new scheduling system within any organization. And, I fear, any installation without these safeguards is almost sure to fail.

In addition to these internal dangers the mutant must also survive in competition with scheduling rules of other firms—for here is where its real benefits to the firm will be generated.

In my opinion the responsibility for the survival of new scheduling systems must be shared by those who devise the systems and those who expect to use them. Those who devise them should not only inform those who may use them of the auxiliary controls which are necessary but also insist on their implementation—for without them any new system will almost surely fail. Similarly, those who expect to use the new systems must recognize the extensive changes which may, as a result of the systems, be required in the plant organization outside the scheduling function and must be willing to make these changes. Otherwise, not only will their new system not work—it may be worse than the one they already have.

2

Optimal Two= and Three=Stage Production Schedules With Set=up Time Included

S. M. Johnson
THE RAND CORPORATION

1. TWO-STAGE PRODUCTION SCHEDULE

Let us consider a typical multistage problem formulated in the following terms by R. Bellman:

"There are n items which must go through one production stage or machine and then a second one. There is only one machine for each stage. At most one item can be on a machine at a given time.

"Consider $2n$ constants A_i, B_i, $i = 1, 2, \ldots, n$. These are positive but otherwise arbitrary. Let A_i be the set-up time plus work time of the ith item on the first machine, and B_i be the corresponding time on the second machine. We seek the optimal scheduling of items in order to minimize the total elapsed time."

A simple decision rule leads to an optimal scheduling of the items minimizing the total elapsed time for the entire operation. For

Reprinted from the *Naval Research Logistics Quarterly* **1** (1954), 61–68.

example, the decision rule permits one optimally to arrange twenty production items in about five minutes by visual inspection.

In the second section a three-stage problem is also discussed and solved for a restricted case.

Lemma 1.   The production sequence on either machine can be made the same as that of the other machine without loss of time.

Proof.   On the time scales for each machine place the A's and B's in any position *subject to the rules*; i.e., the start of a B_j must be to the right of the end of an A_j. If the orders are different, the elements out of order will be placed something like the following.

Then without loss of time we can make the ordering of stage 1 the same as the ordering of stage 2 by successive interchanges, starting from the left of consecutive pairs of those items which are out of order. Symmetrically we could order items on stage 2 to match that of stage 1.

Next, since the orders are now the same, we may start each item as soon as possible to minimize the total time. Thus there are no delay times on the first stage.

Notation.   Let X_i be the inactive period of time for the second machine immediately before the ith item comes onto the second machine.

If, for example, we consider the sequence $S = 1, 2, 3, \ldots, n$, we have the following time scales for each machine:

We have

$$X_1 = A_1$$

$$X_2 = \max (A_1 + A_2 - B_1 - X_1, 0)$$

$$X_1 + X_2 = \max (A_1 + A_2 - B_1, A_1)$$

$$X_3 = \max \left(\sum_1^3 A_i - \sum_1^2 B_i - \sum_1^2 X_i, 0 \right)$$

$$\sum_1^3 X_i = \max \left(\sum_1^3 A_i - \sum_1^2 B_i, \sum_1^2 X_i \right)$$

$$= \max \left(\sum_1^3 A_i - \sum_1^2 B_i, \sum_1^2 A_i - B_1, A_1 \right).$$

In general,

$$\sum_1^n X_i = \max_{1 \le u \le n} K_u$$

where

$$K_u = \sum_{i=1}^u A_i - \sum_{i=1}^{u-1} B_i.$$

Let

$$F(S) = \max_{1 \le u \le n} K_u.$$

We want a sequence S^* such that $F(S^*) \le F(S_0)$ for any S_0.

Solution of Problem. Consider S' the sequence formed by interchanging the jth and the $j+1$-st items in S; then

$$F(S') = \max_{1 \le u \le n} K'_u$$

where

$$K'_u = \sum_{i=1}^u A'_i - \sum_{i=1}^{u-1} B'_i$$

and

$$A'_i = A_i, \qquad B'_i = B_i \qquad \text{for } i \ne j, j+1$$
$$A'_j = A_{j+1}, \qquad B'_j = B_{j+1}, \qquad A'_{j+1} = A_j, \qquad B'_{j+1} = B_j.$$

Then

$$K'_u = K_u \qquad \text{if } u \ne j, j+1.$$

Thus $F(S') = F(S)$ unless possibly if $\max(K_j, K_{j+1}) \max \ne (K'_j, K'_{j+1})$.

Theorem 1. An optimal ordering is given by the following rule. Item (j) precedes item $(j+1)$ if

$$\max(K_j, K_{j+1}) < \max(K'_j, K'_{j+1}). \tag{1}$$

If there is equality, either order is optimal, provided it is consistent with all the definite preferences (see Case 4, Lemma 2).

By subtracting $\sum_1^{j+1} A_i - \sum_1^{j-1} B_i$ from each term in Relation (1), it becomes

$$\max(-B_j, -A_{j+1}) < \max(-B_{j+1}, -A_j)$$

or

$$\min(A_j, B_{j+1}) < \min(A_{j+1}, B_j). \tag{2}$$

This ordering is transitive (proof follows), thus leading to a sequence S^*, unique except for some indifferent elements.

Then $F(S^*) \leq F(S_0)$ for any sequence S_0, since S^* can be obtained from S_0 by successive interchanges of consecutive items, according to Relation (2), and each interchange will give a value of F smaller than or the same as before.

Lemma 2. Relation (2) is transitive. Suppose min $(A_1, B_2) \leq$ min (A_2, B_1) and min $(A_2, B_3) \leq$ min (A_3, B_2). Then

$$\min (A_1, B_3) \leq \min (A_3, B_1)$$

except possibly when item 2 is indifferent to both items 1 and 3.

Proof.

Case 1. $A_1 \leq B_2$, A_2, B_1 and $A_2 \leq B_3$, A_3, B_2.
   Then $A_1 \leq A_2 \leq A_3$ and $A_1 \leq B_1$ so that $A_1 \leq$ min (A_3, B_1).

Case 2. $B_2 \leq A_1$, A_2, B_1 and $B_3 \leq A_2$, A_3, B_2.
   Then $B_3 \leq B_2 \leq B_1$ and $B_3 \leq A_3$ so that $B_3 \leq$ min (A_3, B_1).

Case 3. $A_1 \leq B_2$, A_2, B_1 and $B_3 \leq A_2$, A_3, B_2.
   Then $A_1 \leq B_1$ and $B_3 \leq A_3$ so that min $(A_1, B_3) \leq$ min (A_3, B_1).

Case 4. $B_2 \leq A_1$, A_2, B_1 and $A_2 \leq B_3$, A_3, B_2.
   Then $A_2 = B_2$ and we have item 2 indifferent to item 1 and item 3. In this case, item 1 may or may not precede item 3, but there is no contradiction to transitivity as long as we order item 1 and item 3 first and then put item 2 anywhere.

If Relation (2) is used, there is an extremely simple, practical way of ordering the items in n steps.

Working Rule.

1. List the A's and B's in two vertical columns.

i	A_i	B_i
1	A_1	B_1
2	A_2	B_2
.	.	.
.	.	.
.	.	.
n	A_n	B_n

2. Scan all the time periods for the shortest one.

3. If it is for the first machine (i.e., an A_i), place the corresponding item first.

4. If it is for the second machine (i.e., a B_i), place the corresponding item last.

5. Cross off both times for that item.

6. Repeat the steps on the reduced set of $2n-2$ time intervals, etc. Thus we work from both ends toward the middle.

7. In case of ties, for the sake of definiteness order the item with the smallest subscript first. In case of a tie between A_i and B_i order the item according to the A.

To illustrate the method, the following somewhat extreme example is worked out. Consider

i	A_i	B_i
1	4	5
2	4	1
3	30	4
4	6	30
5	2	3

The rule gives an optimal sequence (5, 1, 4, 3, 2). The total delay time for this sequence is four units, and the total elapsed time is 47 units. If one reversed the order of the items, the total time would be 78 units, the worst value possible.

2. THREE-STAGE PRODUCTION SCHEDULE

For three different machines or stages (at most, one item at a time on each machine), the problem loses some of the nice structure of the two-stage case. The problem is formulated, however, and for the special cases where min $A_i \geq$ max B_j or min $C_i \geq$ max B_j the complete solution is found analogously to the two-stage problem.

Lemma 3. An optimal ordering can be reached if we assume the same ordering of the n items for each machine.

Proof. By Lemma 1 the orders on the first and third machines can be made the same as that of the second; i. e., the first two machines have the same orders and the last two machines have the same orders. Thus the lemma is proved.

For four or more stages, the optimal scheduling may call for a shift in ordering of the items. Consider two items going through four stages with times listed below:

i	A_i	B_i	C_i	D_i
1	3	3	3	3
2	3	1	1	3

It can be verified that the optimal scheduling here calls for a shift of ordering from the second to the third stage. Thus the general solution is apt to be very complicated.

Notation.

Let A_i, B_i, X_i be defined as in the two-stage problem.

Let $C_i =$ set-up time plus work time for the ith item on the third machine.

Let $Y_i =$ the delay interval on the third machine immediately preceding the entry of the ith item onto the third machine.

Consider the time scales for each machine.

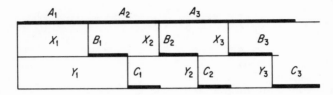

We have

$$Y_1 = X_1 + B_1 = A_1 + B_1$$

$$Y_n = \max\left(\sum_1^n B_i + \sum_1^n X_i - \sum_1^{n-1} C_i - \sum_1^{n-1} Y_i, 0\right)$$

so that

$$\sum_1^n Y_i = \max\left(\sum_1^n B_i - \sum_1^{n-1} C_i + \sum_1^n X_i, \sum_1^{n-1} Y_i\right)$$

$$= \max\left(\sum_1^n B_i - \sum_1^{n-1} C_i + \sum_1^n X_i,\right.$$

$$\left. \sum_1^{n-1} B_i - \sum_1^{n-2} C_i + \sum_1^{n-1} X_i, \ldots, B_1 + X_1\right).$$

Let

$$H_v = \sum_1^v B_i - \sum_1^{v-1} C_i, \qquad v = 1, 2, \ldots, n$$

and

$$K_u = \sum_1^u A_i - \sum_1^{u-1} B_i, \qquad u = 1, 2, \ldots, n, \text{ as before.}$$

Then

$$\sum_1^n Y_i = \max_{1 \le u \le v \le n} (H_v + \max K_u) = \max_{1 \le u \le v \le n} (H_v + K_u).$$

As before, we interchange the jth and $j+1$-st items. Then the H's and K's are unchanged except possibly those with subscripts j and $j+1$.

Now we compare

$$\max (H_{j+1} + K_u, 1 \le u \le j + 1; H_j + K_u, 1 \le u \le j)$$

with $\quad \max (H'_{j+1} + K'_u, 1 \leq u \leq j + 1; H'_j + K'_u, 1 \leq u \leq j)$.

Notice that these terms no longer involve just the subscripts j and $j + 1$, and thus the decision is not independent of what precedes the interchanged elements.

3. SPECIAL CASE WHERE MIN $A_i \geq$ MAX B_j

Here $\max\limits_{u \leq v} K_u = K_v$, so that we now compare fewer terms. Our rule now states that the jth item precedes the $j + 1$-st item if

$$\max (H_{j+1} + K_{j+1}, H_j + K_j) < \max (H'_{j+1} + K'_{j+1}, H'_j + K'_j). \quad (3)$$

In case of equality, we make the ordering of indifferent items consistent with the ordering given by the definite inequalities.

Then by subtracting

$$\sum_1^{j+1} A_i - \sum_1^{j-1} B_i + \sum_1^{j+1} B_i - \sum_1^{j-1} C_i$$

from two sides of (3), it becomes

$$\max (-B_j - C_j, -B_{j+1} - A_{j+1}) < \max (-B_{j+1} - C_{j+1}, -B_j - A_j)$$

or

$$\min (A_j + B_j, C_{j+1} + B_{j+1}) < \min (A_{j+1} + B_{j+1}, C_j + B_j). \quad (4)$$

Lemma 4. Relation (4) is transitive.

Proof. Proof is the same as for Lemma 2.

By the same arguments as before, we can reach an optimal sequence by successive interchanges of adjacent elements in any sequence following this rule. Thus we have

Theorem 2. If $\min A_i \geq \max B_i$, $1 \leq i \leq n$, then an optimal three-stage production schedule is given by the following rule: Item i precedes item j if

$$\min (A_i + B_i, C_j + B_j) < \min (A_j + B_j, C_i + B_i).$$

If equality holds, the two items are indifferent and either is permissible, provided we order these items in a manner consistent with the orders given by the definite inequalities.

As in the two-stage case, there is a short working rule providing the optimal scheduling very quickly. Here A_i is replaced by $A_i + B_i$, and B_j is replaced by $B_j + C_j$.

Note that the same results hold if $\min C_i \geq \max B_j$.

Another special three-stage case is when the two-stage rule applied to the first two stages gives the same ordering as that for the last two stages.   Then this ordering is the optimal for the three-stage case.

An equivalent statement of the three-stage problem is as follows:
Notice that

$$\max_{u \leq v \leq n} \left(K_u + H_v + \sum_{i=1}^{n} C_i \right)$$

is the maximum sum of elements passed through on all "walks" in
the time matrix from the upper left-hand corner to the lower right-
hand corner, when steps are taken to the right or downward.   The
problem is to find a scheduling of items which minimizes this maximum walk.

This interpretation is useful in numerical work for three-stage
problems but does not carry over to four or more stages.

As we noted previously, the optimal ordering is not always the
same on each stage when there are more than three stages.   As a
practical working rule, however, one could assume the same order
for each stage and then use the "maximum walk" interpretation to
eliminate candidates for an optimal schedule.

Author's Note.   Since this paper was written in 1953, there have
been several extensions and generalizations by various authors, for
example, S.M. Johnson, "Discussion: Sequencing in Jobs on Two
Machines with Arbitrary Time Lags," *Management Science* **5**, 3,
(April, 1959).

3

Numerical Experience with the Linear and Monte Carlo Algorithms for Solving Production Scheduling Problems

B. Giffler, G. L. Thompson, V. Van Ness
INTERNATIONAL BUSINESS MACHINES CORPORATION

In a previous article by the first two authors [1], algorithms were developed to enummerate feasible active schedules. We have programmed these algorithms for a computer (IBM 704) and have accumulated considerable experience with them. We wish to report on that computational experience here. Our aim in the computations was not primarily to obtain answers to specific problems, but rather to see experimentally how difficult the combinatorial problem is.

1. THE NONNUMERICAL COMPLETE ENUMERATION PROGRAM

The first program was written for the linear nonnumerical algorithm (in which all operation times are unity) and worked out all possible conflict resolutions which arose. It did this by constructing all permutations of queues before machines and actually trying them all. In other words, it searched the entire "tree" of active schedules.

G. L. Thompson is at the Graduate School of Industrial Administration, Carnegie Institute of Technology. Part of his work was supported by the Office of Naval Research through grants to the Carnegie Institute of Technology.

We had fully expected that the combinatorial problem posed by the complete enumeration version of the algorithm would increase in difficulty very rapidly, and our experience with this algorithm fully confirmed our expectations. The size of the combinatorial problem is especially striking in view of the fact that we confined our investigations to the set of *active feasible* schedules, which is a much smaller set than the set of all feasible schedules.

The computational immensity of the scheduling problem is well illustrated by the following 6 × 6 problems, which were among the first with which we experimented. These scheduling problems are referred to as "6 × 6 problems" because in each one, six commodities are processed over one or more of six facilities. The facility ordering matrix, for the case in which each commodity is processed by each facility, is as shown in Figure 1.

Commodity	Facility order matrix
1	3 1 2 4 6 5
2	2 3 5 6 1 4
3	3 4 6 1 2 5
4	2 1 3 4 5 6
5	3 2 5 6 1 4
6	2 4 6 1 5 3

Figure 1

The facility ordering matrix, Figure 1, was used to generate a series of problems, referred to as 6 × 6 * 1, 6 × 6 * 2, . . . , 6 × 6 * 6. The first of these problems was obtained by considering that each commodity is produced by performing one operation on the facility indicated in column 1 of the matrix in Figure 1. Similarly, the second problem was obtained by considering that each commodity is produced by performing two operations on the facilities indicated in columns 1 and 2, and so on. As might be expected, the number of active schedules in each of these problems increased very rapidly. The actual numbers of active schedules for these problems is given in Figure 2. For obvious reasons, we did not try to enumerate completely the schedules for the 6 × 6 * 6 problem.

Problem	Number active schedules	Time in minutes
6 × 6 * 1	36	.00
6 × 6 * 2	290	.09
6 × 6 * 3	914	.48
6 × 6 * 4	7,546	4.82
6 × 6 * 5	84,802	70.18

Figure 2

Observe that, in the $6 \times 6 * 5$ case, that a combinatorial problem is defined by giving data involving 30 integers each between 1 and 6, and the resulting problem kept the computer busy for 70 minutes producing 84,802 active, feasible schedules! In examining some of the schedules produced we estimate that, corresponding to each active feasible schedule, there are approximately 100 inactive feasible schedules equivalent in the sense of [1]. Thus the total number of feasible schedules for the $6 \times 6 * 5$ problem is approximately eight million.

Still another instance of the computational "stone wall" of the problem is given by a $10 \times 10 * 4$ problem that we ran having data consisting of 40 integers each between 1 and 10. With this problem the computer produced 112,783 feasible active schedules in 75.1 minutes without completing the enumeration. We estimate that completion would have taken another two hours.

Because of the enormous numbers of feasible active schedules found, even for such trivially small problems as these, we quickly concluded that it was necessary to adopt a Monte Carlo approach, that is, to sample from the set of feasible active schedules. A program was written to implement this approach. The results obtained with the program are discussed in the following section.

2. THE MONTE CARLO ALGORITHM FOR THE NONNUMERICAL CASE

In the complete enumeration algorithm, conflicts are resolved in all possible ways. For the Monte Carlo argorithm, conflicts are resolved by choosing at random among the possible resolutions. Thus, in the construction of a schedule, there are a number of random decisions made at each conflict point. As we shall see, this is not the same as choosing at random with equal probability from the set of all feasible active schedules.

Since we wanted to get an idea of the structure of the combinatorial problem involved, we had the computer work out samples of 200, 500, or 1000, active feasible schedules, saving in most cases only the completion time of each schedule. It then printed the distribution of completion times of the sample, together with a few of the shortest schedules found.

In comparing the sample distributions with the true distribution obtained by the linear complete enumeration algorithm, for those cases in which comparison was possible, we noted immediately that short schedules had higher probability in the Monte Carlo distribution than in the true distribution. We called this effect the "amplification factor."

The reason for the amplification factor is that short schedules have, on the average, fewer conflicts to be resolved than long ones. In the Monte Carlo algorithm each conflict was resolved at random, and, therefore, the probability of obtaining a particular schedule is approximately proportional to the number of resolved conflicts it has. Hence, longer schedules, having more conflicts to resolve, are less probable than short ones. Unfortunately, the amplification factor does not necessarily hold in the numerical case, since the length of a schedule in that case does not necessarily depend upon the number of conflicts that need to be resolved to get it.

Another indication of the size of the combinatorial problem is illustrated by the data of Figure 3. We picked three problems for

Run	Number of active schedules produced	Observed probability of shortest schedule	Number of shortest schedules found	Number of duplications
6×6	5000	.008	40	3 triples, 7 doubles
7×7	5000	.007	34	5 doubles
$10 \times 10*8$	3000	.009	28	No duplications

Figure 3

which the observed probability of the shortest schedule occurring was very small, and generated for each problem a large number of feasible active schedules, saving in each case the shortest schedules observed. Although the sampling process used is sampling with replacement, observe that the greatest number of duplications occurs in the 6×6 case, that somewhat fewer occur in the 7×7 case, and that none at all occur in the $10 \times 10*8$ case. We conclude from this (and other) data that the set of active optimal schedules, even though a very small part of the set of all active feasible schedule, must increase very rapidly as the size of the problem increases.

To demonstrate the usefulness of the Monte Carlo process as a computational device, let us regard the Monte Carlo process as a binomial trials process in which either we obtain an optimal schedule with a fixed, but unknown, probability, or we do not. If p is the probability of a favorable event, then $1 - p$ is the probability of the unfavorable event, and $1 - (1 - p)^n$ is the probability of getting an optimal schedule in n trials. The table in Figure 4 shows how these probabilities vary with p and n. From Figure 4 we see that if there is .1 probability of getting an optimal schedule, then in 50 runs we are 99.5 percent certain, and in 1000 runs essentially certain, of observing an optimal schedule. However, if the probability of observing an optimal schedule is .02, then to make ourselves 95 per-

n p	10	25	50	75	100	200	500	1000
.100	.651322	.928210	.994846	.999630	.999973	1.000000	1.000000	1.000000
.050	.401263	.722610	.923055	.978656	.994079	.999965	1.000000	1.000000
.020	.182927	.396535	.635830	.780236	.867380	.982412	.999959	1.000000
.010	.095618	.222179	.394994	.529413	.633968	.866020	.993430	.999957
.005	.048890	.117780	.221687	.313357	.394230	.633042	.918428	.993346
.002	.019821	.048818	.095253	.139421	.181433	.329948	.632489	.864935
.001	.009955	.024702	.048794	.072291	.095208	.181351	.393621	.632305

Figure 4

cent certain of observing an optimum, we have to sample between 100 and 200 schedules. As the probability goes down, we have to sample more and more schedules to be reasonably sure of observing an optimal one.

From this we see that the Monte Carlo process is a true approximate computational method. If the amount to be spent on computation is specified, the probability of getting answers can be computed from Figure 4, if various assumptions are given. It is encouraging that, for events of probability .02 or greater, the Monte Carlo process is 98 percent certain of observing one of them with a sample size of only 200. In our experience, the time to run 200 schedules is only a few minutes for problems ranging up to 2000 operations.

3. DATA FROM THE NONNUMERICAL MONTE CARLO RUNS

The data from the nonnumerical Monte Carlo runs are summarized in Appendix 2. Three important conclusions are evident from this appendix.

1. In comparing this data with the complete enumeration data of Appendix 1, we note the amplification factor for the Monte Carlo case that increases the probability of short schedules and decreases the probability of long ones. The effect can be seen from the data of Figure 5, which compares the 6×6 runs. The reason for the amplification factor was explained in Section 2.

Run	Minimum length	Complete enumeration probability	Monte Carlo probability
$6 \times 6 * 2$	4	.145	.314
$6 \times 6 * 3$	6	.488	.633
$6 \times 6 * 4$	7	.117	.406
$6 \times 6 * 5$	8	.011	.136

Figure 5

2. The *spread*, that is, the difference of the time to complete the longest schedule found with the time to complete the shortest schedule found, exceeded ten only once and for reasonably large-sized problems was approximately constant at eight or nine.

3. The *time to complete* a fixed number of runs varies approximately linearly with the "size" of the problem. This observation can be refined in the following two ways:

    a. The time to complete varies approximately linearly with the *area* of the problem, i.e., with $A = m \cdot n$.

    b. The time to complete varies approximately linearly with the *volume* of the problem, that is, with $V = m \cdot n \cdot L$, where L is the length (or expected length) of the problem.

We shall discuss observations 2 and 3 in more detail.

Observation 2 is contrary to intuition, since, as the size of the problem goes up, it is most reasonable to expect that the worst schedule found would be much worse than the best. But this is not so, as the data shows. The importance of this conclusion lies in the fact that it makes the Monte Carlo algorithm work as well on a large problem as on a small one, since the distribution of probabilities of getting schedules of various lengths is the same for each one. Incidentally, the form of the distribution in the nonnumerical case is a bell-shaped curve truncated from above and below, as illustrated in Figure 6.

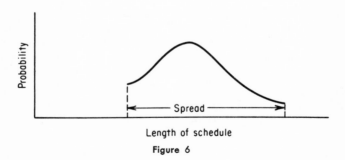

Figure 6

As the data in Appendix 2 show, the shortest schedule is rarely the most probable one, and the most probable schedule is usually only three or four time periods longer than the shortest one. The amplification factor actually makes it improbable that a very long schedule will be generated, and increases the probability of generating a short one. The amplification factor may be regarded as an explanation of the narrowness of the spread.

The narrow spread is disturbing in one sense, since it means that as problems get bigger, practically any method of choosing a schedule will produce one not far off from the optimal one. However, we shall see that in the numerical case the constancy of spread no longer holds, and consequently the latter conclusion also does not hold for that case.

As for observation 3, it is most easily seen in the graphs of Appendix 3, in which we have plotted the time in minutes against the product mn, a statistic we refer to as the "area of the data." The area is simply the number of numbers in the facility ordering matrix that is used. The lines in the two graphs fall quite close to all of the observed points with only two exceptions—the $100 \times 10 * 10$ and the $200 \times 10 * 10$ problems. However, observe that in these cases every commodity is processed by every facility. This has two effects: first, it makes the time to complete a schedule very long, since the minimum completion time is then obviously close to m; second, it makes waiting lines very long, so the random number conflict resolver (which is relatively slow) is used very often by the program, making the time factor rise considerably.

The area conjecture (that is, the time to complete a given number of runs varies linearly with the area mn of the data) is seen to hold quite well when, on the average, at most 20 percent of the facilities process any given commodity. In this case we can use the approximate formula $t = A/70 = mn/70$ to estimate the time to run 200 schedules. The values of A, t, and A/t are computed in Appendix 4.

To take into account the length of the schedules, and hence the average number of decisions that have to be made to complete a schedule, we consider the "volume" of the problem, $V = mnL$, where L is either the shortest length observed or (better) the most probable length (as an estimate for the expected length). All of these quantities are computed in the table of Appendix 4. Notice that V^* (the most probable volume) is a good measure of the problem size and that $V^* = 1400t$ approximately, where t is the time to run 200 schedules. The ratio V^*/t is less than 1400 for small problems where there are no long waiting lines, and it is greater than 1400 for larger problems where long waiting lines require a more inefficient code to be used.

Of the two, the area conjecture is the easier to use, because one does not know in advance what the expected length will be. However, for explaining date already in existence, the volume conjecture provides a better fit.

4. THE NUMERICAL MONTE CARLO ALGORITHM

The algorithm for the numerical case is presented in reference [1]. Since we did not work out the complete enumeration version of the algorithm, our only experience was with the Monte Carlo version.

As in the nonnumerical case, problems were made up by a computer program. For the numerical case it was necessary to make up operation times for each job, and these were also selected by the computer. These times were positive integers, and the parameter that we varied in selecting them was the ratio R of longest to shortest job time (the shortest job time was always 1). The job times were then picked with equal probability to lie between 1 and the longest job time. We made a number of runs with values of R being 2, 3, 5, 8, 10, and 15. The results are summarized in Appendices 5–8.

Appendix 7 shows how the length of time to complete a schedule varies with the ratio R. Note that the spread is, as before, the difference between the longest and shortest schedules observed. Another parameter of interest is the number of "peaks" the distribution has. In Figure 7, which is the distribution of 200 runs of

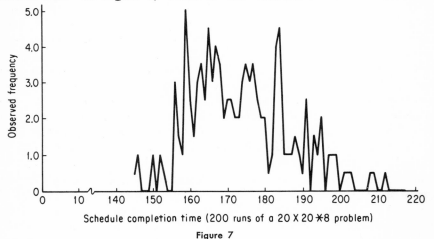

Schedule completion time (200 runs of a 20 X 20 ＊8 problem)

Figure 7

a $20 \times 20 * 8$ problem with $R = 15$, observe that there are 20 peaks, counting a peak as being any time at which the observed frequency stops decreasing and starts increasing. This kind of distribution is typical of the numerical problems which are quite rectangular (i. e., $m \gg n$) and which have a large job ratio R.

In order to explain the various results obtained, including the phenomenon of peaks, let us consider the following model of the problem we are trying to solve: represent jobs by rectangles, all of unit width, whose length is proportional to the job time. We wish to construct from these a Gantt chart by putting all the rectangles representing work to be done by a given facility in a row, in such a way that the precedence relations are satisfied. We want to solve the puzzle of putting these rectangles together into a Gantt chart which is of shortest length.

Examination of the graphs in Appendix 7 shows that both the spread and the number of peaks increase approximately linearly as R increases. When $R = 1$, we have the nonnumerical case for which there is one peak and a spread of seven. When $R = 15$, there are 16 peaks and a spread of 92. Interpreting in terms of the above puzzle idea, we find that it follows that it is possible to put together Gantt charts of a wide range of lengths, but within the range, some lengths are much easier to achieve than others. Thus, as R increases, the combinatorial aspects of the problem increase rapidly.

A measure of the worth of the Monte Carlo process is the length of the shortest schedule observed. In order to get an idea of how good the shortest schedule is, we make two comparisons : first, with the most probable schedule observed in the Monte Carlo process, which we take to be representative of the scheduling process when it is done in a completely decentralized way, i. e., with each man at his machine making the necessary scheduling decisions; second, with the SIO (for "shortest imminent operation," also called FOFO for "first off, first on") loading rule, which is a local scheduling rule that says that the operator should assign that operation to the machine which will be completed first. In Appendix 8 we have graphed, for the $20 \times 20 * 10$ series of problems, the average shortest schedule, the average most probable schedule, and the average SIO schedule as a function of R. Clearly, the average shortest and average SIO schedules are superior to the average most probable schedule for all values of R. And the SIO schedule is slightly superior to the average shortest schedule for several values of R.

The SIO schedule, as we constructed it, made a unique choice whenever there was a set of choices. We suspect that we could have done even better with this rule if we had run it several times and chosen at random whenever there was more than one possibility. Unfortunately, this idea was not tried in our series of runs.

In the Monte Carlo choice process, the most probable schedules are, as in the nonnumerical case, those with fewest conflict resolutions. However, in the numerical case the shortest schedules are not necessarily those which have the fewest conflict resolutions. For instance, in the example on p. 501 of [1], the two shortest schedules (length 16) have three conflict resolutions and have probability 1/8 each of being chosen, whereas the schedule of length 18 has two conflict resolutions and hence has probability 1/4 of being chosen by the

Monte Carlo process. Thus the amplification factor does not necessarily work to our advantage in the numerical case. What it does is to select a certain group of schedules (the ones with fewest conflict resolutions) and to increase the probability of choosing them while decreasing the probability of choosing others.

5. CONCLUSIONS

For the reasons just mentioned, it seems likely that a Monte Carlo process that uses rules as guides in its random choices will be considerably superior to a purely random choice device. In fact, Fischer and Thompson in [2] report on a study which logically follows the one here, in which they devised some learning strategies to guide the program in its use of rules.

Among the definite conclusions of the present study is that a correlated strategy (the best schedule found in k tries) is considerably better than an uncorrelated strategy (the most probable). Second, the SIO rule does about as well as a correlated strategy. And a correlated SIO rule (the best of several tries with the SIO rule, when conflicts are resolved at random) should do even better. Of course, the installation of a correlated rule in a factory would require considerable amounts of hardware, involving perhaps a signalling device located at each machine. The question is whether the installation would be profitable when the cost of the additional equipment and complication versus the expected benefits are taken into consideration, and the answer is far from clear at the present time.

The reason the SIO rule appears to be good in the present context is probably because it tends to keep work moving as quickly as possible, and hence to build up queues before many different machines. The longer the queues, the more likely it is that a machine can be kept usefully occupied.

It appears desirable that learning programs which utilize mixtures of loading rules should be developed as the next step. A start on these is reported on in [2].

REFERENCES

1. Giffler, B. and G. L. Thompson, "Algorithms for Solving Production Scheduling Problems," *Operations Research* **8** (1960), 487–503.

2. Fischer, H. and G. L. Thompson, "Probabilistic Learning Combinations of Local Job-Shop Scheduling Rules," Chapter 15 of this volume.

APPENDIX 1: SUMMARY OF DATA — COMPLETE ENUMERATION CASE

Run Identity	Number of schedules	Time in minutes	Minimum length	Probability of minimum length	Length most probable	Probability of most probable length	Spread
4 × 4 * 1	2	.00	2	1.000	2	1.000	1
4 × 4 * 2	12	.00	4	.667	4	.667	2
4 × 4 * 3	16	.001	5	.563	5	.563	2
4 × 4 * 4	71	.06	6	.155	7	.563	3
5 × 5 * 1	4	.00	2	1.000	2	1.000	1
5 × 5 * 2	12	.001	3	.333	4	.667	2
5 × 5 * 3	61	.018	5	.574	5	.574	3
5 × 5 * 4	687	.31	7	.261	8	.517	4
5 × 5 * 5	1,894	1.30	8	.181	9	.479	4
6 × 6 * 1	36	.00	3	1.000	3	1.000	1
6 × 6 * 2	290	.09	4	.145	5	.607	3
6 × 6 * 3	914	.48	6	.488	6	.488	3
6 × 6 * 4	7,546	4.82	7	.117	9	.362	5
6 × 6 * 5	84,802	70.18	8	.011	11	.306	6
10 × 10 * 1	8	.00	2	1.000	2	1.000	1
10 × 10 * 2	256	.05	5	1.000	5	1.000	1
10 × 10 * 3	27,673	20.62	6	.096	7	.500	3
10 × 10 * 4	112,783 [a]	75.10 [a]	8	.734	8	.734	3

[a] The 10 × 10 * 4 run was incomplete.

APPENDIX 2: SUMMARY OF DATA—MONTE CARLO NONNUMERICAL CASE

Run identity	Number of schedules	Time in minutes	Minimum length	Probability of minimum length	Length most probable	Probability of most probable length	Spread
4 × 4 * 2	1000	.57	4	.678	4	.678	2
4 × 4 * 3	500	.32	5	.548	5	.548	2
4 × 4 * 4	500	.46	6	.188	7	.594	3
5 × 5 * 2	1000	.57	3	.368	4	.632	2
5 × 5 * 3	1000	.91	5	.623	5	.623	3
5 × 5 * 4	1000	1.27	7	.657	7	.657	4
5 × 5 * 5	1000	1.56	8	.419	8	.419	4
6 × 6 * 2	1000	.84	4	.314	5	.633	3
6 × 6 * 3	1000	1.10	6	.633	6	.633	3
6 × 6 * 4	3113	4.60	7	·406	7	.406	4
6 × 6 * 5	3861	7.57	8	.136	9	.354	6
6 × 6 * 6	1000	2.76	9	.004	11	.378	7
6 × 6 * 6	5000	11.70	9	.008	11	.346	7
7 × 7 * 2	1000	.90	4	.369	5	.631	2
7 × 7 * 3	1000	1.30	6	.541	6	.541	3
7 × 7 * 4	1000	1.74	7	.251	8	.596	4
7 × 7 * 5	1000	1.90	8	.048	10	.441	5
7 × 7 * 6	1000	3.40	10	.139	12	.355	5
7 × 7 * 7	1000	3.60	11	.009	13	.411	6
7 × 7 * 7	5000	17.20	11	.007	13	.393	8
8 × 8 * 1	1000	.54	3	1.000	3	1.000	1
8 × 8 * 2	1000	.86	4	.554	4	.554	2
8 × 8 * 3	1000	1.31	5	.127	6	.567	4
8 × 8 * 4	1000	1.88	6	.025	8	.495	5
8 × 8 * 5	1000	2.54	8	.058	9	.452	5
8 × 8 * 6	1000	3.16	9	.016	11	.387	6
8 × 8 * 7	1000	3.95	11	.017	13	.358	7
8 × 8 * 8	1000	4.63	12	.016	14	.321	7
9 × 9 * 2	1000	.65	3	1.000	3	1.000	1
9 × 9 * 3	1000	1.37	6	1.000	6	1.000	1
9 × 9 * 4	1000	1.93	7	.657	7	.657	3
9 × 9 * 5	1000	2.46	8	.271	9	.674	3
9 × 9 * 6	1000	3.36	10	.262	11	.384	5
9 × 9 * 7	1000	4.32	12	.193	13	.391	6
9 × 9 * 8	1000	5.09	13	.077	15	.339	6
9 × 9 * 9	1000	5.90	14	.027	16	.341	7
10 × 10 * 2	1000	1.14	5	1.000			
10 × 10 * 3	5000	9.43	6	.356	7	.584	3
10 × 10 * 4	3037	7.50	8	.795			3

Run identity	Number of schedules	Time in minutes	Minimum length	Probability of minimum length	Length most probable	Probability of most probable length	Spread
10 × 10 * 5	2177	7.02	9	.188	10	.621	5
10 × 10 * 6	2076	8.65	11	.230	12	.415	5
10 × 10 * 7	1680	8.28	12	.069	14	.430	5
10 × 10 * 8	1156	6.61	13	.006	15	.439	6
10 × 10 * 8	1000	5.60	13	.009	15	.407	7
10 × 10 * 8	1000	5.55	13	.013	15	.390	7
10 × 10 * 8	1000	5.63	13	.006	15	.397	6
10 × 10 * 9	1775	10.17	15	.081	17	.369	6
10 × 10 * 9	1321	9.05	15	.076	16	.349	6
10 × 10 * 10	1109	8.88	16	.012	18	.327	8
20 × 20 * 10	200	3.62	19	.005	22	.270	7
30 × 30 * 10	200	5.43	18	.005	21	.355	7
30 × 30 * 15	200	8.95	27	.015	29	.250	9
40 × 40 * 10	200	7.40	19	.005	23	.305	9
40 × 40 * 20	100	10.13	37	.010	42	.250	10
50 × 50 * 1	200	.71	4	1.000			
50 × 50 * 2	200	1.26	5	.090	6	.910	2
50 × 50 * 2	1000	6.10	5	.077	6	.923	2
50 × 50 * 3	200	1.85	7	.380	8	.585	4
50 × 50 * 4	200	2.62	9	.315	10	.530	3
50 × 50 * 5	200	3.47	11	.155	12	.570	4
50 × 50 * 6	200	4.33	12	.010	14	.460	5
50 × 50 * 7	200	5.61	14	.010	16	.430	7
50 × 50 * 8	200	6.43	16	.060	18	.435	7
50 × 50 * 9	200	7.65	18	.045	20	.425	9
50 × 50 * 10	200	8.80	19	.015	21	.315	8
50 × 50 * 10	1000	43.45	19	.004	21	.325	9
50 × 50 * 15	100	8.09	30	.040	32–3	.210	8
50 × 50 * 20	100	12.63	38	.040	40	.220	9
100 × 50 * 10	100	12.10	31	.040	33	.340	8
200 × 10 * 10	50	54.57	202	.080	203	.240	8
200 × 25 * 10	100	57.86	96	.050	101	.210	12
100 × 10 * 10	50	16.1	104	.020	106	.220	7
40 × 40 * 15	200	12.86	28	.010	32	.270	10
10 × 50 * 25	100	2.77	28	.040	30	.470	6
20 × 50 * 25	100	5.60	32	.020	34	.300	9
30 × 50 * 25	100	9.08	37	.050	40	.240	9
40 × 50 * 25	100	14.23	41	.020	44	.250	9

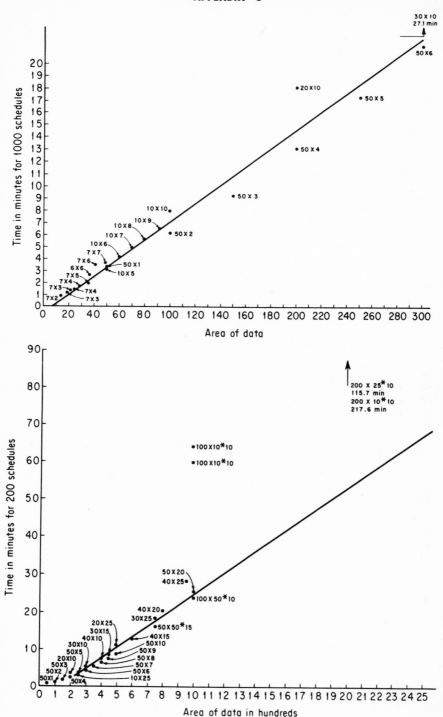

APPENDIX 4:   AREA, VOLUME FOR MONTE CARLO RUNS

Run	t Time for 200	Minimum length	A Area	$\dfrac{A}{t}$	V Volume	$\dfrac{V}{t}$	Most probable length	$V*$ Probable volume	$\dfrac{V*}{t}$
10 × 10 * 8	1.14	13	80	70.0	1,040	910	15	1,200	1050
10 × 10 * 8	1.12	13	80	71.5	1,040	930	15	1,200	1070
10 × 10 * 8	1.11	13	80	72.0	1,040	940	15	1,200	1080
10 × 10 * 8	1.13	13	80	71.0	1,040	924	15	1,200	1070
10 × 10 * 9	1.15	15	90	78.5	1,350	1180	17	1,530	1340
10 × 10 * 9	1.37	15	90	65.7	1,350	995	16	1,440	1050
10 × 10 * 10	1.60	16	100	62.5	1,600	995	18	1,800	1120
20 × 20 * 10	3.62	19	200	55.4	3,800	1050	22	4,400	1220
30 × 30 * 10	5.43	18	300	55.2	5,400	995	21	6,300	1160
30 × 30 * 15	8.95	27	450	50.2	12,150	1360	29	13,050	1480
40 × 40 * 10	7.40	19	400	54.0	7,600	1030	23	9,200	1240
40 × 40 * 20	20.26	37	800	39.5	29,500	1450	42	33,600	1660
50 × 50 * 1	.71	4	50	70.4	200	282	4	200	282
50 × 50 * 2	1.26	5	100	79.5	500	398	6	600	476
50 × 50 * 2	1.25	5	100	80.0	500	400	6	600	480
50 × 50 * 3	1.85	7	150	81.0	1,050	568	8	1,200	650
50 × 50 * 4	2.62	9	200	76.4	1,800	687	10	2,000	765
50 × 50 * 5	3.47	11	250	72.0	2,750	793	12	3,000	865
50 × 50 * 6	4.33	12	300	69.2	3,600	832	14	4,200	970
50 × 50 * 7	5.61	14	350	62.3	4,900	873	16	5,600	998
50 × 50 * 8	6.43	16	400	62.2	6,400	995	18	7,200	1120
50 × 50 * 9	7.65	18	450	58.8	8,100	1060	20	9,000	1180
50 × 50 * 10	8.80	19	500	56.8	9,500	1080	21	10,500	1190
50 × 50 * 10	8.68	19	500	57.5	9,500	1092	21	10,500	1210
50 × 50 * 15	16.18	30	750	46.5	22,500	1390	32–3	24,000	1480
50 × 50 * 20	25.26	38	1000	39.6	38,000	1500	40	40,000	1580
100 × 50 * 10	24.20	31	1000	41.3	31,000	1280	33	33,000	1360
100 × 10 * 10	63.00	104	1000	15.9	104,000	1650	109	109,000	1730
200 × 10 * 10	217.60	202	2000	9.2	404,000	1860	203	406,000	1870
200 × 25 * 10	115.72	96	2000	17.3	192,000	1670	101	202,000	1750
40 × 40 * 15	12.86	28	600	46.6	16,800	1306	32	19,200	1493
10 * 50 * 25	5.54	28	250	45.0	7,000	1264	30	7,500	1354
20 * 50 * 25	11.20	32	500	44.7	16,000	1428	34	17,000	1517
30 * 50 * 25	18.16	37	750	41.3	27,750	1528	40	30,000	1651
40 * 50 * 25	28.46	41	1000	33.9	41,000	1440	44	44,000	1546

APPENDIX 5

Run identity	Minimum length	Probability	Most probable		SIO length	Probability	Spread	Number humps	Time 500 scheds.
			Length	Probab.					
6 × 6 * 2 * 3	9	.320	10	.442	8	.32	4	2	.65
6 × 6 * 3 * 3	11	.056	13	.294	14	.102	9	1	.92
6 × 6 * 4 * 3	15	.006	19	.180	18	.170	11	2	1.22
6 × 6 * 5 * 3	19	.004	22	.204	22	.204	14	1	1.61
6 × 6 * 6 * 3	19	.008	23	.158	20	.040	15	1	1.79
6 × 6 * 2 * 10	31	.200	33	.246	40	.136	15	5	.66
6 × 6 * 3 * 10	32	.080	34	.226	32	.080	21	4	.93
6 × 6 * 4 * 10	41	.018	48	.138	47	.122	21	3	1.25
6 × 6 * 5 * 10	43	.004	58	.070	45	.006	36	6	1.57
6 × 6 * 6 * 10	63	.002	79	.090	69	.030	31	7	1.81
8 × 8 * 2 * 3	9	.432	9	.432	9	.432	6	2	.86
8 × 8 * 3 * 3	12	.042	14	.312	17	.098	8	3	1.19
8 × 8 * 4 * 3	13	.012	16	.234	15	.124	11	1	1.64
8 × 8 * 5 * 3	17	.002	21	.212	17	.002	12	1	2.08
8 × 8 * 6 * 3	23	.002	29–30	.156	28	.142	17	1	2.50
8 × 8 * 7 * 3	24	.004	29	.166	26	.082	15	2	2.94
8 × 8 * 8 * 3	26	.012	30	.182	26	.012	15	1	3.44
8 × 8 * 2 * 10	19	.078	21	.386	21	.386	11	5	.82
8 × 8 * 3 * 10	32	.024	42	.224	35	.066	20	6	1.20
8 × 8 * 4 * 10	34	.004	42	.112	47	.098	27	8	1.65
8 × 8 * 5 * 10	58	.002	72	.092	66	.050	35	7	2.07
8 × 8 * 6 * 10	58	.002	73	.072	83	.014	50	9	2.54
8 × 8 * 7 * 10	71	.006	86	.060	68		44	10	3.03
8 × 8 * 8 * 10	74	.006	89	.066	83	.040	39	9	3.43
20 × 20 * 4 * 1	7	.005	9	.62	8	.26	4	1	.0226
20 × 20 * 4 * 2	12	.015	15	.305	13	.085	8	1	.0220
20 × 20 * 4 * 3	19	.115	20	.260	18		9	1	.0213
20 × 20 * 4 * 5	29	.025	33	.180	28		16	5	.0214
20 × 20 * 4 * 8	35	.005	40	.155	38	.03	22	5	.0216
20 × 20 * 4 * 10	49	.01	58	.08	58	.08	28	8	.0217
20 × 20 * 4 * 15	77	.005	97	.06	83	.015	99	13	.0222
20 × 20 * 8 * 1	14	.03	16	.39	15	.265	6	1	.0459
20 × 20 * 8 * 2	24	.04	29	.255	26	.09	12	1	.0449
20 × 20 * 8 * 3	31	.005	38–9	.16	32	.01	15	3	.0442
20 × 20 * 8 * 5	49	.005	60	.10	47		24	7	.0441
20 × 20 * 8 * 8	88	.02	97–8	.075	90	.005	28	7	.0438
20 × 20 * 8 * 10	90	.005	103	.09	88		34	7	.0437
20 × 20 * 8 * 15	145	.005	159	.05	154	.00	68	13	.0441
20 × 20 * 2 * 1	21	.085	23	.32	21	.05	7	1	.0707
20 × 20 * 2 * 2	35	.01	39	.205	32		13	1	.0689
20 × 20 * 2 * 3	45	.015	51	.165	46	.03	16	3	.0678
20 × 20 * 2 * 5	73	.015	83, 85	.095	70		34	7	.0677
20 × 20 * 2 * 8	111	.005	125	.07	101		51	10	.0667
20 × 20 * 2 * 10	137	.005	166	.05	138	.00	61	15	.0664
20 × 20 * 2 * 15	205	.005	229	.045	201		104	18	.0683

Run identity	Minimum length	Probability	Most probable		SIO length	Probability	Spread	Number humps	Time 500 scheds.
			Length	Probab.					
20 × 20 * 16 * 1	27	.02	30	.28	27	.02	9	1	.0959
20 × 20 * 16 * 2	43	.02	48	.18	39		14	2	.0939
20 × 20 * 16 * 3	60	.005	67	.125	56		25	3	.0937
20 × 20 * 16 * 5	96	.005	109	.10	96	.005	37	6	.0923
20 × 20 * 16 * 8	146	.01	164	.07	142		47	11	.0916
20 × 20 * 16 * 10	175	.005	204	.05	175	.005	71	15	.0912
20 × 20 * 16 * 15	276	.01	294	.045	256		94	19	.0903
20 × 20 * 20 * 1	34	.015	37	.250	33		11	1	.1225
20 × 20 * 20 * 2	55	.01	61	.13	53		17	3	.1203
20 × 20 * 20 * 3	77	.015	89	.115	75		27	7	.1188
20 × 20 * 20 * 5	121	.005	129 136	.065	116		34	8	.1175
20 × 20 * 20 * 8	185	.01	206	.06	181		61	11	.1160
20 × 20 * 20 * 10	233	.005	254 257	.05	226		60	14	.1158
20 × 20 * 20 * 15	330	.005	367	.06	309		94	17	.1158
50 × 50 * 10 * 3	42	.005	47	.195	43	.025	18	3	.1112
50 × 50 * 10 * 5	66	.005	80	.095	80	.095	24	6	.2095
50 × 50 * 10 * 8	105	.01	115	.07	103		48	7	.2064
50 × 50 * 10 * 10	121	.005	140	.08	118		55	12	.2063
50 × 50 * 10 * 15	180	.005	203	.055	175		72	14	.2055

APPENDIX 6: 20×20 SERIES

R	Average spread	Average peaks	Average shortest	Average most probable	Average SIO
1	7	1	21	23	21
2	13	2	33	38	33
3	18	3	46	56	45
5	29	7	74	84	71
8	42	9	113	126	110
10	55	12	157	185	157
15	92	16	207	229	201

APPENDIX 7

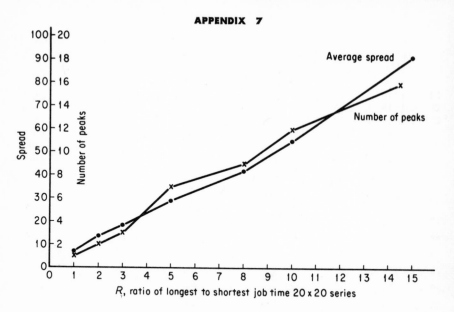

R, ratio of longest to shortest job time 20 x 20 series

APPENDIX 8

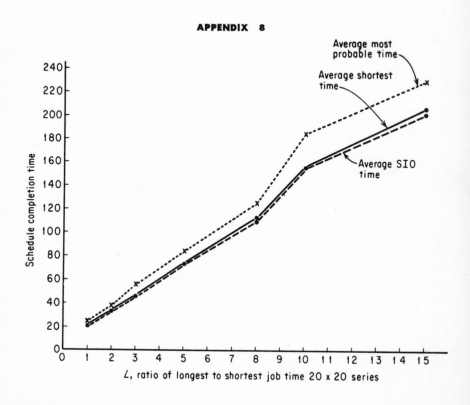

L, ratio of longest to shortest job time 20 x 20 series

4

Schedule Algebras and their Use in Formulating General Systems Simulations

Bernard Giffler

INTERNATIONAL BUSINESS MACHINES CORPORATION

The intent of this paper is to summarize some theory of scheduling[1] and, in particular, to show how the theory is used to define and solve production scheduling problems ordinarily solved by simulation. Two basic types of problems are considered: (1) determinate problems in which the desired answers are implicit in the given data, e.g., problems to determine the start times of tasks, if the order relations which connect them and the time required to perform each task are given; (2) indeterminate problems in which there is insufficient data to determine the answers and for which it is necessary to define functions to generate the missing data, e.g., production scheduling problems in which the order of performing tasks on facilities is not given a priori but must be determined by the repeated application of a schedule rule.

[1] B. Giffler, "Mathematical Solution of Production Planning and Scheduling Problems", *IBM ASDD Technical Report*, October 1960.

A paper presented at the Factory Scheduling Conference, Carnegie Institute of Technology, May 10–12, 1961.

The primary objective of this work is to display new and more efficient ways to solve production scheduling problems and to simplify the effort required to write computer programs to implement these solutions. Sample problems are solved, both mathematically and in the algorithmic form suitable for computer programming.

1. ORDER RELATIONS IN SCHEDULING

Underlying every scheduling problem is an order system whose elements are the tasks to be scheduled. The basic order relation, which connects the tasks, is called the *precedes* relation and is designated by the symbol $\leq$. The statement $a \leq b$ is taken to mean that task a must start at the same time or before task b or, more simply, that task a precedes task b.[2] The relation $\leq$ is transitive, reflexive, and antisymmetric. That is, (1) $a \leq a$ for all a, (2) $(a \leq b) \wedge (b \leq c) \rightarrow a \leq c$, and (3) $(a \leq b) \wedge (b \leq a) \rightarrow a = b$.

Note that a precedes relations does not exist between two tasks simply because one happens to start at the same time or before the other. For this relation to exist, there must be a compelling technological necessity for one of the tasks to start at the same time or before the other. For example, if there are two tasks, one to prime a surface for painting and the other to paint it, then a precedes relation would exist between the tasks, since the priming task must start at the same time or before the painting task. Similarly, two tasks that are performed by the same facility will have a precedes relation with each other if, for some reason, one is compelled to start at the same time or before the other.

The precedes relation $\leq$ includes the relation *next-precedes*, denoted by the symbol $\ll$. We take the statement $a \ll b$ to mean that task a next-precedes task b, or, more specifically, that there exists a transitive chain of relations $\leq$ from a to b which includes no other task as an intermediary. The distinction between the relations $\leq$ and $\ll$ may be clarified by the example which follows.

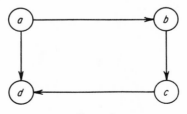

Figure 1

----

[2] The word "precedes" is used as though it had precisely the same meaning as the longer phrase "must start before or at the same time."

Order systems may be conveniently represented by·directed graphs as in the following example. Figure 1 illustrates a system of four tasks : a, b, c, and d. The precedes relations are $a \leq a$, $a \leq b$, $a \leq c$, $a \leq d$, $b \leq b$, $b \leq c$, $b \leq d$, $c \leq c$, $c \leq d$, $d \leq d$. The next-precedes relations are $a \ll b$, $a \ll d$, $b \ll c$, $c \ll d$. This order system, being an abstract conception, could conceivably represent the under-lying order system of any number of specific, concrete problems. For example, tasks a and b could be successive tasks to produce a commodity 1 ; tasks c and d could be successive tasks to produce a commodity 2. The technological requirements for the building of the two commodities could thus account for the two next-precedes rela-tions, $a \ll b$ and $c \ll d$. The two remaining next-precedes relations could arise if tasks a and b must, for technological reasons, be perform-ed consecutively by a production facility and, similarly, tasks b and c.

Each precedes relation $a \leq b$ contains one or more chains of zero or more relations $\ll$. With reference to Figure 1, the relation $a \leq d$ consists of two chains of relations $\ll$, namely, $a \ll b \ll c \ll d$ and $a \ll d$. The first of these chains is said to be of level 3, since it con-sists of three relations $\ll$; the second is said to be of level 1. Each precedes relation of a task to itself is said to consist of one chain of level zero.

2. QUANTIFYING ORDER RELATIONS

Each chain of (zero or more) relations $\ll$ is quantified by associat-ing with it a number which is the minimum interval of time neces-sary to traverse the chain. Thus, with a one-level chain, $a \ll b$, we would associate a number which is a minimum time after task a has started before task b can start. A two-level chain, say $a \ll b \ll c$, would be quantified by a number which is the conventional sum of the quantifiers of the two one-level chains of which it is composed. Before attempting to continue this discussion, we pause briefly to introduce a new notation which will make this subject easier to comprehend.

We express the fact that task i does not next-precede task j by the notation,

$$s_{ij}^{(1)} = 0. \tag{1}$$

The superscript (1) tells us we are talking about one-level chains ; the subscripts i and j, that we are talking about a one-level chain from i to j ; the number 0 (to which the symbol $s_{ij}^{(1)}$ is equated) tells us that there is no one-level chain from i to j or, in other words, that i does not next-precede j.

If task i does next-precede j we would write that

$$s_{ij}^{(1)} = t_{ij} \qquad (2)$$

where t_{ij} is a minimum interval of time, after task i has started, before task j can start. Since, theoretically, t_{ij} can represent a time interval of "zero magnitude" and since the symbol 0 has already been spoken for (its use in the expression $s_{ij}^{(1)} = 0$ means that $i < / < j$),[3] we introduce a new symbol for zero magnitude, namely, the Greek letter iota, ι. To avoid confusing 0 for ι, and vice versa, we refer to the symbol 0 always as zero. We refer to the symbol ι always as iota or zero magnitude.

The number ι has immediate application in quantifying all chains of level 0. We simply say that

$$s_{ij}^{(0)} = \iota, \qquad \text{if } i = j$$
$$= 0, \qquad \text{if } i \neq j. \qquad (3)$$

It is characteristic in production scheduling problems that there can be, at most, one chain of level 0 between any two tasks. This does not hold, of course, for chains of level greater than zero. For this reason, we introduce the concept of the "set of all chains of given level" which connect two tasks.

The notation for the set of all chains of level 0 from i to j is $(s_{ij}^{(0)})$. We already know that this set can contain at most one member, namely, zero, if $i \neq j$, or iota, if $i = j$. Similarly, the set of all chains of level 1 from i to j is written as $(s_{ij}^{(1)})$. This set will contain the number zero if $i < / < j$, or it will contain one or more positive numbers,[4] t_{ij}'s, if $i \ll j$. These definitions are expressed by the equality statements.

$$(s_{ij}^{(0)}) = (\iota), \qquad i = j$$
$$= (0), \qquad i \neq j \qquad (4)$$

and

$$(s_{ij}^{(1)}) = (t_{ij}\text{'s}), \qquad i \ll j$$
$$= (0), \qquad i < / < j. \qquad (5)$$

The set of the times to traverse all chains of level 2 can be obtained easily from the sets of the times to traverse all chains of level 1. We write that

$$(s_{ij}^{(2)}) = (t_{ik} + t_{kj}) \qquad (6)$$

for all tasks k such that $i \ll k \ll j$.

[3] The symbol $< / <$ is to be read "does not next-precede."

[4] A set $(s_{ij}^{(1)})$ will contain as many positive entries as there are independent reasons for a next-precedes relation to exist between the tasks i and j. For example, a task i may have to next-precede a task j because i and j are successive tasks to produce a single commodity and also because the technology of the facility (or facilities) which performs the tasks requires that they be performed consecutively.

Another, and potentially more useful, way to summarize the calculation of the set $(s_{ij}^{(2)})$ is to write that

$$(s_{ij}^{(2)}) = \sum_k (s_{ik}^{(1)}) \odot (s_{kj}^{(1)}) \qquad (7)$$

where "multiplying" $(s_{ik}^{(1)})$ and $(s_{kj}^{(1)})$ means to add each entry in $(s_{ik}^{(1)})$ to all entries in $(s_{kj}^{(1)})$ when they are both nonzero, and the "summation over k" means to collect all the "products" into one set. The computation indicated in Equation (7) leads one to conjecture that, by a suitable redefining of the operations of plus and times, a mathematical system could evolve which would make it possible to reduce the logical and computational operations in scheduling problems to routine manipulation of suitably defined matrices. Two mathematical systems of this character, called "schedule algebras," have in fact been developed. They are described in Section 3.

3. SCHEDULE ALGEBRAS

This section describes two special algebras (actually, matrix rings) for scheduling problems. The first of these algebras is equivalent in terms of its postulates to conventional matrix algebra and is called schedule algebra. The other algebra, to be described further on, is equivalent in terms of its postulates to the conventional matrix algebra of nonnegative matrices. This latter algebra is called schedule* algebra.

The elements of schedule algebra are rectangular matrices whose (i, j)th entries are sets. To avoid possible confusions, we always refer to the elements of the algebra as *matrices* and enclose all symbols for matrices in brackets. We refer to the sets as *sets* or (*element-sets*) and enclose symbols for these sets in parentheses. We reserve the term "element" to refer only to the individual entries in the sets. Symbols for elements are never enclosed.

The set (0), which contains only the number zero, is said to be empty. If a set is not empty, it may contain any number of positive or negative numbers, except that no two numbers may have precisely the same magnitude and opposite sign. The numbers we have in mind are the numbers of conventional arithmetic with the one exception that the conventional number for zero magnitude is to be replaced by the pair of numbers, ι and $-\iota$.

Matrices $[A]$ and $[B]$ may be added if they are of the same size. We write, in this case, that $[A] \oplus [B] = [C]$ and understand the matrix $[C]$ to be the schedule algebraic sum of the matrices $[A]$ and $[B]$. The (i, j)th set, (c_{ij}), of $[C]$ is formed, in a manner similar to that of conventional matrix algebra, by "adding" the corresponding (i, j)th sets, (a_{ij}) and (b_{ij}), of the matrices $[A]$ and $[B]$. Thus to complete the definition of schedule algebraic addition, we have only to state how one "adds" two sets. To add two sets we perform the following sequence of operations:

1. Collect the entries of both sets.
2. Replace by a zero all pairs of entries which have the same magnitude but opposite sign.
3. If one entry remains which is not zero, suppress all zeros. If all remaining entries are zeros, suppress all zeros but one.

The following example illustrates the addition of two 2 by 3 matrices:

$$\begin{bmatrix} (\iota) & (1, -\iota) & (-5) \\ (0) & (\iota) & (0) \end{bmatrix} \oplus \begin{bmatrix} (0) & (-1) & (5) \\ (\iota) & (-\iota) & (-\iota) \end{bmatrix}$$

$$= \begin{bmatrix} (\iota, 0) & (1, -1, -\iota) & (-5, 5) \\ (0, \iota) & (\iota, -\iota) & (0, -\iota) \end{bmatrix} = \begin{bmatrix} (\iota) & (-\iota) & (0) \\ (\iota) & (0) & (-\iota) \end{bmatrix}. \quad (8)$$

Matrix multiplication in schedule algebra resembles conventional matrix multiplication. For example, a matrix $[B]$ can be premultiplied by a matrix $[A]$ only if $[A]$ has exactly as many columns as $[B]$ has rows. The product matrix, in this case, will have as many rows as $[A]$ and as many columns as $[B]$.

We indicate that $[B]$ is to be premultiplied by $[A]$ by writing $[A] \odot [B]$ or, if there is no ambiguity, $[A]\,[B]$. We determine the (i, j)th set of the product, $[A]\,[B]$, by performing the operation indicated by the following equation:

$$(p_{ij}) = \sum_k (a_{ik}) \odot (b_{kj}). \quad (9)$$

In this equation the set (p_{ij}) is the (i, j)th set of the product $[A] \odot [B]$; (a_{ik}) and (b_{kj}) are (i, k)th and (k, j)th sets of $[A]$ and $[B]$. The equation tells us to add the "products" of all kth pairs of sets (a_{ik}) and (b_{kj}), where addition is the schedule algebraic addition just previously defined. To form the schedule algebraic product of two sets, (a_{ik}) and (b_{kj}), we form and add the product of each element in (a_{ik}) with all elements in (b_{kj}). Again, addition is the schedule algebraic addition previously defined. Thus to complete the rule for multiplication we need only to define how to multiply two elements. The rule for this multiplication follows.

$$\begin{aligned} a \odot b = |a| + |b| = c \quad & \text{if } a \text{ and } b \text{ have the same sign,} \\ = -c \quad & \text{if } a \text{ and } b \text{ have opposite signs,} \\ = 0 \quad & \text{if } a \text{ or } b \text{ is zero.} \end{aligned}$$

The plus sign in the above rule indicates a conventional operation of addition.[5] Consequently, $\iota \odot a = a$ for all a and, similarly, $-\iota \odot a = -a$ for all $a \neq 0$.

Following is an example of the schedule algebraic multiplication of a 1 by 2 vector by a 2 by 2 matrix.

$$[(\iota, -1) \quad (1,1)] \begin{bmatrix} (\iota, 1) & (0) \\ (\iota) & (-1) \end{bmatrix} = [(\iota, 1, -1, -2, 1, 1) \quad (-2, -2)]$$

$$= [(\iota, -2, 1, 1) \quad (-2, -2)] \qquad (10)$$

Matrices in schedule algebra obey, with respect to $\oplus$ and $\odot$, the same postulates as do matrices in conventional matrix algebra. The identity matrix in addition is written $[0]$; all of its sets are (0); that is, empty. Every matrix $[A]$ has a unique inverse in addition. The (i, j)th set of the inverse has the same elements as the (i, j)th set of $[A]$, except that respective entries will have opposite signs.

The identity matrix in multiplication is the square matrix $[I]$, having sets (ι) on its main diagonal and (0) elsewhere. As in conventional matrix algebra, inverses in multiplication will be unique (when they exist).

The matrix $[-I]$ is defined the same as $[I]$ except that its diagonal sets are $(-\iota)$. Premultiplying or postmultiplying any matrix by $[-I]$ serves to change the sign of all nonzero elements in the matrix. The matrix $[-I]$ enables us formally to define a schedule algebraic operation of subtraction. We simply say that

$$[A] \ominus [B] = [A] \oplus [-I] \odot [B] \qquad (11)$$

It may be instructive, at this point, to remark that all theorems in conventional matrix algebra which depend solely on the postulates of the algebra apply also in schedule algebra.

3.1. An Alternative Rule For Addition

In many scheduling problems it is computationally convenient to change the rule for matrix addition so that it becomes a "maximizing" operation. When this change in the rule for addition, and its several unavoidable consequences, are introduced into schedule algebra, we call the algebra schedule* algebra. The same postulates apply in schedule* algebra as in schedule algebra, except that there are no inverses in addition. This change makes schedule* algebra equivalent, in terms of its postulates, with the conventional matrix algebra of all nonnegative matrices. A brief description of the algebra follows.

---

[5] Note that conventional addition is not a formal operation in schedule algebra but is used only as a device to simplify the explanation of how one is to form the magnitude of a schedule algebraic product.

Matrices in schedule* algebra have entries which are either zero or a nonnegative number (including iota). The symbol for schedule* algebraic addition is *. As in schedule (and conventional) matrix algebra, two matrices may be added only if they are of the same size. The (i, j)th entry of the sum matrix $[A] * [B]$ is max (a_{ij}, b_{ij}), where a_{ij} and b_{ij} are the (i, j)th entries $[A]$ and $[B]$. The number 0 in these maximizations is treated as though it were negative infinity. The identity matrix for addition in schedule* algebra is written $[0]$ and has zero entries everywhere.

Schedule* algebraic multiplication of matrices is exactly the same as in schedule algebra, except that all additions which occur in the matrix multiplications are to be carried out according to the maximizing rule, defined above. The identity matrix in multiplication is the square matrix $[I]$ having entries ι on its main diagonal and 0 elsewhere. Schedule* algebraic multiplication of matrices is denoted by the symbol #. Examples of a schedule* algebraic matrix addition and multiplication follow

$$
\begin{bmatrix} 1 & 0 \\ \iota & 1 \end{bmatrix} * \begin{bmatrix} 0 & 1 \\ 1 & 5 \end{bmatrix} = \begin{bmatrix} \max (1,0) & \max (0,1) \\ \max (\iota,1) & \max (1,5) \end{bmatrix} = \begin{bmatrix} 1 & 1 \\ 1 & 5 \end{bmatrix}
$$

$$
\begin{bmatrix} 1 & 0 \\ \iota & 1 \end{bmatrix} \# \begin{bmatrix} 0 & 1 \\ 1 & 5 \end{bmatrix} = \begin{bmatrix} \max (1 \odot 0, 0 \cdot 1) & \max (1 \odot 1, 0 \cdot 5) \\ \max (\iota \odot 0, 1 \cdot 1) & \max (\iota \odot 1, 1 \cdot 5) \end{bmatrix}
$$

$$
= \begin{bmatrix} 0 & 2 \\ 2 & 6 \end{bmatrix}. \tag{12}
$$

4. SCHEDULE ALGEBRAIC FORMALIZATIONS

We define a one-level (or next-precedes) matrix $[S]$, whose (i, j)th set

$$
\begin{aligned}
(s_{ij}^{(1)}) &= (t_{ij}\text{'s}), && \text{if } i \ll j \\
&= (0), && \text{if } i < l < j
\end{aligned} \tag{13}
$$

where the t_{ij}'s are minimum intervals, after task i has started, before task j can start.

We define the zero-level precedes matrix $[S^0]$ to be a square matrix with (i, j)th set

$$
\begin{aligned}
(s_{ij}^{(0)}) &= (\iota), && \text{if } i = j \\
&= (0), && \text{if } i \neq j.
\end{aligned} \tag{14}
$$

$[S^0]$ is, of course, the identity matrix $[I]$.

The set $(s_{ij}^{(2)})$ of all two-level chains from task i to task j is the schedule algebraic sum of all kth products, $(s_{ik}^{(1)}) \odot (s_{kj}^{(1)})$. That is,

$$
(s_{ij}^{(2)}) = \sum_k (s_{ik}^{(1)}) \odot (s_{kj}^{(1)}). \tag{15}
$$

The above process may be extended to determine the set of all w-level chains from i to j. The equation is

$$(s_{ij}^{(w)}) = \sum_k (s_{ik}^{(w-k)}) \odot (s_{kj}^{(k)}) \tag{16}$$

where k is any nonnegative integer equal to or less than w.

Equation (15) is compactly expressed for all (i, j)th pairs of tasks by the schedule algebraic matrix equation,

$$[s^w] = [s^{w-k}] \odot [s^k]. \tag{17}$$

The (i, j)th set, $(s_{ij}^{(w)})$, of $[S^w]$ will contain as many nonzero elements as there are chains of w relations $\ll$ between i and j. Further, each element, being the sum of the wt's in one chain, is a lower bound on the time to traverse all w-level chains from i to j. If there are no w-level chains from i to j, the attempt to calculate $(s_{ij}^{(w)})$ will produce the empty set, (0). We designate the set of the lengths of all chains (of any level) from i to j by the symbol (θ_{ij}), and write that

$$(\theta_{ij}) = (s_{ij}^{(0)}) \oplus (s_{ij}^{(1)}) \oplus \cdots \oplus (s_{ij}^{(\lambda^*)}) \tag{18}$$

where λ^* is the maximum number of relations $\ll$ in any chain from i to j. We assemble the (θ_{ij}) into the matrix $[\theta]$ and write that

$$[\theta] = [I] \oplus [S] \oplus \cdots \oplus [S^\lambda] \tag{19}$$

where λ is the maximum of all λ^*. It is clear that $[S^k] = [0]$ for all $k > \lambda$.

We now state that $\qquad [\theta] = [I \ominus S]^{-1}. \tag{20}$

To prove this result we multiply both sides of Equation (20) by $[I \ominus S]$ and rearrange terms to produce the equation

$$[\theta] = [I] \oplus [S][\theta]. \tag{21}$$

We now expand this result by repeated premultiplications of both sides by $[S]$ and additions of $[I]$ to obtain

$$[\theta] = [I] \oplus [S] \oplus \cdots \oplus [S^{\lambda+1}][\theta]$$

and, consequently, since $[S^{\lambda+1}][\theta] = [0]$,

$$[\theta] = [I] \oplus [S] \oplus \cdots \oplus [S^\lambda]. \tag{22}$$

The matrix $[\theta]$ summarizes all the restrictions on the starts of jth tasks which are the consequence of the relations $\ll$ and the time intervals associated with these relations. Each set (θ_{ij}) contains (if it is not empty) the lengths of time to traverse all chains of relations $\ll$ from i to j, and is a lower bound on the closeness of the starts of i and j. The maximum entry in the set is denoted by the symbol φ_{ij}. It is greatest of the lower bounds and represents the shortest possible interval of time which can separate the tasks' respective starts.

It is possible to show that, if all unpreceded tasks start at time (say) t_0, then j can start exactly at time $t_0 + \max (\varphi_{ij})$, and not sooner.

To show some of the manipulative power of schedule algebra, we consider briefly the problem to determine the effect on the matrix $[\theta]$ of changing one or more entries in $[S]$. In the argument to follow, we assume that we know $[\theta_0] = [I \ominus S_0]^{-1}$ and wish to compute the matrix $[\theta_1]$ which results if we change $[S_0]$ to (say) $[S_1]$. We begin by defining the change matrix

$$[\Delta S_1] = [S_1] \ominus [S_0]$$

and write that

$$[\theta_1] = [I \ominus S_1]^{-1} = [I \ominus S_0 \ominus \Delta S_1]^{-1}. \tag{23}$$

Premultiplying the right-hand side of Equation (23) by

$$[I \ominus S_0]^{-1}[I \ominus S_0] = [I]$$

and noting that

$$[I - S_0][I \ominus S_0 \ominus \Delta S_1]^{-1} = [[I \ominus S_0 \ominus \Delta S_1][I \ominus S_0]^{-1}]^{-1}$$

we obtain

$$\begin{aligned}[\theta_1] &= [I \ominus S_0]^{-1}[I \ominus S_0][I \ominus S_0 \ominus \Delta S_1]^{-1} \\ &= [I \ominus S_0]^{-1}[[I \ominus S_0][I \ominus S_0]^{-1} \ominus \Delta S_1[I \ominus S_0]^{-1}]^{-1} \\ &= [\theta_0][I \ominus \Delta S_1 \theta_0]^{-1}. \end{aligned} \tag{24}$$

When there have not been many changes to $[S_0]$, $[\Delta S_1 \theta_0]$ will tend to be sparse, with the result that $[I \ominus \Delta S_1 \theta_0]$, the matrix to be inverted, will be nearly an identity matrix and, consequently, relatively easy to invert. In any event, there is a great variety of known numerical methods for speeding and compacting inversions of matrices of this general form. Several of these methods are treated in detail in reference [1].

For the cases in which one needs to know only the maximum chains connecting (i, j)th pairs of tasks, it is possible to define a schedule* algebraic matrix $[\varphi]$, whose (i, j)th entry is the number φ_{ij} (previously defined), and to solve directly for this matrix by using the equation

$$[\varphi] = [I] * [S] * \cdots * [S^\lambda]$$

or, noting that $S^{\lambda+1} = [0]$,

$$[\varphi] = [I] * [S] \, \# \, [\varphi]. \tag{25}$$

In the above equations, an entry in $[S]$ is assumed to contain, at most, one element: zero, if the set is empty, or the maximum of the set. This assumption is implied whenever we use schedule* algebraic formalizations and is the reason that each set is represented always by the entry it contains.

Equation (25), and also Equation (20), may be solved with much economy of effort by iterative eqations of which the following are examples. These iterative solutions are possible because $[S^{2+1}]$ contains only zero entries.

$$(\theta_{ij}) = (\iota), \qquad\qquad i = j$$

$$= \sum_k (s_{ik}^{(1)}) \odot (\theta_{kj}), \qquad i \neq j$$

$$\varphi_{ij} = (\iota), \qquad\qquad i = j$$

$$= \sum_k s_{ik}^{(1)} \mathbin{\sharp\!\sharp} \varphi_{kj}, \qquad i \neq j \qquad\qquad (26)$$

Starting (and/or complete) times of tasks may also be computed iteratively. We begin by defining the row vector $[T_0]$ whose jth element $t_j^{(0)}$ is the earliest time the jth task can start if it is an unpreceded task and is zero, otherwise.[6] We then define the row vector $[T]$ whose jth element t_j is the actual time at which the jth task starts. These t_j's may be computed iteratively by the following schedule* algebraic equation:

$$t_j = t_j^{(0)} * \sum_k t_k \mathbin{\sharp\!\sharp} s_{kj}^{(1)}. \qquad\qquad (27)$$

5. DETERMINATE SCHEDULING PROBLEMS

We recognize two classes of scheduling problems: determinate problems and indeterminate problems. We say that a problem is determinate if the answer which is sought is implicit in the given restraints of the problem. The determinate problem, as a type of problem, is similar to a problem of solving a set of simultaneous equations in that the answer (namely, the values of the unknowns) is implicit in the equations.

A scheduling problem in contrast is indeterminate if the restraints do not imply the answer but, at most, a set of possible (or feasible) answers. To solve the indeterminate problem, one must first make it determinate. This is customarily accomplished in scheduling problems by specifying a rule for selecting next tasks to be performed; that is, when the next task is not prescribed by (or implicit in) the given restraints. The rule essentially narrows down the set of feasible answers by successively adding restraints to the initial set of restraints until finally one answer remains.

---

[6] Generally, the $t_j^{(0)}$'s can be arbitrary restraints on the starting times of any task, whether it is preceded or not.

5.1. Example of a Determinate Scheduling Problem

In this section we consider briefly the following problem: we are given a set of n tasks and are told that certain pairs of these tasks must be performed consecutively (that is, without a third task intervening), and we are given, for each of these pairs, the minimum time interval, after the first task starts, before the second can start. We are finally told when each unpreceded task starts and are asked to find when all tasks start.[7]

One approach to the solution of the above problem has already been indicated; see Equation (27). We, however, will take this opportunity to display an alternative approach. We note first that we are given the matrix $[S]$ and a row vector $[T_0]$, whose jth entry, $t_j^{(0)}$, is the start time of task j, if j is unpreceded, and is zero otherwise. Now if we let $[T]$ with jth entry t_j be a row vector of the starting times which are to be determined, we can write that

$$[T] = [T_0] \,\sharp\, [\varphi]$$
$$= [T_0] \,\sharp\, [I * S * S^2 * \cdots * S^\lambda]$$
$$= [T_0] * [T_0 S] * [T_0 S][S] * [T_0 S^2][S] * \cdots * [T_0 S^{\lambda-1}][S]. \quad (28)$$

This last equation can be put into the following form:[8]

$$[T] = [T_\lambda]$$

where

$$[T_\lambda] = [T_{\lambda-1}] * [T_{\lambda-1}][S] = [T_{\lambda-1}][I * S]$$

and   (29)

$$[T_1] = [T_0] * [T_0][S] = [T_0][I * S].$$

To solve the given problem, we need only to solve Equation (29), and for this we need a computing algorithm. One possible algorithm is the following.

Step 1. Prepare a sequence of n boxes (or words) to be called T. Place the given start time of an ith task in the ith box of T. Place a zero in all other boxes of T. (The algorithm, as it proceeds, will eventually place the start of each task in its corresponding box in T.)

Step 2. Prepare a triplet of boxes for each given next-precedes relation. In the first box of each triplet, place the index i of the task which next-precedes; in the second box, place the index j of the task which is next-preceded; in the third box, place the given minimum time t_{ij}, after the first task starts, before the second can

---

[7] The problem is equivalent to determining the earliest possible starting times of tasks on a critical path diagram.

[8] The derivation of Equation (29) makes use of a special property of Schedule* Algebraic addition, namely, that $[A] * [A] = [A]$ for all $[A]$.

start. Sequence the triplets, j indices within i indices. Call this set of boxes N.

Step 3. Set an index $K = 0$ and place this index in (or next to) each ith box in T which contains a nonzero entry. Call the number attached to an ith box the K_i number of the box.

Step 4. Note the "leftmost" box in T with $K_i = K$; say it is the ith box. (Initially, all nonzero boxes will have $K_i = 0$.)

Step 5. Add (in the conventional sense) the entry in the ith box above to the first t_{ij} in N. Compare the sum with the entry in the jth box of T. If the sum is greater, replace the entry in the jth box by the sum and check the box. Repeat this step with each jth successive t_{ij}.

Step 6. Repeat from Step 3 until there are no boxes with $K_j = K$. When this happens, increase the K_i number of all checked boxes by one and uncheck; advance K to $K + 1$ and repeat from Step 4. If there are no checked boxes, transfer to OUT.

OUT. When this step is reached, the ith box in T will contain the start time of the ith task.

6. INDETERMINATE SCHEDULING PROBLEMS

The basic distinction between a determinate and indeterminate scheduling problem having already been made (Section 5), we shall, in this section, proceed directly to outline solutions to a specific class of indeterminate scheduling problems commonly referred to as production simulations. We characterize these scheduling problems and the context in which they occur as follows.

1. There are n tasks to be performed. For each task there is specified a group of facility-types which is needed to perform the task. There may be one or more facilities of each type available to perform the task.

2. Certain pairs of tasks, because of the structure of the products being produced, must be performed consecutively. For each of these pairs there is given a number which is the minimum delay, after the first task starts, before the second can start.

3. Certain pairs of tasks, because they are to be performed by a same facility-type and possibly by a same facility of the given type, may be performed consecutively.[9] For each of these pairs there is given a number which is the minimum delay, after the first task in the pair starts, before the second can start—if we assume, of course, that

[9] This means, in the context of the particular problem being considered, that tasks i and j are to be performed by a same facility-type and that they may, consequently, be performed consecutively by asame facility of the type.

the second task ultimately next-follows the first task on a same facility.

4. For some tasks there will be given an earliest time at which the tasks may be started. These times are likely to be specified in the following circumstances: (a) The task is associated with a product which is not to be released for manufacture until the specified time. (In this case it is sufficient to specify these times only for the un-preceded tasks.) (b) The task requires special equipment, raw material, service, etc., which will not be available before the specified time.

5. For each task there may be given a number which is the time necessary to perform the task to completion.

The problem is to determine, for each task, the particular facilities which perform it and the time it starts. Also, if the time to perform the task to completion is given, the ending time is determinable. To solve the problem, we assume that there is given a rule for determining which task is to be performed next. A mathematical solution to the problem using the schedule* algebra follows.

We begin by redefining the problem. We assemble the information in items 1, 2, and 3 (above) into an open $[S_0]$ matrix whose (i, j)th entry,

$$
\begin{aligned}
s_{ij} &= t_{ij}, &&\text{if it is given that } i \ll j, \\
&= t_{ij}x_{ij}, &&\text{if it is possible that } i \ll j, \\
&= 0, &&\text{if it is impossible that } i \ll j. \quad (30)
\end{aligned}
$$

The variable x_{ij} is given the value ι if tasks i and j are assigned to be performed consecutively by a same facility; otherwise, x_{ij} is set equal to 0. S_{ij} is set equal to 0 at the outset, if it is given that $i = j$, that $j \le i$ or $j \ll i$, or if it is given that i and j are to be performed by facilities of different types, and it is not given that $i \ll j$.

The information in item 4 (above) is assembled into the schedule* algebraic vector $[T_0]$ whose jth entry is the earliest permitted start time of j, if this is specified, and is zero otherwise.

The information in item 5 does not require special treatment, its main use being to determine the completion times of tasks, if their starting times are given. In many cases the time intervals, referred to in item 5, will be the same as one or the other of the intervals referred to in items 2 and 3.

To simplify explanations, we shall assume that there is exactly one facility of each type, that each task requires exactly one of these facilities for its performance, and that next tasks are selected to be performed by these facilities by the FOFO (first off, first on) rule. This rule has many variations. However, for our sample problem it means simply that each task selected to be performed next by a facility must be that particular task which will first make the facility (which performs it) available to perform another task. Note that the rule does not require that a task be available to start when the facility is next available to start, or that the selected task be picked from the queue of tasks which may have been waiting for the availability of the facility. The rule will occasionally schedule a facility to be idle even though some one or more tasks are waiting for the facility. When this happens, the rule will likely be holding the facility available for a short-running job which is on its way.

We are now ready to display an iterative procedure for determining the starting times of all tasks. This procedure is imitative of the procedure used to determine the starting time of tasks in the determinate scheduling problem considered in Section 5. See Equation (29).

Step 1. Construct the vector $[T_0]$ and the matrix $[S_0]$ described above.

Step 2. Locate each null or potentially null column in $[S_0]$. (A column is potentially null if it could be made null by setting all x's in the column equal to zero and striking all entries in rows of tasks previously selected to start.)

Step 3. Determine, for each jth task whose column was located in Step 2, a "test number" equal to the jth entry of the vector $[T_0]$, increased by the minimum coefficient of an x in the jth tasks row in $[S_0]$. These computed numbers, called *FACATS* (facility available time), are the earliest times that the facility which performs j could be available to start a next task, if j were to be selected to start next. Select that jth task whose calculated *FACAT* is minimum.

Step 4. Update $[S_0]$ to $[S_1]$ as follows: (a) set each ith x_{ij} in column j equal to zero; (b) set each x_{jk} (if there are any) equal to y_{jk} (this change of variable is explained in a following paragraph); (c) if there is a y_{hj}, set it equal to iota and all other y_{hk} (if any) equal to zero.

Step 5. Compute $[T_1] = [T_0] * [T_0 \sharp S_1]$. In multiplying $[S_1]$ by $[T_0]$, treat all x_{ij}'s as though they were 0, all y_{ij}'s as though they were iota.

Steps 1 through 5 show how the first task is selected to start and how the problem is then transformed so that the process may be repeated. Specifically, to select a next task to start, one repeats Steps 3, 4, and 5, replacing in the process $[S_0]$ by $[S_1]$, $[T_0]$ by $[T_1]$, $[S_1]$ by $[S_2]$, and $[T_1]$ by $[T_2]$. One continues in this vein until all tasks are selected, at which time all variables (x and y) in the original $[S_0]$ will have been replaced by an iota or a zero. The final jth entries in $[T]$ are the starting times of the jth tasks.

The variables y are of a transitory nature. They represent the value which x_{ij} may assume on its way to becoming an iota or a zero. The reason for its introduction is that when a jth task is selected to start, we know immediately the tasks which can no longer next-precede it. We do not, however, know the particular task (if any) which will next-follow it. We only know that (possibly) one of the x_{jk} will be set equal to iota and the others to zero. While the x_{jk}'s are in this "status," we call them y_{jk}'s.

6.1. A Numerical Example

We consider the following numercial problem: two products, $P1$ and $P2$, are to be manufactured. $P1$ is assumed to have been released at time iota; $P2$, at time 3. Each product requires for its manufacture the performance of three tasks. The interrelation of the tasks and their relevant processing times are depicted in the flow diagrams of Figure 2.

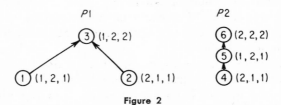

Figure 2

In the figure, the numbers in the nodes of the flow charts identify the tasks. The ordered triplet (x, y, z) of numbers, which is placed adjacent to each node, has the following meaning: x is the index of the facility-type needed to perform the task (note that each task is performed by one or the other of two facility-types); y is the minimum time, after i starts, before the next task to advance the product can start; z is the minimum time, after i starts, before a next task can follow i on the same facility. There are no a priori restrictions on the order in which the tasks are to be performed by the facilities.

The first step is to construct the matrices $[T_0]$ and $[S_0]$, as shown below. These matrices are constructed so that the ith row and (or) column represent the ith task. Each x in $[S_0]$ is a different variable.

$$[T_0] = [\iota \quad \iota \quad \quad 0 \quad \quad 3 \quad 0 \quad 0]$$

$$[S_0] = \begin{bmatrix} 0 & 0 & \max(2, 1x) & 0 & 1x & 0 \\ 0 & 0 & 1 & 1x & 0 & 1x \\ 2x & 0 & 0 & 0 & 2x & 0 \\ 0 & 1x & 0 & 0 & 1 & 1x \\ 1x & 0 & 1x & 0 & 0 & 2 \\ 0 & 2x & 0 & 2x & 0 & 0 \end{bmatrix}$$

(31)

Having constructed $[S_0]$, we note that tasks 1, 2, and 4 are potentially null and have respective FACATS of 1, 1, and 4. Since tasks 1 and 2 are tied, we select task 1 (arbitrarily) to start. This act of selection changes $[S_0]$ to

$$[S_1] = \begin{bmatrix} 0 & 0 & \max(2, 1y) & 0 & 1y & 0 \\ 0 & 0 & 1 & 1x & 0 & 1x \\ 0 & 0 & 0 & 0 & 2x & 0 \\ 0 & 1x & 0 & 0 & 1 & 1x \\ 0 & 0 & 1x & 0 & 0 & 2 \\ 0 & 2x & 0 & 2x & 0 & 0 \end{bmatrix}. \tag{32}$$

We compute $[T_1] = [T_0] * [T_0 \; \sharp \; S_1]$ and obtain

$$[T_1] = [\iota \quad \iota \quad 2 \quad 3 \quad 4 \quad 0]. \tag{33}$$

We now note that the tasks with potential null columns are 2 and 4 (task 1 having started, we overlook its row and column) and that their FACATS happen to remain 1 and 4, respectively. Consequently, we select task 2 to start next. This selection changes $[S_1]$ to

$$[S_2] = \begin{bmatrix} 0 & 0 & \max(2, 1y) & 0 & 1y & 0 \\ 0 & 0 & 1 & 1y & 0 & 1y \\ 0 & 0 & 0 & 0 & 2x & 0 \\ 0 & 0 & 0 & 0 & 1 & 1x \\ 0 & 0 & 1x & 0 & 0 & 2 \\ 0 & 0 & 0 & 2x & 0 & 0 \end{bmatrix}. \tag{34}$$

Computing $[T_2] = [T_1] * [T_1 \; \sharp \; S_2]$, we obtain

$$[T_2] = [\iota \quad \iota \quad 2 \quad 3 \quad 4 \quad 6]. \tag{35}$$

The tasks with potential null columns are now 3 and 4 and have FACATS of 4 and 4, respectively. We select task 3 to start, again arbitrarily breaking a tie in the process. This selection changes $[S_2]$ to

$$[S_3] = \begin{bmatrix} 0 & 0 & 2 & 0 & 0 & 0 \\ 0 & 0 & 1 & 1y & 0 & 1y \\ 0 & 0 & 0 & 0 & 2y & 0 \\ 0 & 0 & 0 & 0 & 1 & 1x \\ 0 & 0 & 0 & 0 & 0 & 2 \\ 0 & 0 & 0 & 2x & 0 & 0 \end{bmatrix}. \tag{36}$$

Computing $[T_3] = [T_2] * [T_2 \; \sharp \; S_3]$, we get

$$[T_3] = [\iota \quad \iota \quad 2 \quad 3 \quad 4 \quad 6]. \tag{37}$$

The tasks with potential null columns are now just one task, namely, task 4. Since there is only one possible selection, there is no point in computing its FACATS. It is selected to start next, and we have

$$[S_4] = \begin{bmatrix} 0 & 0 & 2 & 0 & 0 & 0 \\ 0 & 0 & 1 & 1 & 0 & 0 \\ 0 & 0 & 0 & 0 & 2y & 0 \\ 0 & 0 & 0 & 0 & 1 & 1y \\ 0 & 0 & 0 & 0 & 0 & 2 \\ 0 & 0 & 0 & 0 & 0 & 0 \end{bmatrix} . \tag{38}$$

Computing $[T_4] = [T_3] * [T_3 \,\sharp\, S_4]$, we get

$$[T_4] = [\iota \quad \iota \quad 2 \quad 3 \quad 4 \quad 6]. \tag{39}$$

Again, there is only one task with a potential null column, namely, task 5. Consequently, it is the next selection to start and gives us

$$[S_5] = \begin{bmatrix} 0 & 0 & 2 & 0 & 0 & 0 \\ 0 & 0 & 1 & 1 & 0 & 0 \\ 0 & 0 & 0 & 0 & 2 & 0 \\ 0 & 0 & 0 & 0 & 1 & 1y \\ 0 & 0 & 0 & 0 & 0 & 2 \\ 0 & 0 & 0 & 0 & 0 & 0 \end{bmatrix} . \tag{40}$$

from which we compute $[T_5] = [T_4] * [T_4 \,\sharp\, S_5]$, or

$$[T_5] = [\iota \quad \iota \quad 2 \quad 3 \quad 4 \quad 6]. \tag{41}$$

The last task to be selected is task 6. Its selection gives us

$$[S_6] = \begin{bmatrix} 0 & 0 & 2 & 0 & 0 & 0 \\ 0 & 0 & 1 & 1 & 0 & 0 \\ 0 & 0 & 0 & 0 & 2 & 0 \\ 0 & 0 & 0 & 0 & 1 & 1 \\ 0 & 0 & 0 & 0 & 0 & 2 \\ 0 & 0 & 0 & 0 & 0 & 0 \end{bmatrix} . \tag{42}$$

and

$$[T_6] = [T_5] * [T_5] \,\sharp\, [S_6] = [\iota \quad \iota \quad 2 \quad 3 \quad 4 \quad 6]. \tag{43}$$

$[S_6]$ is the final determinate $[S]$. $[T_6]$ is the start time vector $[T]$. Each jth entry of $[T]$ is the starting time of the jth task.

6.2. Duplicate Facilities

There are many possible directions in which to generalize the problem and solution presented in the sections immediately preceding. Unfortunately, there is not sufficient space to discuss more than one of these possible generalizations, namely, the modification in the solution which is necessary when there are arbitrary numbers of facilities of each type. We point out, in passing, that no modification is required to accommodate the case where the tasks require the simultaneous availability of two or more different facility-types for their performance. In this event, one simply sets s_{ij} equal to $t_{ij} x_{ij}$ if one or more of the facility-types needed to perform i is needed also to perform j. One could conceivably have a different t_{ij} for each facility-type. However, it is sufficient (for the problem we are considering) to use the t_{ij} which is maximum.[10]

Where there are any number of facilities of each type, we add to the number of tasks to be performed by each facility-type a number of dummy tasks which take iota time for processing and which neither precede or are preceded by any other task. The dummy tasks, however, may next-precede, or be next-preceded by, any of the legitimate tasks to be performed by the same facility-type for which they were invented.

In a problem with dummy tasks of the above description, we make the dummies the first tasks to start. This is done in one operation by changing all x's in the dummies' columns to zeros and all x's in their rows to y's. Having done this, we could proceed with the solution in the normal way if it were not for the fact that there may now be more than one entry with a coefficient of y in the column of a task which is a candidate to start. (There will, in fact, be as many entries with coefficients of y as there are duplicate facilities available to perform the condidate.) In this case, we do *not*, in multiplying $[S_0]$ by the vectors $[T_k]$, set all y_{ij} equal to ι, but only that y_{ij} (in each column j) which will make the jth entry of the vector product a minimum. The effect of this modification in the solution of the scheduling problem is to cause each jth task (selected to start) to be started by that particular facility (of the required type) which has been waiting longest for a next job or, if none happens to be waiting, by that particular facility which will be first available to take a next job.

6.3. Alternative Schedule Rules

An essential property of a solution to an indeterminate problem is that it must be able, after each selection of a task to start, to trans-

---

[10] It is also worth noting in passing that the formulation automatically takes account of possible savings in set-ups which are the consequence of the particular order in which tasks are started on facilities. This is accomplished as follows: we assume that the interval of time t_{ij} to perform a task i is composed of two components, namely, $t_{ij} = t'_{ij} + s_{ij}$, where t'_{ij} is the time needed to perform i, assuming that the facility (or facilities) needed to perform i are set up to perform i, and that s_{ij} is the time to tear down and set up the facility to perform the particular j which may next-follow i. Clearly, we can have a different t_{ij} for each j which may next-follow i on a same facility. Also, no task which i might firmly next-precede need be delayed while a facility, which performs i, is being torn down and set up for a next-following j.

form the original problem so that the rule may be applied again. The specific object of the transformation is to make available that information about the new status of the system which is needed to reapply the schedule rule.

In the FOFO problem considered in Section 6, the essential information needed to apply the schedule rule is the possible starting times of each task whose column in $[S]$ is a potential null column. This information is routinely generated by the repeated calculation of the vectors $[T_k]$. (It will be recalled that the jth entry of $[T_k]$ is precisely the earliest possible starting time of the jth task.)

Alternative schedule rules may require more or less information about the status of the system than FOFO. For example, one can conceive of schedule rules for which it would be necessary to compute, after each kth selection of a task to start, the matrix $[\varphi_k]$, or even $[\theta_k]$, corresponding to an $[S_k]$. On the other hand, one can conceive of schedule rules for which we would need only to know which tasks are available to be selected next.

REFFERENCES

1. Giffler, B., *Mathematical Solution of Production Planning and Scheduling Problems*, IBM ASDD Technical Report, (October 1960).

2. Giffler, B., *Production Control Formalizations Suitable for Electronic Data Processing*, IBM Research Report RC-20, (May 1957).

3. Giffler, B., *SIMPRO I: An IBM 704-7090 Simulation Program for Planning, Scheduling and Monitoring Production Systems*, IBM ASDD Technical Report, (December 1961).

4. Kelley, J. E., Jr., "Critical-Path Planning and Scheduling: Mathematical Basis," *Opns. Res.*, (May 1961).

5. Giffler, B. and G. L. Thompson, "Algorithms for Solving Production Scheduling Problems," *Opns. Res.*, (July 1960).

5

On the Job=shop Scheduling Problem

Rudolph C. Reinitz
SOCONY MOBIL OIL CO., INC.

1. GENERAL IDEAS AND METHOD OF APPROACH OF THIS PAPER

The job-shop operation is a complex system by its nature. It is a dynamic process with a continuous flow of orders. As much as we would desire to follow the history of every order through the shop, the task appears to be so formidable that an analytical treatment becomes prohibitive. But is it necessary to follow every order? Can we not look upon an order as a member of a population of orders and evaluate the statistical properties of the population as influenced by the parameters of the job shop? Such parameters may be labor and machine capacities, know-how of the personnel, storage facilities, etc.

We feel that such an approach may lead to a manageable analytical representation of the problem. This approach is a combination of

This paper is based on a Ph. D. thesis submitted to Case Institute of Technology, Cleveland Ohio. The author wishes to express his sincere gratitude to Professor John D. C. Little of Case Institute of Technology whose constant advice, encouragement, and many suggestions made the preparation of this work possible.

the queuing approach (the shop is viewed as a network of waiting lines) and the thermodynamic approach [1] (no attempt is made to know the location of the job at any particular time; instead, the probability of its being in various locations of the shop is defined).

A basic assumption in the models that are developed is that the service facilities in the shop operate independently and that the arrivals of jobs to a service center have a Poisson process. Empirical observations of job shops and related operations (e.g., airfields) have revealed that the arrivals of units to the various service departments approximated very closely the Poisson distribution [2, 3]. But there is also a rational basis for using the Poisson process as a model for a real-system input. The Poisson process may be looked upon as a limit of disintegration of scheduled processes. The arrivals to a service department originate from completed services in other departments. Each process at each department has some distribution of service time, and the divergence of events from the scheduled times randomizes the input process, an intrinsic characteristic of the Poisson Law.

This assumption makes it possible to reduce the formidable n-machine center sequencing problem to n one-machine center problems.

We also assume that the shop is able to handle all incoming orders (i.e., the utilization factor is less than one) and that the shop operates in statistical steady state.

With respect to the service time distribution, it is assumed to be exponential, or it may be approximated by either a hyperexponential or a k-Erlang distribution. The Markov process (discrete in space and continuous in time) proves to be an ideal mathematical representation of the system; it includes the stochastic properties of arrivals and departures of the orders.

We distinguish between two decision levels which are strongly interrelated :

1. Decisions concerning the *over-all shop* activity, such as accepting or rejecting orders, quoting delivery dates.

2. Decisions concerning the *machine center* operation, such as the sequencing of jobs through the machine center.

Mathematical models representing both decision levels are developed. We present a method for obtaining the waiting time distribution function, using the Kolmogorov equations [4], by introducing artifical absorbing states into the Markovian transition matrix and modifying the arrival rates. These time functions enable us to estimate the completion time of an order and its distribution function if a certain sequencing procedure is given. Delivery commitments are then based on the properties of the completion time distribution function.

The sequencing problem in a job shop is not a static problem. Because of the steady flow of orders, it is by no means clear that selecting the optimal sequence at each individual period will attain an over-all optimal procedure. For this reason, the problem has been formulated as a dynamic programming problem, and we use Howard's algorithm [5] to solve the recursive relations that have been expressed as N linear, constant-coefficient differential equations. These equations include the cost structure of our problem, and by Howard's policy iteration method we arrive at a sequencing procedure which yields the minimum total expected loss rate.

Solving for the optimal sequencing procedure requires the description of the system by the number of possible states that can occur (which may run into the thousands). In solving a real-life problem this may introduce serious limitations. It is hoped that within ten years or so computing machines that will solve large-scale programs quickly and inexpensively will be available.

2. INDIVIDUAL MACHINE CENTER MODEL (ANALYSIS)

We have indicated in the introduction of this paper that the performance of the individual machine centers has a direct effect on the performance of the over-all shop. The choice of a sequencing procedure affects the time a job waits to be processed, which in turn affects the waiting-time costs. It also affects the processing cost by selecting the order and the number of set-ups required to process the various jobs.

We shall show here how to calculate the waiting time of a job for a given sequencing procedure and how to obtain an optimal sequencing procedure.

2.1 Estimation of Waiting Time

a. The System

1. Machine center. The machine center consists of a fixed number of identical machines. Test, assembly, packaging stations, or any other department through which the job must go is included under this heading.

2. Input. The input to the system is composed of a steady flow of semifinished jobs to be processed by the machines. The jobs are grouped into r classes.

3. Output. The output of a center is either a semifinished job or a completed job.

b. Parameters of the Model

For each class we have :

λ_p = mean arrival rate, $p = 1, 2, \ldots, r$.

μ_{pk} = mean processing rate if job k follows p, where p, $k = 1$, 2, ..., r. The processing time of class p job includes the tear-down and make-ready operations (set-up) of the next job k.

c. Assumptions of the Model

1. The machine center is able to handle all the incoming orders (i.e., the utilization factor is less than one).

2. The arrival distribution of jobs is Poisson.

3. The service time distribution is exponential or may be approximated by either a hyperexponential distribution or a k-Erlang distribution.

4. The system is in steady state.

5. The number of possible states is finite. (A state is defined by the number of class p jobs waiting for service, $p = 1, 2, \ldots, r$, and the type of jobs being served at a given instant of time.) This assumption is required since the computers are limited with respect to the size of the problems they can solve. On the other hand, if in-process storage limitations are imposed on the system, the assumption is necessary in order to comply with such restrictions.

6. Each machine center with m identical machines, having $(1/m)\mu$ service rate, is approximated to a single channel system with service rate μ. This assumption is due primarily to computational savings. There is no conceptual difficulty in solving the problem for a set of multichannel service centers, except that the number of states will increase considerably.

7. Each operation, once started, must be performed to completion; i.e., irrespective of the classification of the job, it may not cut in on any job that has been started servicing (nonpre-emptive servicing procedure), but may displace all those waiting in the line if the procedure requires it.

8. Within each class, "first come, first served" discipline holds.

9. The sequencing procedure is fixed and known; i.e., given a state E_i, we know which of the waiting jobs to sequence next into the service facility once it becomes empty.

d. Mathematical Representation of a Service Center

In a small interval of time dt, a transition may occur from state i to a number of possible states. If the jobs are grouped into r classes, the states are represented by an $r + 1$ dimensional vector space. Thus a state vector $(p; n_1, n_2, \ldots, n_r)$ indicates that a class p job is served and waiting in line are n_1 of class 1, n_2 of class 2, $\ldots$, n_r of class r.

In the described system the transitions occur randomly in time. If a state E_i at time t_0 is given, no additional information concerning the states of the system at previous times can alter the probability of being in a state E_j at any future time $t_0 + t$.   For such systems the Chapman-Kolmogorov equation holds [4].

Let p_{ij} = the probability of making a transition from state i to state j in a short interval of time h.

$p_i(t)$ = the probability that the system is in state i at time t.

The Chapman-Kolmogorov equation gives the following recursive relation :

$$P_j(t + h) = \sum_i P_i(t) p_{ij} \tag{1}$$

where

$$\sum_j p_{ij} = 1. \tag{2}$$

Subtracting $P_j(t)$ from both sides of (1) gives

$$P_j(t + h) - P_j(t) = \sum_i P_i(t) p_{ij} - P_j(t) \tag{3}$$

$$P_j(t + h) - P_j(t) = \sum_i P_i(t)[p_{ij} - \delta_{ij}] \tag{4}$$

where δ_{ij} is the Kronecker delta such that

$$\delta_{ij} = \begin{cases} 1, & \text{if } i = j \\ 0, & \text{if } i \neq j. \end{cases} \tag{5}$$

Dividing Equation (4) by h and passing to the limit, we obtain

$$\lim_{h \to 0} \left[\frac{P_j(t + h) - P_j(t)}{h} \right] = \sum_i P_i(t) \lim_{h \to 0} \left[\frac{p_{ij} - \delta_{ij}}{h} \right]. \tag{6}$$

Define

$$T_{ij} = \lim_{h \to 0} \frac{p_{ij} - \delta_{ij}}{h}. \tag{7}$$

We assume that the T_{ij} exists.   For $i \neq j$, T_{ij} is called the transition rate from state i to state j.   Equations (6) and (7) finally give the well-known Kolmogorov forward equation

$$\frac{d}{dt} P_j(t) = \sum_i P_i(t) T_{ij}. \tag{8}$$

Equation (8) gives the rate of change of state probability P_j at time t and represents a *continuous* Markov chain process in *time* with discrete states.   Let $P(t)$ be a row vector; in matrix notation Equation (8) becomes

$$\frac{d}{dt} \boldsymbol{P}(t) = \boldsymbol{P}(t) T. \tag{9}$$

Since

$$\sum_j p_{ij} - 1 = 0 \tag{2}$$

and

$$\sum_j (p_{ij} - \delta_{ij}) = \sum_i p_{ij} - 1 \tag{10}$$

it follows that

$$\sum_j T_{ij} = 0; \qquad T_{ii} = -\sum_{j \neq i} T_{ij} \tag{11}$$

i.e., each row of a continuous Markov chain sums to zero.

We see that our system may be described by a set of Markov chains—one for each center.

e. The Waiting-Time Distribution Function To evaluate the waiting-time distribution of a job of class p in department d, we select one at random as it arrives and call it the "tagged job." Let us assume that the decision of which job to sequence next depends on the state the system is in and is known.

The following device enables us to keep track of our tagged job: all class p jobs which arrive after the tagged job are designated p'. In other words, we introduce an additional class of jobs, p', with the same transition rate as p, but all arrivals after the tagged job will join $n_{p'}$, and all departures of class p will deplete n_p. Since within each class we maintain "first come, first served" rule, the tagged job will enter the service facility when $n_p = 0$, and the unit in service is p.

Thus, we create absorbing states of the form $(p; n_1, \ldots, n_{p-1}, n_p = 0, n_{p'}, \ldots, n_r)$. Let all these states belong to the set A and the transient states to the set B.

Let $J =$ maximum number of jobs permitted to wait.

The transition matrix for this situation is obtained as follows: the system goes from state

$$(k; n_1, \ldots, n_p, n_{p'}, \ldots, n_r)$$

to state

$$(k; n_1, \ldots, n_p, n_{p'} + 1, \ldots, n_r)$$

with transition rate λ_p, if

$$\sum_{k=1}^{r} n_k < J$$

or to

$$(k; n_1, \ldots, n_h + 1, \ldots, n_p, n_{p'}, \ldots, n_r)$$

with transition rate λ_h, $h \neq p$, if

$$\sum_{k=1}^{r} n_k < J$$

or to

$$(p; n_1, \ldots, n_p - 1, n_{p'}, \ldots, n_r)$$

with transition rate μ_{kp}, if $n_p > 0$ and the procedure, according to which the system operates, sequences class p next; or it goes to

$$(h, n_1, \ldots, n_h - 1, \ldots, n_p, n_{p'}, \ldots, n_r)$$

with transition rate μ_{kh}, if $n_h > 0$ and the procedure, according to which the system operates, sequences class h next.

All other transitions have zero rates. The diagonal elements are the negative of the sum of all the transition rates in that row [see Equation (11)].

For the sake of a more compact notation, let the state be denoted by 1, 2, ... , i,... , j, ... , N and the transition rates by T_{ij}. Omitting the subscripts designating the tagged job and the department under consideration, let $q_j(t)$ be the probability that a given job p is still in the queue at time t after arrival, given that at time zero it joined the system, putting this system in state $j \epsilon B$.

$q_j(t)$ may be studied by applying the Chapman-Kolmogorov equation :

$$q_j(t + dt) = \sum_{\substack{k \in B \\ k \neq j}} T_{jk} q_k(t) \, dt + (1 - \sum_{\substack{k \in A \cup B \\ k \neq j}} T_{jk} dt) q_j(t). \qquad (12)$$

Equation (12) may be interpreted as follows : p will still be in queue an instant dt later if one of the following happens.

1. It may make a transition to state $k \in B$ $(k \neq j)$ an instant dt after it joined the queue. This event has the probability $T_{jk} dt$.

2. It does not make a transition to any other state an instant dt after it joined the queue. This event has a probability

$$(1 - \sum_{\substack{k \in A \cup B \\ k \neq j}} T_{jk} dt).$$

Noting that

$$T_{jj} = - \sum_{\substack{k \in A \cup B \\ k \neq j}} T_{jk}$$

transposing $q_j(t)$, dividing by dt and taking the limit, we get

$$\frac{dq_j(t)}{dt} = \sum_{k \in B} T_{jk} q_k(t), \qquad \text{for all } j \in B. \qquad (13)$$

Thus we can express the rate of change of the relevant time distribution function by properly defining the set of transient states.

Let us form a new transition matrix X which will include only the transient states of T. The transition rates of X will be such that

$$X_{jk} = T_{jk}, \qquad \text{if } j, k \in B.$$

From Equation (13) we have

$$\frac{dq_j(t)}{dt} = \sum_k X_{jk} q_k(t) \qquad (14)$$

Letting $Q(t)$ be a column vector of the $q_k(t)$, in matrix notation we have

$$\frac{dQ(t)}{dt} = XQ(t) \tag{15}$$

The Laplace transform of Equation (15) is

$$sQ(s) - Q(0) = XQ(s) \tag{16}$$

$$(sI - X)Q(s) = Q(0) \tag{17}$$

where I is the identity matrix. Multiplying both sides of Equation (17) with the inverse of $(sI - X)$, we obtain

$$Q(s) = (sI - X)^{-1}Q(0) \tag{18}$$

but

$$Q(0) = (1 \ldots 1)^T \tag{19}$$

since the probability that the tagged unit p is still in queue a time zero after it joined the system is one. Hence,

$$Q(s) = (sI - X)^{-1}(1 \ldots 1)^T. \tag{20}$$

Let $H(t)$ be the inverse transform of $Q(s)$. Then the unconditional cumulative waiting-time distribution $G_q(t)$ is obtained by weighting column vector $H(t)$ with the appropriate steady-state probability vector[1] P, of matrix T. Note that the matrix T contains all the states, transient and absorbing; i.e., the dimension of T is N, whereas the dimension of H is the number of states constituting the set B only.

$$G_q(t) = \sum_{j \in B} h_j(t) P_j' \tag{21}$$

where P_j' has the following meaning: let
$\quad P_j =$ steady-state probability of E_j using T.
$\quad B =$ transient states.
Then $P_i' = Prob\{$system in $E_j \in B$ immediately after an arrival of a job of class $p_j\}$. Each P_j' equals one of the steady state P_i, namely, the one such that, upon the arrival of a job of class p, E_i is transformed to E_j.

If we recall that our calculations pertain to the tagged job p, we obtain the cumulative waiting-time distribution of class p jobs by labeling Equation (21) with the pertinent index; i.e.,

$$G_{qp}(t) = \sum_{j \in B_p} h_{jp}(t) P_j'. \tag{22}$$

---

[1] The steady-state probability vector P is obtained by solving the set of simultaneous equations $PT = 0$ plus the normalizing requirement

$$\sum_{j=1}^{N} P_j = 1.$$

Let W_p = expected waiting time of job p in queue.

$E(t_{qp}^2)$ = the second moment of the waiting time of job p in queue.

$(\Delta t_{qp})^2$ = the variance of the waiting time of job p in queue.

We have

$$W_p = \int_0^\infty G_{qp}(t)\,dt \tag{23}$$

$$E(t_{qp}^2) = 2\int_0^\infty t\,G_{qp}(t)\,dt \tag{24}$$

$$(\Delta t_{qp})^2 = \int_0^\infty (2t - W_p)G_{qp}(t)\,dt. \tag{25}$$

Example Let J (the maximum number in queue) be two, and r (the number of classes) be one. In this model, jobs which arrive to find two jobs in queue are turned away. In calculating the waiting-time distributions and its moments, such jobs are considered to wait zero time. In this case we need not create an artificial class, since within each class the "first come, first served" rule holds. To distinguish the state at which the tagged job enters service, it is sufficient to make the arrival rate equal zero the moment the job joins the system. The absorbing states are then: the state in which there is no queue in the system and the service is busy, and the state when the facility is empty.

The X matrix is

State	$(1,1)$	$(1,2)$
$(1,1)$	$-\mu$	0
$(1,2)$	μ	$-\mu$.

$$\tag{26}$$

$(sI - X)$ and its inverse are

State	$(1,1)$	$(1,2)$
$(1,1)$	$s+\mu$	0
$(1,2)$	$-\mu$	$s+\mu$

$$(sI - X) = \tag{27}$$

State	$(1,1)$	$(1,2)$
$(1,1)$	$\dfrac{1}{s+\mu}$	0
$(1,2)$	$\dfrac{\mu}{(s+\mu)^2}$	$\dfrac{1}{s+\mu}$.

$$(sI - X)^{-1} = \tag{28}$$

$Q(s)^T$ is obtained by multiplying $(sI - X)^{-1}$ by the column vector $(1;\,1)^T$; thus

$$Q(s)^T = \left(\frac{1}{s + \mu}; \frac{\mu}{(s + \mu)^2} + \frac{1}{s + \mu}\right)^T. \tag{29}$$

The conditional cumulative waiting-time distributions, $B(t)^T$ are obtained by the inverse transform of $Q(s)^T$

$$B(t)^T = (e^{-\mu t}; \mu t e^{-\mu t} + e^{-\mu t})^T. \tag{30}$$

$B(t)^T$ is interpreted as follows: the probability that the unit is still in queue a time t after arrival, if we are given that the system was in state $(1, 1)$ after it joined the queue, is $e^{-\mu t}$. The probability that the unit is still in queue a time t after arrival, if we are given that the system was in state $(1, 2)$ after he joined the queue, is $(1 + \mu t)e^{-\mu t}$.

These results are well-known from queuing theory. The advantage the above derivation has for calculating waiting-time distributions is that it is applicable to any queuing discipline, irrespective of the rule it follows.

We still have to calculate the unconditional waiting-time distribution $G_q(t)$; the transition matrix T for the given case is

State   (0, 0)   (1, 0)   (1, 1)   (1, 2)

$$T = \begin{array}{c} (0,0) \\ (1,0) \\ (1,1) \\ (1,2) \end{array} \left|\begin{array}{cccc} -\lambda & \lambda & & \\ \mu & -\lambda - \mu & \lambda & \\ & \mu & -\lambda - \mu & \mu \\ & & \mu & -\mu \end{array}\right. \tag{31}$$

The steady-state probabilities of T are

$$P = (P_0; \ P_0\rho; \ P_0\rho^2; \ P_0\rho^3) \tag{32}$$

where

$$P_0 = \frac{1 - \rho}{1 - \rho^4} \qquad \rho = \frac{\lambda}{\mu}. \tag{33}$$

Finally,

$$G_q(t) = \rho P_0[e^{-\mu t} + \rho(1 + \mu t)e^{-\mu t}]. \tag{34}$$

The relevant steady-state probabilities are $P(1, 0)$ and $P(1, 1)$, since only in the states $(1, 0)$ and $(1, 1)$ is the unit joining the queue and waiting. Since $r = 1$, the index of the class is omitted in our notation.

The mean waiting time is

$$W = \int_0^\infty G_q(t)\,dt. \tag{23}$$

Substituting Equation (34) into Equation (23) and integrating, we obtain

$$W = P_0\rho\left[-\frac{1}{\mu}e^{-\mu t} - \frac{\rho}{\mu}e^{-\mu t} - \frac{\rho e^{-\mu t}}{\mu}(\mu t + 1)\right]_0^\infty \tag{35}$$

$$W = P_0 \frac{\rho}{\mu}(1 + 2\rho). \tag{36}$$

The second moment is

$$E(t_q^2) = 2 \int_0^\infty t G_q(t) \, dt \tag{24}$$

$$E(t_q^2) = 2P_0 \frac{\rho}{\mu^2}(1 + 3\rho). \tag{37}$$

The variance is

$$(\Delta t_q)^2 = \int_0^\infty (2t - W) G_q(t) \, dt \tag{25}$$

$$(\Delta t_q)^2 = 2P_0 \frac{\rho}{\mu^2}(1 + 3\rho) - \left[\frac{P_0 \rho}{\mu}(1 + 2\rho)\right]^2. \tag{38}$$

The actual calculation of the waiting-time distribution function $G_{pq}(t)$ is quite complicated, to say the least, since the functional form of Equation (20) must be preserved to find the inverse transform of $(sI - X)^{-1}$.

An alternative, but not so elegant, approach for finding $G_{pq}(t)$ is presented in which high-speed electronic computers may be utilized.

If we do not require the closed form of the waiting-time distribution but only its moments (as is the case for obtaining the over-all completion time distribution of an order), the computations become simpler, as will be illustrated after the alternative procedure for finding $G_{pq}(t)$ is presented.

Alternative procedure for finding the waiting-time distribution $G_{pq}(t)$. In Equation (15) we had

$$\frac{d}{dt} \boldsymbol{Q}_p(\boldsymbol{t}) = X_p \boldsymbol{Q}_p(\boldsymbol{t}). \tag{15}$$

The solution of Equation (15) is

$$\boldsymbol{Q}_p(\boldsymbol{t}) = \boldsymbol{Q}_p(0) e^{X_p t} \tag{39}$$

where

$$e^{X_p t} = \left[I + X_p t + \frac{1}{2!} X^2 t^2 + \cdots\right] \tag{39}$$

where $\boldsymbol{Q}(\boldsymbol{0})$, as before, is the probability that p is in the system at time zero (at the time of its arrival). Hence

$$\boldsymbol{Q}_p(\boldsymbol{t}) = e^{X_p t}(1, \ldots, 1)^T. \tag{40}$$

Then

$$\boldsymbol{Q}_p(\boldsymbol{t}) = \left(I + X_p t + \frac{1}{2!} X_p^2 t^2 + \frac{1}{3!} X_p^3 t^3 + \cdots\right)(1, \ldots, 1)^T. \tag{41}$$

$\boldsymbol{Q}_p(\boldsymbol{t})$ may be easily calculated, since it involves matrix multiplications and additions only. $e^{X_p t}$ can be approximated by the power series to a desired degree of accuracy by taking enough terms of expantion of Equation (41).

$Q_p(t)$ is conditional on the state the system is in at p's arrival. Arguing similarly as before, we find that the unconditional cumulative waiting-time distribution in steady state is

$$G_{qp}(t) = \sum_{j \in B} q_{jp}(t) P'_j, \qquad p = 1, 2, \ldots, r. \tag{42}$$

Deriving the rth moment of the waiting time.

In Equation (15) we obtained the rate of change of the cumulative waiting-time distribution vector $Q(t)$. The same relation will hold for the density function $W(t)$, since the density function may be obtained by differentiating the cumulative distribution function, and since the matrix X (of the transient states) pertains to both functions. Hence

$$\frac{dw_j(t)}{dt} = \sum_k X_{jk} w_k(t). \tag{43}$$

Let $Y_j =$ the time when the tagged job enters the service facility, if it is given that at time zero it joined the system, putting this system in state $j \in B$.

We have

$$w_j(t)\, dt = P[Y_j \in (t, t + dt)].$$

The rth moment of Y_j is

$$E(Y_j^r) = (-1)^r \frac{d^r}{ds^r} w_j(s) \Big|_{s=0} \tag{44}$$

where $w_j(s)$ is the Laplace transform of $w_j(t)$. The Laplace transform of Equation (43) is

$$s w_j(s) - w_j(0) = \sum_k X_{jk} w_k(s). \tag{45}$$

Taking the first derivative with respect to s in Equation (45),

$$w_j(s) + s \dot{w}_j(s) = \sum_k X_{jk} \dot{w}_k(s) \tag{46}$$

we have

$$w_j(0) = 1 \tag{47}$$

$$\dot{w}_j(0) = - E(Y_j) = - K_j \tag{48}$$

where K_j is the conditional mean waiting time.

Substituting Equations (47) and (48) into Equation (46) (evaluated at $s = 0$), we have

$$\sum_k X_{jk} K_k = - 1. \tag{49}$$

In matrix notation, let K be a column vector of the K_j:

$$XK = -(1, \ldots, 1)^T \tag{50}$$

or, assuming that the inverse of X exists,

$$K = -X^{-1}(1, \ldots, 1)^T. \tag{51}$$

The second moment of Y_j is obtained by differentiating Equation (46) with respect to s and setting $s = 0$.

$$\dot{w}_j(s) + \dot{w}_j(s) + s\ddot{w}_j(s) = \sum_k X_{jk}\ddot{w}_k(s)\Big|_{s=0}. \tag{52}$$

We have

$$\ddot{w}_j(0) = E(Y_j^2) = R_j \tag{53}$$

where R_j is the conditional second moment of the waiting time

$$-2K_j = \sum_k X_{jk}R_k \tag{54}$$

$$-2K = XR \tag{55}$$

or

$$R = (X^{-1})^2(2, \ldots, 2)^T. \tag{56}$$

We see that both the first and second moments of the conditional time an order spends in the queue are easily computed by simple manipulations such as matrix inversion and matrix multiplication. Given the state the center is in when the order arrives, we may estimate the time it will take to enter the service facility.

The unconditional mean and second moment vectors are obtained by weighting them with the *appropriate* steady-state probability vector P. (Note again the difference in the dimensions of K, R, and P, as in the cumulative time distribution case.)

To illustrate the point, let us take the same example as before:

$$X^{-1} = \begin{array}{c} \quad \\ (1,1) \\ (1,2) \end{array} \begin{array}{c} \text{State} \quad (1,1) \quad (1,2) \\ \left| \begin{array}{cc} -\dfrac{1}{\mu} & 0 \\[2mm] -\dfrac{1}{\mu} & -\dfrac{1}{\mu} \end{array} \right. \end{array} \tag{57}$$

$$K = \left(\frac{1}{\mu}, 2\frac{1}{\mu}\right)^T \tag{58}$$

$$W = K_1 P(1,0) + K_2 P(1,1) \tag{59}$$

$$W = P_0\frac{\rho}{\mu}(1 + 2\rho). \tag{60}$$

For calculating the second moment we have

$$\text{State } (1,1)(1,2)$$

$$(X^{-1})^2 = \begin{array}{c} (1,1) \\ \\ (1,2) \end{array} \left| \begin{array}{cc} \dfrac{1}{\mu^2} & 0 \\ \\ \dfrac{2}{\mu^2} & \dfrac{1}{\mu^2} \end{array} \right. \tag{61}$$

$$\boldsymbol{R} = 2\left(\frac{1}{\mu^2}, \frac{3}{\mu^2}\right)^T \tag{62}$$

$$E(t_q^2) = R_1 P(1,0) + R_2 P(1,1) \tag{63}$$

$$E(t_q^2) = 2P_0\left(\frac{\rho}{\mu^2}\right)(1 + 3\rho). \tag{64}$$

For calculating the variance of t_q, we have

$$(\Delta t_q)^2 = E(t_q^2) - W^2 \tag{65}$$

$$(\Delta t_q)^2 = 2P_0\frac{\rho}{\mu^2}(1 + 3\rho) - \left[P_0\frac{\rho}{\mu}(1 + 2\rho)\right]^2. \tag{66}$$

Until now we have discussed the waiting-time distribution of job p in department d. If we are interested in the completion-time distribution (time it takes for job p to leave the department), our computational procedures will hold, except for the absorbing states, which have to be redefined as

$$A = (k; n_1, \ldots, n_{p-1}, n_p = 0, n_p' \ldots n_r), \qquad \text{for all } k \neq p.$$

2.2. Deriving an Optimal Sequencing Procedure

a. The System Identical to Section 2.1

b. Parameters of the Model In addition to the center load parameters discussed in Section 2.1, we have the following cost parameters for each service center:

c_p = the in-process inventory cost rate of job p waiting to be served.

c_{pk} = the tear-down and set-up cost rate if job k follows p, $(k \neq p)$. c_{pk} is obtained by allocating the expected set-up cost over the expected service time.

d_p = customers' delay cost rate. Operationally, d_p has the following meaning: some contracts may specify penalties if delivery commitments are not met, and rewards for early deliveries. Such costs (rewards) may be of the form of dollars per unit time being late (early). In other cases the penalty (reward) of being late (early) may be associated with loss (gain) of anticipated profits. This can happen if late (early) deliveries cause loss (gain) of future business.

c. Assumptions of the Model Identical to Section 2.1, except for assumption 9. (Instead of assuming that the sequencing procedure is known, we shall show how to derive an optimal procedure.)

d. Decision Variable and Objectives in the Model Let a_j = the set of alternative choices while system is in state j. In each state of the system we have to decide which job should be processed next.

The objective is to minimize total expected costs due to in-process inventories, set-ups, and delays. This objective is achieved by finding the sequencing procedure that will minimize the total expected cost.

e. An Optimal Sequencing Procedure The sequencing problem in a job shop is not a static problem. Because of the steady flow of orders, it is by no means clear that selecting the optimal sequence at each individual period will attain an over-all optimal procedure. Therefore, we shall formulate the problem as a dynamic decision-making problem.

At each point in time, we have the alternative to sequence any of the jobs waiting for service ("first come, first served" within class is observed). We also have the alternative not to sequence any of the waiting jobs until a transition to another state occurs. Such a decision may be economically justified if we have a high enough cost to change the process.

The problem, then, is to sequence the stochastically arriving jobs so that the total expected cost will be minimum. This calls for selecting the alternatives that will optimize the objective function. The set of these alternatives for all states establishes the optimal policy.

To find the optimal policy, we apply Bellman's "Principle of Optimality" of dynamic programming [6], which states:

"An optimal policy has the property that, whatever the initial state and initial decision are, the remaining decisions must constitute an optimal policy with respect to the states resulting from the first decision."

Let
$f_i(t)$ = the total expected cost a service center will incur in the remaining t units of time starting in state i, if an optimal policy is followed.
C_{ii} = cost rate the center incurs while it is in state i.
C_{ij} = cost rate the center incurs while it makers a transition from state i to state j.

We have

$$C_{ii} = c_{pk} + \sum_{h=1}^{r} n_{ih}(c_h + d_h)$$

$$c_{pk} = 0, \quad \text{if } p = k$$

where n_{ih} is the number of class h jobs waiting for service in state i. c_{pk}, c_p, d_p are defined in paragraph b of this section.

By the principle of optimality we have

$$f_i(t + dt) = \min_{\{a_i\}} \left\{ (1 - \sum_{j \neq i} T_{ij}^{a_i} dt)(C_{ii}^{a_i} dt + f_i(t)) \right.$$

$$\left. + \sum_{j \neq i} T_{ij}^{a_i} f_j(t) dt \right\}, \quad \text{for } i = 1, 2, \ldots, N \quad (67)$$

where $\{a_i\}$ represents the set of possible alternatives in state i.

The recurrence relation in Equation (67) is obtained from the following reasoning : during the time interval dt the center may remain in state i or make a transition to some other state j. If it remains in state i for a time dt, it will incur a cost $C_{ii} dt$ plus the expected cost that it will incur in the remaining time t, which is $f_i(t)$. The probability that this happens is one minus the probability that it makes a transition in dt. On the other hand, there may be a transition to some state $j \neq i$ during a time interval dt with a probability $T_{ij} dt$. In this case, the center incurs a cost $C_{ij} dt$, which, multiplied by $T_{ij} dt$, is a higher-order term of dt and, therefore, neglected. Hence, the expected cost incurred if the center starts in state j with time t remaining, is $f_j(t)$. The second term must be summed over all possible states $j \neq i$. From the available set of alternatives $\{a_i\}$, we shall choose the one which will minimize the righthand side of Equation (67). (Note that the transition rates and the cost rates are functions of the alternative chosen.)

Substituting Equation (11) into Equation (67) and neglecting higher-order terms of dt gives

$$f_i(t + dt) = \min_{\{a_i\}} \left\{ (C_{ii}^{a_i} dt + f_i(t) + T_{ii}^{a_i} f_i(t) dt \right.$$

$$\left. + \sum_{j \neq 1} T_{ij}^{a_i} f_j(t) dt \right\} \quad (68)$$

$$f_i(t + dt) = \min_{\{a_i\}} \left\{ (C_{ii}^{a_i} dt + f_i(t) + \sum_{j=1}^{N} T_{ij}^{a_i} f_j(t) dt \right\},$$

$$\text{for } i = 1, 2, \ldots, N. \quad (69)$$

Subtracting from both sides of (69) $f_i(t)$, dividing by dt, and passing to the limit, we obtain

$$\frac{d}{dt} f_i(t) = \min_{\{a_i\}} \left\{ C_{ii}^{a_i} dt + \sum_{j=1}^{N} T_{ij}^{a_i} f_j(t) \right\}, \quad i = 1, 2, \ldots, N. \quad (70)$$

R. Howard has developed a procedure to solve such recursive relations [5]. It is composed of two consecutive calculations for each iteration, the policy evaluation and the policy improvement. We shall not go into the details of deriving Howard's method, but give the procedure relevant to our case. The procedure is shown in Figure 1.

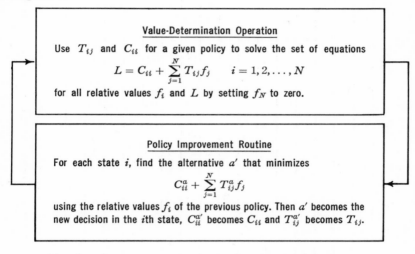

Value-Determination Operation

Use T_{ij} and C_{ii} for a given policy to solve the set of equations

$$L = C_{ii} + \sum_{j=1}^{N} T_{ij} f_j \qquad i = 1, 2, \ldots, N$$

for all relative values f_i and L by setting f_N to zero.

Policy Improvement Routine

For each state i, find the alternative a' that minimizes

$$C_{ii}^a + \sum_{j=1}^{N} T_{ij}^a f_j$$

using the relative values f_i of the previous policy. Then a' becomes the new decision in the ith state, $C_{ii}^{a'}$ becomes C_{ii} and $T_{ij}^{a'}$ becomes T_{ij}.

Note: L is the loss rate; f_i is the transient value of the total cost independent of time. (For details see [5].)

Figure 1. Iteration cycle for completely ergodic continous-time decision processes.

Figure 2. Transition matrix with alternatives.

Jobs served	n_1	n_2	state	1	2	3	4	5	6	7	8	9	10	11	12	13	14	15	16
0_1	0	0	1	$-\lambda$		λ_1						$\lambda_2^{a_2}$						$\lambda_2^{a_1}$	
0_2	0	0	2		$-\lambda$	$\lambda_1^{a_2}$						λ_2							$\lambda_1^{a_1}$
1	0	0	3	μ_{11}		$-\lambda-\mu_{11}$	λ_1	λ_2											
1	1	0	4			μ_{11}	$-\lambda-\mu_{11}$		λ_2	λ_1									
1	0	1	5					$-\lambda-\mu_{1i}$	λ_1		λ_2	$\mu_{12}^{a_1}$						$\mu_{11}^{a_2}$	
1	1	1	6					μ_{1i}	$-\mu_{1i}$			$\mu_{12}^{a_2}$							
1	2	0	7				μ_{11}		μ_{1i}	$-\mu_{11}$									
1	0	2	8								$-\mu_{12}$			μ_{12}					
2	0	0	9		μ_{22}							$-\lambda-\mu_{22}$	λ_1	λ_2					
2	1	0	10			$\mu_{21}^{a_1}$							$-\lambda-\mu_{2i}$		λ_2	λ_1			$\mu_{22}^{a_2}$
2	0	1	11								μ_2			$-\lambda-\mu_{2i}$	λ_1		λ_2		
2	1	1	12					$\mu_{21}^{a_1}$				$\mu_{22}^{a_2}$			$-\mu_{2i}$	λ_1			
2	2	0	13												μ_{21}	$-\mu_{21}$			
2	0	2	14											μ_{22}			$-\mu_{22}$	$-\mu_{22}$	
0_1	0	1	15					λ_1						λ_2				$-\lambda$	
0_1	1	0	16				λ_1					λ_2							$-\lambda$

Transition matrix T for deriving the optimal sequencing procedure

Number of classes $r = 2$ Maximum number of jobs waiting $J = 2$ Maximum number of states $N = 16$.

In general: State $(0_h; n_1, n_2, \ldots, n_r)$ represents a state in which the service facility is set up to process job h but is currently idle and n_p jobs of class p are waiting for service:

$$\sum_{p=1}^{N} n_p < J.$$

In service	n_1	n_2	State	Cost elements	Alternative cost elements
0_1	0	0	1	0	c_{12}
0_2	0	0	2	0	c_{21}
1	0	0	3	0	
1	1	0	4	$c_1 + d_1$	
1	0	1	5	$c_{12} + c_2 + d_2$	$c_2 + d_2$
1	1	1	6	$c_1 + d_1 + c_2 + d_2$	$c_{12} + c_1 + d_1 + c_2 + d_2$
1	2	0	7	$2(c_2 + d_2)$	
1	0	2	8	$c_{12} + 2(c_2 + d_2)$	
2	0	0	9	0	
2	1	0	10	$c_{21} + c_1 + d_1$	$c_1 + d_1$
2	0	1	11	$c_2 + d_2$	
2	1	1	12	$c_{21} + c_1 + d_1 + c_1 + d_2$	$c_1 + d_1 + c_2 + d_2$
2	2	0	13	$c_{21} + 2(c_1 + d_1)$	
2	0	2	14	$2(c_2 + d_2)$	
0_1	0	1	15	$c_2 + d_2$	
0_2	1	0	16	$c_1 + d_1$	

Note : c_p = In-process inventory cost rate of class p jobs waiting for service.
d_p = customer's delay cost rate of class p jobs.
c_{pk} = set-up cost rate if k follows p.

Figure 3. Cost vector $C_{ii}^{a_i}$ for deriving the optimal sequencing procedure.

In Figure 2 we illustrate the transition matrix T, and in Figure 3 the cost rate vectors C for the various possible alternatives. The example refers to the case of $J = 2$ and $r = 2$, where

I = maximum number of jobs permitted to wait.

J_i = number of jobs waiting in state i.

n_{ip} = number of class p jobs waiting in state i.

We have

$$J_i = \sum_{p=1}^{r} n_{ip}; \qquad J_i \leq J$$

From Figure 2 we see that even for a simple case, where the maximum number of jobs does not exceed two and the number of classes is also two, there are 16 possible states. As J and r increase, the number of possible states N increases rapidly.

In the Appendix we show the relationship between N, J, and r. From the results we see that if, for example, the maximum number of jobs permitted to wait is ten and the jobs are classified into three classes, then the number of possible states is 1023.

In solving a real-life problem, the large number of possible states may introduce serious computational limitations. Alternatively, we can always suboptimize the system by selecting one of the suboptimal sequencing methods discussed by the author in another publication [9].

3. AN OVER-ALL JOB-SHOP MODEL (SYNTHESIS)

An over-all model is obtained by synthesizing the individual service center models. We take up the topic of *estimating completion time and establishing delivery commitments.*

a. The System

1. Job Shop. The job shop consists of a collection of machine centers, each containing a fixed number of identical machines.

2. Input. The input to the system is composed of a steady flow of jobs to be processed by some or all of the production facilities. These jobs may have different service rates, set-up requirements, level of importance, etc., and may be classified into any combination of such characteristics. The jobs are grouped into r classes.

3. Output. The output of the shop is made up of completed jobs.

b. Parameters of the Model   For each machine center we have

t_{pd} = the time class p job spends in department d.
$\overline{U}_{pd} = E(t_{pd})$, the mean of t_{pd}.
$\sigma^2_{pd} = E(t_{pd} - \overline{U}_{pd})^2$, the variance of t_{pd}.
m = number of departments which a class p job goes through.

For each job we have

$S_p = \sum_d t_{pd},$ the completion time of job p (the summation being over the set of departments p has to go through).

$M_p = E(S_p),$ the mean completion time of job p.

$s^2_p = \text{Var}(S_p),$ the variance of S_p.

c. Assumptions of the Model

1. The shop is able to handle all the incoming orders.

2. The expected time a class p job spends in department d and its variance is known. In Section 2.1 we developed a method for finding these parameters for a given sequencing procedure. Note that $\overline{U}_{pd}$ and σ^2_{pd} are functions of

    a. The arrival and service rates associated with each class of job at each department.

    b. The sequencing procedure followed in each department.

3. After an order is discharged from a service facility, it is transfered immediately to the next assigned department. This assumption may be removed, however, by creating an additional service center whose function would be to transfer the jobs to their next assignment.

4. The input to each service center may originate from outside the

system or from any other service center. The routes of the jobs through the shop are viewed as an interwoven network of paths.

5. The times t_{pd} which class p jobs spend in department d are mutually independent random variables.

d. Distribution Function of Completion Time An approximate completion-time distribution function is obtained by applying the central limit theorem. We know that S_p tends to the normal distribution as m increases if the following (sufficient) conditions are satisfied [8].

1. The times t_{pd} which class p jobs spend in department d are mutually independent random variables, $d \in m$, $p = 1, 2, \ldots, r$.

2. Two positive constants α and β exist such that for all p and d

$$\sigma_{pd}^2 > \alpha$$

$$E(|\, t_{pd} - \overline{U}_{pd}\,|^3) < \beta.$$

3. $\qquad\qquad s_p^2 \to \infty \quad \text{as} \quad m \to \infty, \qquad p = 1, 2, \ldots, r. \qquad (71)$

4. $\qquad\qquad \lim_{m \to \infty} \dfrac{\sigma_{pd}^2}{s_p^2} = 0, \qquad \text{for all } p \text{ and } d.$

It is reasonable to hypothesize that these conditions hold, since jobs are usually sent through many different departments in a variety of routings, and since each department works independently with respect to sequencing the incoming jobs.

We have

$$M_p = \sum_d \overline{U}_{pd} \qquad (72)$$

$$s_p^2 = \sum_d \sigma_{pd}^2 \qquad (73)$$

the summation being over all the departments which p goes through. Applying the central limit theorem, we obtain the approximate cumulative distribution function of completion time

$$P(S_p \le t) \cong \Phi\left(\frac{t - M_p}{s_p}\right) \qquad (74)$$

where Φ is the standardized cumulative normal distribution function.

If the company tolerates missing its delivery commitments a fraction α_p on the average, then it will set its due dates D_p, such that

$$\Phi\left(\frac{D_p - M_p}{s_p}\right) = 1 - \alpha_p \qquad (75)$$

is satisfied.

For example, if $\alpha_p = 10$ percent, D_p is obtained by adding 1.3 standard deviations to the expected mean completion time, M_p:

$$D_p = M_p + 1.3 s_p. \qquad (76)$$

The basic approach of setting due dates is indicated in Equation (76). Due date should be set realistically on the basis of shop operating levels, and the sequencing rules instituted at the individual processing centers should be taken into account. This is not the usual practice, which is to set the due dates and then to schedule the shop so as to try not miss them. Frequently, the due dates are set without a clear idea whether they can be met, and almost never is there a good understanding of the effect of trying to meet them on the costs in the shop.

In calculating the due dates we have used steady-state operating levels. Perhaps higher accuracy would be possible by taking into account actual queues. There are, however, two major difficulties in doing so :

1. The time and effort required to collect the necessary data and make the required calculations may be excessive, especially in a large shop.

2. The situation in the shop may change considerably between the time quotation is made and the order is received.

Thus, taking into account actual queues for higher accuracy may not always be feasible or practical.

APPENDIX : THE NUMBER OF POSSIBLE STATES, N

We may calculate the number of possible states by looking at the problem as an occupancy problem.

In each state i we have J_i balls ($=$ number of jobs waiting for service) which may be placed in r cells ($= i$ number of classes the jobs may belong to). Cell p is occupied by n_q balls. For each state i we have

$$n_1 + n_2 + \cdots + n_r = J_i \qquad J_i = 0, \ldots, J. \qquad (A.1)$$

Feller proves, Lemma 2.5 in [7], that the number of different solutions of Equation (A. 1) is

$$A_{J_i, r} = \binom{J_i + r - 1}{J_i}, \qquad J_i = 0, \ldots, J. \qquad (A.2)$$

In addition, we allow the service facility to stay idle even if some jobs are waiting for service. Such a situation may occur if none of the waiting jobs belong to the class last discharged from the service facility and if

$$\sum_{p=1}^{r} n_p < J.$$

(There is no point in keeping the facility idle if no additional jobs can join the waiting line.) For each state i with an idle facility, we have

$$n_1 + n_2 + \cdots + n_{p-1} + (n_p = 0) + n_{p+1} + \cdots + n_r = J_i,$$

$$p = 1, 2, \ldots, r. \quad \text{(A. 3)}$$

The number of different solutions of Equation (A. 3) is

$$A_{J_i, r-1} \binom{J_i + r - 2}{J_i}, \quad J_i = 0, 1, \ldots, J - 1. \quad \text{(A. 4)}$$

With regard to service facility, we may consider it to consist of r cells; only one cell at a time is occupied. This holds for both cases, the busy and the idle facility; in the busy case the cell is occupied by a ball (job); in the idle case the cell is "occupied" by the set-up of the last job.

With each distinguishable situation of J_i, r distinguishable situations are possible in the service facility, giving a total of

$$(A_{J_i, r} + A_{J_i, r-1})r \quad \text{(A. 5)}$$

distinguishable situations (states).

To obtain the total number of possible states, N, we have to sum up $A_{J_i, r}$ over all J_i (from zero to J) and $A_{J_i, r-1}$ over all admissible J_i (from zero to $J - 1$).

Carrying out these operations, we obtain for N

$$N = \left[\sum_{J_i=0}^{J} \frac{(J_i + r - 1)!}{J_i!(r - 1)!} + \sum_{J_i=0}^{J-1} \frac{(J_i + r - 2)!}{(J_i)!(r - 2)!} \right] r, \quad r \geq 2. \quad \text{(A. 6)}$$

REFERENCES

1. Sisson, R. L., "Methods of Sequencing in Job Shops—A Review," *Journal of the Operations Research Society of America* **7**, 1 (1959).

2. Nelson, R. T., "An Empirical Study of Arrival, Service Time, and Waiting Time Distributions of a Job Shop Production Process," Management Sciences Research Project, Research Report No. 60, University of California, Los Angeles (1959).

3. Friend, J. K., "Two Studies in Airport Congestion," *Operations Research* **9**, 3 (1958).

4. *Notes on Operations Research*, Cambridge, Mass.: The Technology Press of Massachusetts Institute of Technology, Chapter 4 (1959).

5. Howard, R. A., *Dynamic Programming and Markov Processes*, Cambridge, Mass.: The Technology Press of Massachusetts Institute of Technology, 1960.

6. Bellman, R., *Dynamic Programming*, Princeton, N. J.: Princeton University Press, 1957.

7. Feller, W., *An Introduction to Probability Theory and its Applications*, 2nd. ed., New York: John Wiley & Sons, Chapter II, Section 5, (1957).

8. Cramer, H., *Mathematical Methods of Statistics*, Princeton N. J.: Princeton University Press, Chapter XV (1954).

9. Reinitz, R. C., "An Integrated Job Shop Scheduling Problem" (Ph. D. thesis, Case Institute of Technology, Cleveland, Ohio, 1961), Chapter 5.

6

Priority Rules for Minimizing the Cost of Queues in Machine Scheduling

Charles C. Holt
UNIVERSITY OF WISCONSIN

1. INTRODUCTION

Even though present knowledge is insufficient to design optimal control rules for large-scale queuing networks, it is not too early to sketch the problem and to seek approximate solutions. The approach taken in this paper is to obtain from a gross analysis of the whole queuing system an optimal allocation of queue delays to individual products. The decision variables for the global analysis are the time each job is to be started in the shop and the expected queue delay for each of its operations. Local priority rules would then be used at each queue in a way consistent with the global decisions. The local rules are intended to be responsive to the detailed situations in each queue which reflect the random events that have occurred in the system.

The author would like to thank Kenneth Shone and Gerald L. Thompson for stimulating his interest in this problem area and to Gene Groff for valuable criticisms of an earlier draft of this paper.

Such a combination of global analysis for the whole system and local decision rules at the queue level will probably work best for production involving many products and machines. Such large and complex stochastic systems tend to be remarkably insensitive to the controls that are introduced, and hence only the most significant factors need be taken into account in designing the controls.

The global analysis is described in Section 2. The object of the analysis is to find the starting times and the queue delays in order to minimize for the system as a whole the sum of inventory holding costs and penalties for late deliveries. It is assumed, for this part of the analysis, that there is a stable relation between the average queue delay and the loading of a given machine. Although a complete algorithm for solution of the problem as formulated is not offered, it appears that good approximations can be obtained for particular applications.

The results of the global analysis are incorporated with local priority rules in the remaining sections. Three rules are examined: the *time schedule priority rule* and two *queue cost priority rules*. The time schedule priority rule is designed to enforce the plan implicit in the global analysis. The queue cost priority rules act, in addition, to reduce the local cost of queue delays. From estimates of the cost of delay for each of the products in the queue at a machine, decentralized decisions are made for each machine. The two rules differ in the approximations used.

2. ALLOCATION OF QUEUE DELAYS TO PRODUCTS

A set of I products is assumed to be scheduled on J machines during a fixed period of time (one month, for example). The expected operation time for each of the operations is represented by M_{ij} ($i = 1, 2, \ldots, I; j = 1, 2, \ldots, J$).[1] For each product the operations are to be performed in a specified order; to reflect this order, let $M_i(s)$ be the expected machining time for the sth operation for the ith product.[2] Each machine is scheduled to be available for operation a given number of hours during the scheduling period; for the jth machine this is M_j. For each product there is assigned a delivery date, denoted by T_i.

Let t_i be the date that the ith product is released to the shop to start operations, and let Q_{ij} represent the expected waiting time of

[1] Since a product may actually be a batch of units that are machined together and moved together from machine to machine, the machining time may include machine set-up time, if we assume that it is independent of the product previously machined.

[2] To simplify the exposition each item is assumed to be machined once on each machine, but only once. Nothing in what follows would be affected by relaxing either assumption. Notation for the general case has been worked out by the author.

product i in the queue before the jth machine; also let $Q_i(s)$ represent the expected waiting time before the sth operation to be performed on the product.

The costs to be considered are the costs of holding in-process inventories and the penalties for late deliveries. The cost function can be written as follows;

$$C = \sum_{i=1}^{I} \sum_{s=1}^{J} v_i(s)[Q_i(s) + M_i(s)] + \sum_{i=1}^{I} f_i'(L_i) \qquad (1)$$

where the first term is the total cost of holding inventory, and $v_i(s)$ is the cost per unit time of holding product i before and during operations.[3] The second term is the total of the lateness penalties for all products where $f_i(\ )$ is the penalty function for the ith product and L_i is the length of time that the shop is late in completing the machining of the ith product measured from its desired delivery date T_i.

The penalty function for lateness is likely to have the form shown by the solid-line curve in Figure 1.

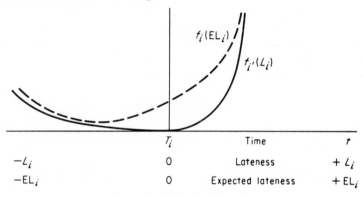

	T_i	Time	t
$-L_i$	0	Lateness	$+L_i$
$-EL_i$	0	Expected lateness	$+EL_i$

Figure 1. Lateness penalty function

As lateness increases, the penalty in terms of customer reaction, etc., increases at an increasing rate. For negative lateness, i.e., early completion, the penalty is either the cost of holding the inventory to the delivery date T_i, or a reflection of the inconvenience to the customer which results from excessively early shipment. In general, the penalties of early completion are relatively low.

Lateness under the best of circumstances will be subject to random

[3] As a product proceeds through a production process, its value and, presumably, the cost of holding it in inventory rises. In many cases this degree of refinement will be unnecessary.

Strictly speaking, actual queue delay and machining time should be used in this function rather than the expected values.

variation but, hopefully, expected lateness EL_i can be controlled.[4] A suitable decision criterion is the expectation of the lateness penalty related to expected lateness; i.e.,

$$f_i(EL_i) \cong Ef_i'(L_i) \tag{2}$$

where E is the expectation operator.

As an illustration, Figure 2 is the probability distribution of lateness

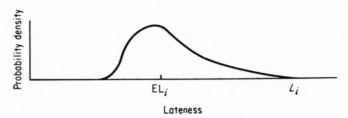

Figure 2. Distribution of lateness

around its expected value. The expected lateness penalty is shown in Figure 1 by the dotted line. The minimum of this function will occur at a negative value of EL_i, so it is best to aim for early completion. If there were no random variability, the ideal expected lateness would, of course, be zero. The size of the early bias reflects the severity of the lateness penalty and the variability in the distribution of lateness. Expected lateness is given by

$$EL_i = t_i + \sum_{s=1}^{J} [Q_i(s) + M_i(s)] - T_i \tag{3}$$

where t_i is the time at which product i is released to start its machining process, i.e., entering the queue for its first machining operation.

When (1), (2), and (3) are combined, expected variable cost is given by

$$EC = \sum_{i=1}^{I} \sum_{s=1}^{J} v_i(s)[Q_i(s)] + \sum_{i=1}^{I} f_i\{t_i + \sum_{s=1}^{J} [Q_i(s) + M_i(s)] - T_i\} \tag{4}$$

where the terms in $M_i(s)$ have been dropped, because they represent fixed costs which are irrelevant for the decisions under consideration.

The average of the queue delays Q_{ij} before machine j must equal its average queue delay D_j. Here it is convenient to use the notation which identifies the machines.

$$\frac{\sum_{i=1}^{I} Q_{ij}}{I} = D_j, \qquad (j = 1, 2, \ldots, J). \tag{5}$$

[4] The control system will, of course, partially offset random variation in lateness. No direct attempt will be made to allocate random variability among products.

A stable relation is assumed to exist between the average queue delay D_j and the fraction of the total available time that machine j is expected to be idle. The percent idle time for the jth machine in any schedule period is given from the original machining time data for the set of products, so that the delays D_j appearing in Equation (5) could be computed from a function of the following form:

$$D_j = g_j\left(1 - \frac{1}{M_j}\sum_{i=1}^{I} M_{ij}\right). \qquad (6)$$

This proposition, of course, needs to be subjected to empirical test, but there appears to be support for it under very general conditions.[5]

Clearly, negative queue delays are impossible, so the solution must be restricted by the relations

$$0 \le Q_{ij}, \quad \begin{array}{l} (i = 1, 2, \ldots, I) \\ (j = 1, 2, \ldots, J) \end{array} \qquad (7)$$

If we designate (current) time at the start of the scheduling period as t, then the following constraint applies to the starting time for each product:

$$t \le t_i, \quad (i = 1, 2, \ldots, I) \qquad (8)$$

i.e., a product cannot be started any sooner than immediately. Since many products will already be in process at the start of the scheduling period, t_i will automatically be equal to t for these products.[6] The machining times that are relevant for determining machine loading will be for those operations that are currently under way[7] and those that are yet to be performed.

The global optimizing problem can now be posed. Find the starting times t_i and the queue delays $Q_i(s)$ for $(i = 1, 2, \ldots, I)$ and $(s = 1, 2, \ldots, J)$ that minimize the criterion function [Equation (4)] subject to the equality constraints [Equation (5)], and the inequality constraints [Equations (7) and (8)]. Note that in these equations two notations are used for the same queue delay variables Q_{ij}.

---

[5] J. R. Jackson [3] has shown a set of conditions under which a decomposition principle applies; i.e., the service centers in a network of queues can be treated independently as simple queues. R. W. Conway and W. L. Maxwell have also shown that a stable relation develops between percent idle time and average queue size per machine. It is highly significant that this result applies both for a pure flow shop, in which all the products follow the same sequence of machine operations, and for a pure job shop, in which the next machine for a product is picked at random with equal probabilities given to the transition from one machine to any other.

[6] For the local decision rules to be considered later, the actual starting date might be used.

[7] Rather than trying to take account of how far these operations have progressed, the simplifying assumption can be made that they are all half completed; i.e., use $M_{ij}/2$ for the operations that are underway.

The following characteristics of the solution to this global problem can be anticipated. The starting date will be set relatively *late* in relation to their delivery dates for those products that are very expensive to hold in inventory, have short machining times, have few queues to pass through,[8] are processed by lightly loaded machines with relatively short queues, and have relatively low penalties for being late. Starting dates will be relatively *early* in the opposite cases. The expected queue delays will be relatively short for those products that should have been started previously to meet their delivery dates, but were not (hence, some of constraints (7) and (8) may be binding), have a high penalty for being late, are expensive to hold in inventory, have many queues to pass through, and are processed by lightly loaded machines. The queue delays will be relatively long under the opposite circumstances.

When the rate of output is high so that idle time is, in general, low, the starting times will be early, indicating long lead times, and the queues will be long, necessitating large in-process inventory.

The computational problem of obtaining a general solution for such a large and complex system is substantial. Consequently, some easily computable approximations to the expected lateness penalty functions should be considered. For example, linear programming solutions or a quadratic programming solution might be used.

This latter approach would involve making a quadratic approximation to the second term of Equation (4).

$$f_i(EL_i) \approx \left\{\frac{P_i}{2}\right\}\left\{t_i + \sum_{s=1}^{J} [Q_i(s) + M_i(s)] - T_i - \hat{L}_i\right\}^2 \qquad (9)$$

where P_i and $\hat{L}_i$ are constants determined by the best quadratic fit in the relevant region of Figure 1.

If the inequality constraint (8) can be handled by segregating the urgent-start products from the others, then t_i can be set equal to t for the urgent products, and the constraint can be ignored for the others. If the constraint (7) is binding, i.e., zero queue delays are needed to hit delivery commitments, the plant is already in serious trouble. If this condition has been avoided by providing adequate lead times,[9] constraint (7) can be ignored and then a Lagrange multiplier solution can be obtained simply by the solution of simultaneous linear equations.

---

[8] This applies to the general case in which different products have different numbers of operations.

[9] There is need for ingenuity in solving the global optimizing problem. For example, if the system is in sufficiently good control that products are started at the proper time, i. e., for virtually all products t_i exceeds t, the troublesome inequality constraint (7) can be neglected. Then by defining a lead time variable,

In the subsequent analyses, $Q_i(s)$ and t_i will refer to the optimal values that have been obtained by solving the problem stated above.

3. THE TIME SCHEDULE PRIORITY RULE

The solution for starting times and queue delays can be combined with machining times and the order of operations to generate for each product an optimal schedule of expected times for each stage of its processing. This is done by arranging the machining times and queue delays for a product in the order in which the operations are to be performed and numbering them in order; i.e., $M_i(s)$ and $Q_i(s)$, where s is the sequence number ($s = 1, 2, \ldots, J$) which appears on a queue delay and the machining time that follows it. The scheduled time for product i to *start* the sth machining operation is designated $t_i(s)$ and is given by

$$t_i(s) = t_i + \sum_{r=1}^{s} Q_i(r) + \sum_{r=1}^{s-1} M_i(r), \qquad (i = 1, 2, \ldots, I)$$
$$(s = 1, 2, \ldots, J). \qquad (10)$$

Such time schedules for each product could not be followed rigidly because (1) internal contradictions can be expected in the schedule, since the order of operations has been neglected in the global optimizing analysis, (2) random variability is inherent in the queuing process on which the analysis rests, and (3) unanticipated random breakdowns of machines, etc., will occur.

J. R. Jackson has investigated the properties of a local priority system that can serve to bridge the gap between the optimal schedules and the operating decisions at the queue level. Suppose, when a product enters the queue of a machine for its next operation, that it is assigned as a priority number the scheduled date at which it is expected to start that operation, i.e., $t_i(s)$. The proposed queue discipline is to select, when the machine is free, the product from the queue that has the lowest priority number, i.e., the earliest scheduled date for starting its operation on the machine.

If the date that the product actually entered the queue is subtracted from this expected starting date, an estimate would be obtained of the expected queue delay that would be necessary to put the product back on schedule exactly. Call this the desired delay. Under such a scheme it appears in [3] that those products which happen to ex-

---

$$\tau_i = T_i - t_i$$

it may be possible by using the quadratic cost function (9) to aggregate similar products and thereby greatly reduce the number of unknowns.

An additional use of the analysis would be to give some indication of sensible lead times in making commitments to customers.

perience relatively long delays in the queue—and the upper tail of the delay distribution obviously is important—will, on the average, have delays that are linearly related to the desired delays with a slope coefficient of unity.

Thus, under this priority system the past random deviations of a product from its schedule will *tend* at each stage to be corrected completely. This constant pressure toward conformity with the schedule will slow down those products that are ahead of schedule by reducing their priorities[10] and will speed up those products that are behind schedule by increasing their priorities.[11] Of course, having a high priority does not in general produce an instantaneous correction, since several behind-schedule (and hence high-priority) products may be in a queue at the same time, and they cannot all be given first choice. Instead of allowing the impact of random deviations to accumulate, this system of local priorities, guided by the optimal time schedule, attenuates the effects of the random disturbances and keeps the system under control. To the extent that the schedules incorporate an optimal balancing of costs and penalties, the decentralized local decisions guided by those schedules will be constantly guided toward the attainment of that optimum which was determined by the global analysis.

4. THE FIRST QUEUE COST PRIORITY RULE

Although the foregoing appears to be a reasonable approach to machine scheduling, several points may be questioned. Why should the optimization analysis be confined to the global decisions and no local cost considerations be taken into account by the local queue decisions— where only control performance was considered? Can a local priority rule be found that has local optimizing characteristics in terms of the situation occurring in the queues that can be used in conjunction with the global optimizing analysis? Since the local queue discipline can affect the average queue delay that was considered in Equation (6), it may be possible to make additional improvements by decreasing the average delays and by decreasing the costliness of the delays that do occur.

R. W. Conway and W. L. Maxwell point out in [1] certain optimal properties of the shortest-operation priority rule in a static situation. A fixed set of products requiring machining times M_i ($i = 1, 2, \ldots, l$) are waiting before a machine to be serviced. If the products are numbered in the order in which they are placed on the machine,

[10] This means increasing their priority number.
[11] Note that reducing the priorities of the ahead-of-schedule products helps to speed up the behind-schedule products.

then the time for completing the ith product is $\sum_{n=1}^{i} M_n$. If it is assumed that the cost of holding the ith product is w_i per period of time, then the total holding cost for all products is $\sum_{i=1}^{l} w_i \sum_{n=1}^{i} M_n$.

This total cost is minimized by ordering the products as follows and renumbering if necessary:

$$\frac{M_1}{w_1} \leq \frac{M_2}{w_2} \leq \cdots \leq \frac{M_l}{w_l}. \tag{11}$$

Conway and Maxwell go on to show by computer simulation (using equal w's) that this rule, when utilized in a complex network of dynamic queues, has low costs reflected by low mean completion times but high variance of completion times.

It would seem desirable to use this rule to minimize the mean local cost of a queue *if* it can be made compatible with the global analysis and *if* sufficient control can be introduced to attenuate the tendency for random variations to accumulate through the system, yielding highly variable performance in hitting delivery dates. To operate this local decision rule in the queue of the jth machine, we need to know for each product in the queue the ratio of its machining time $M_i(s)$ to the incremental cost of waiting per unit of time $w_i(t)$, i.e., the incremental cost of delay currently prevailing at the time t.

The cost of waiting

What is needed is the cost of delay when individual products have deviated significantly from their optimal time schedules. Specifically, estimates of the incremental cost of queue delay are needed for those products that are waiting their turn in a queue at the time t when the machine becomes free. Then a decision must be made to terminate the queue delay for one product and extend it for all others. Consequently, the incremental cost of delay for all these products at the time t is relevant in making the decision.

From a modification of Equation (4), the incremental cost of delay $w_i(t)$ at time t for the ith product, assuming that it is in the queue waiting for its sth operation, is

$$w_i(t) = \frac{\partial EC}{\partial Q_i(s)}$$

$$= v_i(s) + \frac{\partial}{\partial Q_i(s)} f_i[t_i + \sum_{r=1}^{s} \tilde{Q}_i(r) + \sum_{r=1}^{s-1} \tilde{M}_i(r)$$

$$+ \sum_{r=s+1}^{J} Q_i(r) + \sum_{r=s}^{J} M_i(r) - T_i] \tag{12}$$

where $\tilde{Q}_i(r)$ and $\tilde{M}_i(r)$ designate actual queue delays and machining times that have already been experienced, as contrasted with the expected values of the optimal plan. Actually, the queue delay $\tilde{Q}_i(s)$ is not complete unless this product is selected for the next operation on the machine. Nevertheless, it is relevant to estimate the incremental cost of waiting at time t with the queue delay that exists at that time.

Accordingly, the bracketed term in Equation (12) can be written as

$$[t + \sum_{r=s+1}^{J} Q_i(r) + \sum_{r=s}^{J} M_i(r) - T_i]$$

where the current time t replaces the first three terms. Adding the right side of Equation (10) and subtracting the left side yields

$$\{[t - t_i(s)] + t_i + \sum_{s=1}^{S_t} [Q_i(s) + M_i(s)] - T_i\} \tag{13}$$

where $[t - t_i(s)]$ is the amount by which the product currently is behind the planned schedule. Expression (13) can be written more simply by defining a new constant L_i^*:

$$[t - t_i(s) + L_i^*]$$

where L_i^* is the optimal expected lateness for the ith product.

If this result is substituted in Equation (12), the incremental cost of delay is

$$w_i(t) = v_i(s) + \frac{\partial}{\partial Q_i(s)} f_i[L_i^* + t - t_i(s)]. \tag{14}$$

Unless the factory is greatly overloaded or the lead times are too short, the optimal expected lateness will usually be a negative number indicating the desirability of setting t_i early enough to provide a buffer of slack time at the end of the machining process to absorb random fluctuations in completion times and thereby to decrease the risk of incurring the lateness penalty.

The above expression for $w_i(s)$ indicates that the incremental cost of further delay depends upon whether the product already is behind or ahead of schedule. The further it is behind schedule, the higher is the cost of additional delay, as would be expected from an examination of Figure 1.

If, for ease of computation, the quadratic approximation (9) is used, a simple linear expression for the incremental cost of delay is obtained.

$$w_i(t) = v_i(s) + P_i[L_i^* - \hat{L}_i + t - t_i(s)] \tag{15}$$

or, more simply,

$$w_i(t) = a_i(s) + P_i t \tag{16}$$

where

$$a_i(s) = v_i(s) + P_i[L_i^* - \hat{L}_i - t_i(s)].$$

The cost of queue delay, according to Equation (14) or Equation (16), can be substituted in the priority rule (11) to make local decisions on which product should be selected for the next machine operation.

In either case, the priority number depends on time t. Consequently, it should be recalculated each time a decision is made in selecting a product from those that are in the queue. The longer a product stays in the queue, the higher the priority number rises. When a product enters a queue on schedule, its priority is low. The longer it is scheduled to stay in the queue, the lower it is. With such a low priority it is unlikely to start its machining very soon, unless the machine happens to be free. With the passage of time its priority rises, so that by the time scheduled for machining to start, $t_i(s)$, its priority is likely to be high enough to give it the top priority position so that its machining will be started the next time the machine is free. However, the length or composition of the queue may be such, because of random variation, that the product still is not selected. Then the priority continues to rise with the further passage of time until *finally* its priority number is higher than for any other product, so it is selected to be next on the machine.

When its machining is completed, it enters the queue in front of another machine that is to perform its next operation indicated by $(s+1)$. Referring to Equations (16) and (10) it is clear that increasing s will reduce $w_i(t)$. Thus its priority in the new queue will be relatively low as it starts to wait its turn. With the passage of time its priority gradually rises as before.

The priority rises quickly for those products for which lateness quickly becomes very serious, since the slope of expected cost in Figure 1 rises for increases in lateness.

The repeated recalculation of priorities introduces a feedback to the priorities which tends to keep the products on the schedule set by the global optimizing analysis. In addition, machining times and costs of queue delay are taken into account for the particular products in each queue so that the cost of the local queues tends to be minimized.

5. THE SECOND QUEUE COST PRIORITY RULE

The *derivation* of the rule (11) assumed that the cost of queue delay was constant, whereas, in fact, the penalty of delay usually becomes increasingly costly as the delay is extended. Furthermore the derivation was static and did not consider the intermittant inflow and outflow of products from the queue. The second priority rule attempts to surmount these limitations by minimizing the cost which results from each individual decision. The assumption is made that the incremental cost of delay $w_i(s)$ is constant only for the duration of the next machining operation.

Consider the cost of delaying the products that are held in queue while the chosen product is being machined. Suppose that at time t machine j becomes free, and a set of products q_j is waiting in queue to be serviced by that machine. The cost of selecting product i from the queue for the next operation delays all of the other products and incurs the total queue cost given by[12]

$$C_{ij}(t) = M_i(s) \sum_{\substack{k \subset q_j \\ k \neq i}} w_k(t) \tag{17}$$

This cost estimate can be calculated for each of the possible choices of next product to be machined, and the product can be selected that would incur the least queue cost. Thus the cost estimate becomes a priority number, where the lowest number is given preference. Clearly, if the machining time of a product is short, it would not hold up the other products long and hence would have a priority preference. But also if a product is very expensive to delay, for example, it may already be late for delivery, and the cost of the queue would be reduced by not holding up this product further. The interaction of these two factors determines the priority.

The second queue cost priority rule is interesting in that the priority number for a particular product depends upon what other products are in the queue at the same time. One consequence of this is that the rule behaves differently when the queue is long than when it is short. If the queue is long, the rule acts like the shortest operation rule and hence tends to minimize the queue length. When the queue is short, low machining time and high queue cost give a high priority, as is done by the first queue cost priority rule. Indeed, when there are only two products in the queue, the two rules are identical.

Comparing the priority expressions of Equations (11) and (17) it is clear that the computational costs of the second rule will be somewhat higher.

The choice of local queue discipline would affect the average queue delay D_j and hence would need to be taken into account in the delay function of Equation (6) of the global optimizing analysis. Thus, it

---

[12] The summation notation means the sum of the elements contained in the set q_j.

is clear that the global and the local analyses interact so that the system performance needs to be evaluated as a whole.

Simulation testing would be very useful in evaluating these rules. The would author be happy to see someone undertake such a study.

Although no perfection is claimed for the approaches to the scheduling problem that are here proposed, they incorporate in a fairly simple way many of the relevant factors. Hopefully, such approaches will help to close the present gap between uncomputable exact optimizing analyses and practicable but inefficient priority systems.

REFERENCES

1. Jackson, James R., "Networks of Waiting Lines," *Operations Research* **5** (1957), 201–203.

2. Conway, R. W. and W. L. Maxwell, "Network Dispatching by the Shortest-Operation Discipline," *Operations Research* **10** (Jan.–Feb. 1962), 51–73. Reprinted as Chapter 17 of this volume.

3. Jackson, James R., "Queues with Dynamic Priority Discipline," *Management Science* **8**, 1 (Oct. 1961), 18–34. Reprinted as Chapter 19 of this volume.

II

Scheduling Problems in Inventory Control

The possibility of holding inventories of finished goods is an essential part of most of the papers which follow. They do not assume that production quantities and due dates had already been established by the time that the scheduling decision is to be made.

E. H. Bowman ("A New Theory about Managerial Decision-Making," Chapter 7) argues that most of the benefits from research about business decision-making would be realized not so much from changing the nature of decisions as from making the decisions more consistent from one time to another. Illustrating the argument with production and work force smoothing, plant size, and aircraft spare parts problems, he points out that a major function of management is estimating (perhaps implicitly) the costs of intangibles in the firm's operations. These observations are relevant to factory scheduling, especially in asking how much it is worth to avoid making a late delivery.

A highly important problem in managerial control is guaranteeing that decisions made in one division of the firm will be consistent with those made in another. In Chapter 8, "Constrained Inventory Rules for Production

Smoothing," P. R. Winters examines how to make three kinds of decisions consistent with one another: (1) planning total production and employment of the firm, (2) inventory management of individual products, and (3) scheduling the items to be produced through the shop. The analysis leads explicitly to priority indexes for deciding the order in which various products should be started during the scheduling period.

The effectiveness of two scheduling systems are compared by means of computer simulation techniques by B. P. Dzielinski, C. T. Baker, and A. S. Manne in Chapter 9, "Simulation Tests of Lot Size Programming." With data obtained from a metal fabrication plant, a deterministic linear programming model was used for planning lot sizes, work force, and inventories when the actual problem contained random elements. The results of this system are compared with an alternate procedure based upon single-item inventory control. The simulation results suggest that the linear programming model is the more promising method for economic planning of production. The paper also shows how the effectiveness of different "optimization models" may be compared when the assumptions of neither one are satisfied by the actual situation.

K. H. Ishler, R. M. Sharp, and W. W. Staley ("Optimization of a Total Production and Distribution System," Chapter 10) are also concerned with using a linear programming model for processing in various locations and shipments to several markets. Approximations are suggested to reduce the size of the original problem.

The last paper is concerned with a scheduling problem in which it is impossible to hold inventories of the finished product—namely, electric power generation. C. Bachovzeff and J. Corrigan ("Average Cost Method of Scheduling," Chapter 11) suggest a method for scheduling power generation facilities under various load conditions. Simulation tests suggest that the procedure would result in considerable savings over existing practices.

7

Consistency and Optimality in Managerial Decision=making

E. H. Bowman

MASSACHUSETTS INSTITUTE OF TECHNOLOGY

This paper reports some research in managerial decision making, as well as the ideas and a theory stemming from this research. Presented here is a combination of description and prescription. It combines the talents of the manager with those of the analyst in a method and in a theory. The method is pragmatic rather than utopian, in that it offers one way of starting with the managers' actual decisions and building on them to reach a better system.

A referee has summarized this paper as follows: "that managerial decisions might be improved more by making them more consistent from one time to another than by approaches purporting to give 'optimal solutions' to explicit cost models . . . especially for problems where intangibles (run-out costs, delay penalties) must otherwise be estimated or assumed." Although this is a normative statement, it is derived from a number of descriptive concepts (about the world in which we live) which may be of equal interest.

A paper presented at the conference of Factory Scheduling, Carnegie Institute of Technology, May 10–12, 1961. Reprinted from Management Science 9 (1963), 310–321. The research underlying this paper was in part sponsored by the Massachusetts Institute of Technology Operations Research Center contract with the Army Office of Ordnance Research (DA–19–020–ORD–2684) and the Massachusetts Institute of Technology School of Industrial Management Sloan Research Fund. A number of graduate students have helped with this research, particularly Mr. Howard Kunreuther.

The paper is organized essentially in the sequence in which the research was performed and the ideas generated. The problems, research, and decision rules of production scheduling are set forth first. They introduce the cause of this paper. Next, the approach of using management's own past decisions in order to improve present decisions is described. The theory is then set forth in a more general form, after which several additional empirical tests of the theory are described. Finally, the ideas are summarized. Further questions of validity, generality, and operationality must be answered by future research.

1. PRODUCTION-SCHEDULING DECISION RULES

The research which led up to the more basic ideas presented here dealt with the general problem of production and employment scheduling. This work is set forth in some detail in order to convey the spirit of the research.

A very simple decision rule for production scheduling might be

$$P_t = S_t$$

where P_t represents production scheduled in time period t, and S_t represents sales expected in time period t. In this case production would match all fluctuations up and down in sales, and the rule might not be considered a very good one. An extension might be

$$P_t = S_t + x(P_{t-1} - S_t)$$

where x is a decision rule coefficient to be specified between zero and one, and P_{t-1} represents production in the previous time period. If $x = 1$, then the sales terms cancel out, and production in this period equals production in the previous time period (i.e., with no fluctuation). A value for x between zero and one will supply a damping mechanism in this case, where production does change but not as quickly as sales.[1]

However, using this rule (where production does not necessarily match sales each period) would cause inventories to fluctuate. In order to offer some control of these inventory levels, the rule may be further extended:

$$P_t = S_t + x(P_{t-1} - S_t) + y(I_N - I_{t-1})$$

where y is also a decision rule coefficient to be specified between zero and one, I_N represents a concept of "normal" inventory (possibly an easier label than optimum inventory), and I_{t-1} represents the

[1] This rule may be converted into the more standard feedback form:
$$P_t = P_{t-1} + (1 - x)(S_t - P_{t-1}).$$

amount of inventory at the end of the previous period.

Because it is desirable to take into account the anticipated future sales (in the near term), the rule should be extended further:

$$P_t = \sum_{i=t}^{i=t+n} a_i \hat{S}_i + x(P_{t-1} - S_t) + y(I_N - I_{t-1})$$

$$(a_t > a_{t+1} > a_{t+2} > \cdots > a_{t+n})$$

with the a_i's representing weighting coefficients of the sales forecasts, $\hat{S}_i$, for future periods.

Although such a decision rule could be further extended and elaborated, this will suffice for our introduction. The production scheduling behavior of a firm following such a rule would be critically influenced by the numbers supplied for the coefficients, $a_t, \ldots, a_n, x, y$ and I_N (which may be conceived of as a number for the moment). Different sets of numbers in the coefficients would result in different behavior patterns through time. Some patterns would undoubtedly be preferable to others. The challenge, of course, is to determine the preferred set of coefficients. Three methods for making this determination are

1. Simulation (experimentation).
2. Analysis.
3. Management decisions.

Simulation seems to require no justification at present. Many uses are being made today of this activity in universities and in industry,[2] particularly where the mathematics of a more deductive solution scheme break down. Mathematical analysis may be possible even in problems as complex as this.[3] For industrial problems which are framed in less complex form, mathematical analysis is not uncommon. A different source (management decisions) for these decision-rule coefficients is developed later in this paper.

2. THE HMMS DECISION RULES

The production and employment scheduling problem faced by most manufacturing firms, where in each scheduling period both a production quantity and an employment level must be chosen, has been analyzed in research work by Holt, Modigliani, Muth, and Simon (HMMS) on a paint company. Working with quadratic cost forms, and a long-term scheduling horizon, they derived the following production and work force rules:

[2] For a large example, see Jay Forrester, *Industrial Dynamics*, Massachusetts Institute of Technology Press and John Wiley & Sons, Inc., 1961.

[3] See especially Holt, Modigliani, Muth, and Simon, *Planning Production, Inventories, and Work Force*. Englewood Cliffs, N.J.: Prentice-Hall, Inc., 1960.

$$P_t = + .463 O_t + .234 O_{t+1} + \cdots + O_{t+11}$$
$$+ .993 W_{t-1} + 153 - .464 I_{t-1}$$
$$W_t = + .0101 O_t + .0088 O_{t+1} + \cdots + O_{t+11}$$
$$+ .743 W_{t+1} + 2.09 - .010 I_{t-1}$$

where the subscripts are time period notation, P stands for production, W for workers, O for sales orders, and I for inventory. The analyses leading to these decision rules are quite involved and will not be described here, as it is not essential to the major ideas presented in this chapter. They may be found in the literature.[4]

It is important to explain, however, that the rule and the coefficients—the numbers .463, .993, 153, –.464—were derived by mathematical analysis from the cost structure model of this one paint factory studied. Had the company followed these rules, the physical behavior pattern and, therefore, the costs of the behavior would have been different. The HMMS group presents the normalized summary cost data shown in Table 1 for three cases.

Table 1

	Paint Company	
	1949–53 (Korean War included)	1952–54
Decision rule (perfect forecast)	100 %	
Decision rule (moving average forecast)	110 %	100 %
Company performance	139 %	108.5 %
(cost base about $ 3,000,000)		

Since the decision rules require estimates of future sales over the next 12 months, both the actual sales (now known and entitled "perfect forecast"), and a moving average forecast (entitled "naive forecast") were used to reconstruct the behavior of the system over the years listed. The total costs (normalized to 100 percent) for the company's own behavior, as well as the total costs from the decision rules, are given. It can be seen that the decision rule consistently used would have shown an appreciable cost saving.

3. OTHER APPLICATIONS

In our research, we applied the HMMS analysis previously cited

[4] (a) Published in a journal as "A Linear Decision Rule for Production and Employment Scheduling" by Holt, Modigliani, and Simon, *Management Science,* October, 1955, and "Derivation of a Linear Decision Rule for Production and Employment," by Holt, Modigliani, and Muth, *Management Science,* January, 1956.

(b) Then reprinted in *Analyses of Industrial Operations,* edited by Bowman and Fetter, Irwin, Inc., 1959.

(c) Then included in *Planning Production, Inventories, and Work Force,* Holt, Modigliani, Muth, and Simon, Prentice-Hall, Inc., 1960.

to the production and employment scheduling problems of an ice cream company,[5] a chocolate company,[6] and a candy company.[7]

The results, in the same form as before, were as shown in Table 2.

Table 2

	Ice cream	Chocolate	Candy
Decision rule (perfect forecast)	100 %	100 %	100 %
Decision rule (moving average forecast)	104.9 %	102.0 %	103.5 %
Company performance	105.4 %	105.3 %	111.5 %
Approximate cost base	$ 500,000	$ 150,000	$ 1,500,000

With less margin of improvement, it appeared that the linear decision rules, derived from the quadratic approximations to the costs structures of each firm, might have resulted in the cost savings shown.

4. BEHAVIOR AND STATISTICAL REGRESSION

The author of the chocolate company thesis was requested to do a statistical least-squares regression of the company's actual scheduling behavior against the linear decision rule. He added another variable, sales contracted for the next six months, and used a sales level which was derived from exponentially weighted past sales. For the W_t rule he obtained a multiple correlation coefficient of $r = .971$. For the P_t rule he obtained a multiple correlation coefficient of $r = .87$. In other words, the form of these rules gave a pretty fair indication of the chocolate company managers' decisions. That is, the managers were sensitive to these same variables in their decision behavior.

We then did a graphical multiple regression for the candy company, using these rules (with a single "sales level" figure). Again we obtained a fair correlation, with the addition that more inventory was "tolerated" in the busy half of the year.

Next, for all four companies—paint, ice cream, chocolate, and candy—we did a statistical least-squares regression for the company management scheduling behavior on the "open form" of the decision rules; e.g.,

$$P_t = a + b_1\hat{S}_1 + b_2\hat{S}_2 + b_3\hat{S}_3 + b_4\hat{S}_4 + b_5\hat{S}_5 + b_6W_{t-1} + b_7I_{t-1}.$$

These regressions gave us rather poor results. The sales estimates

[5] Rien T. van der Velde, "An Application of a Linear Decision Rule for Production and Employment Scheduling" (Master's thesis, Massachusetts Institute of Technology, 1957).

[6] Wallace Crowston, "An Empirical Study of Actual and Optimum Decision Rules for Production and Employment Scheduling" (Master's thesis, Massachusetts Institute of Technology, 1958).

[7] Constructed from "Production and Inventory Control, Analysis of the Decision-Making Process," Clinton M. Jones (Master's thesis, Massachusetts Institute of Technology, 1958).

S were highly correlated, and the t tests on the coefficients came out poorly.

With advice concerning regression, "Use all the good restrictions you have—you'll get better estimates," we were able to use the feedback form (modified) of the original decision rules.[8]

The versions of the decision rules developed for regression were

$$\Delta W_t = b_1\left(\mathbf{S}_{2-4} - \frac{\mathbf{S}}{\mathbf{W}} W_{t-1}\right) + b_2\left(S_t\frac{\mathbf{I}}{\mathbf{S}} - I_{t-1}\right) + a_1$$

$$P_t = b_3 W_t + b_4\left(\frac{\mathbf{W}}{\mathbf{S}}\mathbf{S}_{2-4} - W_t\right) + b_5\left(S_t\frac{\mathbf{I}}{\mathbf{S}} - I_{t-1}\right) + a_2$$

where W, P, and I are as given before, S_t represents actual sales in current period, $\mathbf{S}_{2-4}$ represents average actual sales in the next three periods, and $\mathbf{S}$, $\mathbf{W}$, and $\mathbf{I}$ represent averages of these variables over the total period of investigation. These rules are a bit simpler although they follow from the feedback rules which Yance proves equivalent to the HMMS rules. The exact form of the rules is not important for this paper, although the modification using variables which are the normalized differences between variables, e.g., $[S_t(\mathbf{I}/\mathbf{S}) - I_{t-1}]$, permitted a more meaningful regression to be made.

With these rules as the form, regressions were done for the four companies to obtain the (estimates of) decision-rule coefficients from management's actual behavior. These gave significant correlations which permitted the development described next.

5. COSTING THE REGRESSION RULES

With the feedback production and employment scheduling rules, and with the coefficients developed from management's own scheduling behavior, it was possible to reconstruct (simulate) the companies' scheduling behavior following these rules (with moving average forecast) as was done in the original work. The results are as shown in Table 3.

Table 3

	Ice cream	Chocolate	Candy	Paint
Decision rule (perfect)	100 %	100 %	100 %	100 %
Decision rule (moving average)	104.9 %	102.0 %	103.3 %	110 %
Company performance	105.3 %	105.3 %	111.4 %	139.5 %
Management coefficients	102.3 %	100.0 %	124.1 %[a]	124.7 %[b]
Correlation	$W_t, r = .78$	$W_t, r = .57$	$W_t, r = .73$	$W_t, r = .40$
	$P_t, \ r = .97$	$P_t, \ r = .93$	$P_t, \ r = .86$	$P_t, \ r = .66$

a Using a perfect sales forecast would have reduced this to 112.5 %.
b This figure must be viewed with some reservation, as we were working with the publications and working papers from HMMS, not the data as such. We could not reconstruct some of their costs, and the five years are 1950–54, rather than 1949–53, although both cover the extreme years of the Korean War.

As can be seen from the table, in all cases but the candy company, if the decision rules with the coefficients supplied by regression of management's own behavior and a rather simple estimating scheme for future sales had been used, the costs would have been less than the company's actual behavior. In the ice cream company and the chocolate company, it would have been even cheaper than the decision rule derived from the standard quantitative analysis and the same sales forecasting scheme.

Several points of explanation may help. It is suspected that the somewhat surprising results of better performance with the managers' coefficients than that supplied by the analysis is due to the fact that the *analysis* is optimum only in the sense that the quadratic cost models from which the rules were derived is a perfect fit for these costs. This, of course, is not the case. It is important to keep in mind that *optimization* is always of a (mathematical) model, which hopefully bears some resemblance to important facets of the real world. The graphical multiple regression done earlier on the candy company (the refuting case here) suggests that had the split inventory policy between slack and busy times of the year been permitted in the rule, the then adjusted management coefficients rule would have been better.

6. THE MANAGEMENT COEFFICIENTS THEORY

An attempt at something like an axiomatic treatment of these concepts is presented *in order to stimulate more ideas*:

1. Experienced managers are quite aware of and sensitive to the criteria of a system.

2. Experienced managers are aware of the system variables which influence these criteria.

3. Managers, in their present position through a process of natural screening, make decisions, i.e., implicitly operate decision rules, with a sense and intuition which relates the variables to the criteria imperfectly—*but which is more erratic than biased*.

4. Most cost or criteria surfaces as a function of the decision variables are shallow, dish-shaped at the bottom (top) and even with bias in the manager's behavior; it is the far-out (variance) examples of behavior which are really expensive or damaging.

5. If manager's behavior had paralleled the decision rules with their average or mean coefficients, their experience would have been better according to the (their) criteria.

It seems useful to attempt an explanation of why decision rules

---

[8] The HMMS rules had been factored into feedback form by Joseph V. Yance in his unpublished paper, "Marshallian Elements in the Carnegie Tech Rules."

derived from management's own average behavior might yield better results than information from the aggregate behavior itself. Man seems to respond to selective cues in his environment; particular things seem to catch his attention at times (the last telephone call), while at other times it is a different set of stimuli. Not only is this selective cueing the case, but a threshold concept seems to apply. He may respond not at all up to some point and then may over-respond beyond that. It is this type of behavior which helps explain the variance in the organization's (or its management's) behavior.

Departures of the decision-making behavior of management from the preferred results in this sense, then, can be divided or factored into two components, one which, in the manner of a grand average departing from some preferred figure, we call bias (which causes a relatively small criteria loss because of the dish-shaped bottom of the criteria surface), and one, representing individual occurrences of experience departing from the grand average, which we call variance (which causes larger criteria losses because of the individual occurrences up the sides of the criteria dish-shaped surface). It is the latter and more important component which seems to offer the tempting possibility of elimination through the use of decision rules incorporating coefficients derived from management's own recurrent behavior.

What can be done with this management coefficients theory?

1. It may yield fresh insight into a management problem or a decision process—it may lead to further ideas. (This is operational in an academic world.)[9]

    a. Several approaches to the same problem are often of benefit.

    b. Patterns of behavior variance against the decision rule may point to missed elements in the analysis.

    c. It gives us a chance to see (indirectly) the criteria through the manager's eyes (or action).

2. Sampling in the current system may be possible; e.g., with 10,000 items in inventory, maybe the managers will look carefully at 100 items and make the necessary decisions for these 100; then these 100 items (along with their relevant variables) may be used in estimating the coefficients in the decision rules for the 10,000 − 100 items (an inventory test case is given later in the chapter).

3. The present system structure may be balanced; e.g., with many branch plants, it may be possible to arrange a better configuration of

---

[9] Harlow Shapely, the Harvard astronomer, in reviewing *The Universe at Large* by Hermann Bondi, includes "'It is not the purpose of any scientific theory,' wisely remarks Dr. Bondi, 'to be infallible or final or true. Its purpose is to be fertile; to suggest new observations that suggest new ramifications of the subject.'"

plant sizes (a plant size test case is given later in the chapter).

4. Let the manager look at the decision rule with his regression coefficients and then decide what his decision will be; e.g., to run in parallel with joint feedback between manager and rules.[10]

5. Decouple the manager, but record his decisions. (This is not seriously offered as a suggestion, but just to stimulate ideas.) The manager has continual access to his changing environment—he makes his decisions; these are filed and this operation (e.g., production and employment scheduling) is determined by the decision rule (not his decision). Then periodically the decision rule is updated from the file of recent decisions. The idea here is to eliminate the effects of the variance in decision behavior, while at the same time permitting the decision rule to reflect the current environment.

6. If the theory can be verified where it is felt that the system criteria can be measured (as in the cases presented in this paper), then some asssurance might exist for using it where the criteria cannot be measured.[11]

7. Automatic decision-making (by computer) to save executive time will require decision rules with coefficients; these may be supplied by regression.

8. At the bounds of analysis, the new theory may help to structure the system. Where aggregation is used in the analysis and the question is raised as to what happens when the clerk breaks open the aggregate, rules with regression coefficients can be supplied.

The management coefficients theory is, of course, not without its

[10] J. G. March and H. A. Simon, *Organizations*, New York: John Wiley Sons, Inc., 1958, p. 209, state: "... since there is no reason to suppose that *any* technique of decision-making, whether centralized or decentralized, will bring the organization into the neighborhood of a genuine 'optimum,' the search for decision mechanisms cannot take criteria of optimization too seriously, but must seek 'workable' techniques for satisficing. The exploration of decision-making techniques along these lines is still in a very undeveloped state.... A number of decision rules for production control and scheduling decisions in individual firms have been developed— but again with only small forays beyond the familiar terrain of optimization." The new theory departs a bit from this familiar terrain.

[11] Herbert Simon in *The New Science of Management Decision*, New York: Harper and Row, Publishers, 1961, makes several statements relevant to this idea. If the new theory offers anything, then the first quotation, p. 17, is not necessarily true. (With reference to operations research) " ... The model will call for certain parameters of its structure (the system) to be estimated before it can be applied in a particular situation. Hence, it is necessary that there be ways of making actual numerical estimates of these parameters [the system, not the decision rules derived therefrom] of sufficient accuracy for the practical task at hand."

The second quotation, p. 18, however, is cited for reinforcement here. "For the operations research approach to work, nothing has to be exact—it just has to be close enough to give better results than could be obtained by common sense without the mathematics."

problems. It may kill the goose that lays the golden eggs. The manager may follow the rule with his past (average) coefficients, and not adjust to new conditions as they take place. March and Simon[12] make the distinction between (a) short-run adaptation as problem solving (here, using the decision rule as fulcrum), and (b) long-run adaptation as learning (here, using the manager to modify decision rules). The problem is how to bypass (a) without inhibiting (b).

7. PLANT SIZE

As an additional check on the theory presented here, an analysis described in the Operations Research Society journal[13] was re-examined. The study concerned the question of the optimum size of ice cream plant for a particular company operating ten plants over a seven-state area. For purposes here, the analysis need not be repeated, but it led to a decision rule for the optimum volume plant:

$$V_{opt} = (K)^{1/3}\left(\frac{2b}{c}\right)^{2/3}$$

where K was the sales density in thousand gallons per square mile (per year), and b and c were particular cost factors relevant to the ice cream production and distribution system. Had the system been restructured according to the analysis and decision rule, gross cost savings appeared to be available. These, along with the results of the new theory, are presented in Table 4.

Table   4

		Savings
Original	$V_{opt} = (K)^{1/3}\left(\frac{2b}{c}\right)^{2/3}$	$ 207,000
Regression (first model)	$V = (K)^{1/3}\, d_1$	$ 133,000
Regression (native Model)	$V = a + d_2 K$	$ 20,000

With the same decision rule form [with $(K)^{1/3}$ as the independent variable and permitting no intercept, $a = 0$], the company's actual plant volumes were used to estimate d_1, the decision rule coefficient. Had the plant system then been restructured with their own (behavior) coefficient in the decision rule, the projected gross cost savings would be $133,000.

For test purposes a naive decision rule, $V = a + d_2 K$, was used in the same manner—it included the relevant variable, sales density, but not to the "right" power, as well as permitting an intercept a.

---

[12] March and Simon, *op. cit.*, p. 170.

[13] E. H. Bowman, "Scale of Operations—An Empirical Study," *Journal of the Operations Research Society of America*, May–June, 1958.

Here a and d_2 were estimated from the actual plants, and, as can be seen, the savings are quite small. In other words, *any old decision rule will not do.* It is certain that the most simple rule, $V = \mathbf{V}$, i.e., all plants should be the average size, would have been more costly for the firm than the present arrangement.

It is interesting to note that the naive rule actually gave a better fit to the data. Although it is the cost savings rather than the good fit which is the choice here, if a collaboration were now in existence between the analyst and the managers, this point would be worthy of discussion and reflection for both parties. That is, *the new theory might be a very useful part of a more general analytic procedure, rather than being directly prescriptive.*

8. IDLEWILD AIRCRAFT SPARES

A further check was made on the new theory using the basic work of a thesis[14] dealing with a spare parts inventory maintained at Idle-wild Airport. Waiting-line theory had been used for the inventory analysis with an n channel service facility for n pieces of an item. An idle channel corresponded to an item in stock; a busy channel corresponded to an empty space; no queues were allowed.

For the management coefficients theory test, an extremely simple decision rule was developed:

$$\text{Spares} = a + bx$$

where
$$x = \frac{\text{usage during repair cycle}}{\text{unit price of item}} \text{ [15]}.$$

The thesis studied in some detail ten stock items of widely scattered characteristics. For our purposes, the results are shown in Table 5.

From this small sample, at least, the simple decision rule with the

[14] Giyora Doeh, "Overhauled Spares Inventory for Aircraft Components" (Master's thesis, Massachusetts Institute of Technology, 1958).

[15] For an incremental approach:
$$\triangle \text{Cost} = \triangle \text{Gain}$$
$$\text{Unit cost} = (\triangle \text{ prob})(\text{run-out cost}).$$

Let
$$\triangle \text{prob } \alpha \left(\frac{1}{\text{spares}}\right)(\text{usage})$$

with tail of hyperbola a rough approximation to tail of Poisson distribution. Then,

$$\text{Unit cost } \alpha \frac{\text{usage}}{\text{spares}}(\text{run-out cost})$$

and

$$\text{Spares } \alpha \frac{\text{usage}}{\text{unit cost}}(\text{run-out cost}$$

Table 5

	Company actual	Thesis analysis	New theory
Investment	$ 17,000	$ 16,000	$ 16,500
Stock-outs in 6 years	186	69	143

behavior coefficients (*a* and *b*) would have saved half as much investment and one-third as many run-outs as the analysis.   No more detailed analysis was made here.

9. OTHER APPLICATIONS

In a very detailed study of equipment replacement policies in the trucking industry,[16] a number of conclusions supporting ideas presented here are found.   A well-accepted model[17] was used with empirical data from industry studies.   The following items were determined:
1. Estimates of obsolescence
    a. Carrying capacity of trailer.
    b. Internal combustion engine technology.
2. Estimates of operating cost
    a. Fuel.
    b. Maintenance.
The study resulted in very flat curves of total yearly average value as a function of equipment life.   Replacement anywhere between 2.2 years and 4.4 years will lead to losses of at most $ 50 short of "exact" optimum.   Smith reports:

"This is a remarkable result especially when one considers that on the average about 2/3 of the total investment of trucking firms is in the form of trucking equipment (i.e., capital goods of intermediate durability requiring regular maintenance).   It would seem that this of all industries would find equipment *replacement* policies of considerable importance, yet precision in such policies turns out to be of minor significance.   It is not argued that it makes no difference when equipment is replaced.   Rather the point is that profits are not sufficiently sensitive to replacement that the firm is likely to miss the optimum by a costly margin even when using relatively crude methods of analysis."

He also states that an optimum service period of three to four years is about one to two years shorter than the actual replacement behavior of the firm in question.

[16] Vernon Smith, "Economic Equipment Policies: An Evaluation," *Management Science*, October, 1957.

[17]
$$V = \sum_{K=0}^{\infty} e^{-\rho kl} \{ \int_0^L Q(KL, t) e^{-\rho t}\, dt - p + S(L) e^{-\rho L} \}.$$

He then goes on to explain that delayed replacement, in effect, is a relatively cheap source of capital for this firm. This is equivalent to saying that the management senses a somewhat different criteria surface than his analysis explicitly considers. Regression of behavior should permit this sensing to be incorporated in the decision rule.

A good deal of interest today seems to exist in heuristics and management problem-solving. Although these processes may be largely programmatic and qualitative, some coefficients are embedded therein. The question of how far to go down some path or how many of these parts to combine may still require parameters. Where this is so, observation and regression of experienced problem solvers may be helpful.

For a case in point, a thesis student has been working on heuristics for a dispatching rule to be associated with a key process in an aircraft plant. The question involves the order in which waiting parts should proceed through the equipment. He has identified four characteristics (e.g., cost, due date) of the parts which are relevant for this sequencing (dispatching). He needs coefficients to weight these characteristics. Simulation had already occurred to him. He agreed that analysis, at least conceptually, might be possible. The new theory suggests to him that he might obtain from the shop the actual dispatching decisions by the men directly involved on a long list of parts along with their characteristics in order to do a regression for the weighting coefficients.

The management coefficients theory says something about the behavior of managers and their organizations. There seems to be no apparent reason why these ideas should apply to production only and not to marketing, or to industrial organizations only and not to governmental organizations, or even to microeconomic problems only and not to macroeconomic problems as well. But perhaps this overstates the case.

10. SUMMARY

The gist of the management coefficients theory is a relatively simple notion:

1. In their decision-making behavior, managers and/or their organizations can be *conceived* as decision rule coefficient estimators (not that they explicitly *are* coefficient estimators).

2. It is the variance in the decision-making rather than the bias that hurts, because of dish-shaped criteria surfaces.

3. A decision rule with mean coefficients estimated from management's behavior should be better than actual performance.

4. It may be better than a rule with coefficients supplied by traditional analysis.

5. Systematic and comparative studies using this idea may lead to further ideas.

8

Constrained Inventory Rules
for Production Smoothing

Peter R. Winters
CARNEGIE INSTITUTE OF TECHNOLOGY

1. INTRODUCTION

"Production smoothing" means planning production levels that reduce the peaks and raise the valleys in translating fluctuating sales
into factory production. This kind of planning is usually done for a
factory that manufactures to finished goods inventory; one of the
principal reasons for the existence of this inventory is that it allows
such smoothing. A variety of methods is available to accomplish production smoothing, or, in other words, to make production decisions.
See, for example, the method of Holt, Modigliani, Muth, Simon [1],
where aggregate production decisions are made to minimize costs of
hiring-firing, overtime-undertime, and inventory holding and run-out.

This paper was presented at the Factory Scheduling Conference, Carnegie Institute of Technology, May 10–12, 1961. Reprinted from Management Science 8 (1962), 470–481. This paper
was written as part of the contract, "Planning and Control of Industrial Operations," with the
Office of Naval Research and the Bureau of Ships. Some of the research was carried on under
arrangements with the Aluminum Company of America. Special thanks go to William Hutchison
and Phillips Whidden of Alcoa.

The last chapter in this book briefly describes other methods and gives references for them.

Production smoothing has probably received more attention in management science literature than any other problem except inventory control. In fact, these two problems are intimately related, if it is finished goods inventory that is being "controlled." Inventory control with the traditional interpretation consists of making two kinds of decisions for the products that are stocked: (1) when to order more, from a supplier or from the firm's own factory, and (2) how much to order. Making these decisions for the factory's own finished goods inventory actually amounts to making production decisions for the factory. Most of the theory of inventory decision-making, however, concentrates on the inventories of isolated products, without taking into account the effect of these decisions on the system the inventory is embedded in. When this type of theory is used for finished goods inventory control, either the factory must ignore the "decisions," or else must suffer additional costs (those noted above) incurred by responding to these inventory (production) decisions that often amplify the seasonal fluctuations that the aggregate production smoothing decisions seek to damp.

If inventory decisions are to be made sensibly, they must be consistent with aggregate factory plans; at the same time, aggregate plans must take into account how total production and inventory will be distributed among individual products. This paper presents a way of accomplishing these goals, or actually, an associated set of ways. We shall first examine a method which minimizes total inventory costs (the sum of individual product inventory costs) subject to an inventory constraint. Second, with the same criterion, we shall use a production constraint. We shall see that neither of these two approaches is entirely satisfactory; the first is not, because it does not accomplish what it tries to do; the second, although it yields the desired results, is unsatisfactory because of the involved calculations required. We shall then show how it is possible, by limiting the extent of the constraint, to make nearly optimal production decisions in a very simple way. This proposed method is based on a comparison of the costs of different ways of developing the trigger and lot-size decisions consistent with desired aggregate plans. The result is a (computationally) inexpensive way of providing the factory at the start of each month (or other planning period) with a list of products to be made during the month, how much of each to make, and a suggested priority of production. This priority is based on inventory and sales considerations, and can be modified by the factory to take into account manufacturing efficiencies.

Cost comparisons between optimal and near-optimal methods are shown in graphs. The mathematical detail is given in the Appendix.

2. AGGREGATE INVENTORY CONSTRAINT

We noted in the introduction that the cost of aggregate finished goods inventory is one of the principal considerations in making production, inventory, and work force decisions for a factory, warehouse system. For any given level of aggregate inventory there are many ways of distributing that total inventory among individual products. Each possible distribution has cost implications—for example, it is possible to have "too much" of one product while another is out of stock. We want to choose a good (the best if we can find it) distribution among products, and then base our production smoothing decisions on the cost of such a distribution. Figure 1 gives a simple illustration.

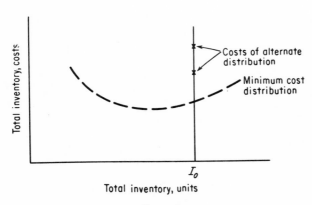

Figure 1

Then, in making inventory decisions for each product, we want to approach that distribution which will minimize total inventory costs. One way to accomplish this is to minimize total inventory costs (the sum of individual product inventory costs) subject to the constraint that the sum of product inventories equals the total inventory specified by the production smoothing decisions. The following notation will help us to be more precise.

For each product (product subscript suppressed):

Q = lot size, or reorder quantity, in units.[1]

I_T = trigger level, or reorder point, in units.

[1] Here, and throughout the paper, quantities are expressed in "units," which in practice should be units suitable for aggregation, such as man-hours of production, or gallons, or sales dollars, or whatever unit is appropriate for the application.

s = expected sales rate during the lead time, units/period.

T_L = lead time in periods.

$C(I_T, Q)$ = expected cost per period of the inventory system for one product.

and I = total desired expected inventory, in units.

$$\text{Total inventory cost} = \sum_i C(I_{Ti}, Q_i).$$

The average inventory for one product is a half-lot plus the buffer

$$\frac{Q}{2} + I_T - sT_L.$$

To minimize total inventory cost subject to the constraint, we would set up the Lagrangian function

$$L = \sum_i C(I_{Ti}, Q_i) + \lambda \left[\sum_i \left(\frac{Q_i}{2} + I_{Ti} - s_i T_{Li} \right) - I \right]$$

and minimize it by taking partial derivatives with respect to each Q_i and I_{Ti}, setting these and the constraint equal to zero, and solving this set of simultaneous equations. For reasonable inventory models, which define $C(I_T, Q)$,[2] and in particular for the model that will be introduced a bit later, this is a formidable task. The task is made easier if we expand the individual cost functions, $C(I_T, Q)$, in a Taylor series, including only terms of second order and lower. Similarly, it is possible to approximate the derivatives by a linear function in Q, I_T, and s. For an example of the former method, see Chapter 1 of [2]; for the latter, see Chapter 13 of [1].

The major difficulty with the aggregate inventory constraint, however, is not a computational one. The trouble is that desired total inventory is obtained only on the average over all products, and hence with a considerable and unacceptable lag. For example, suppose that

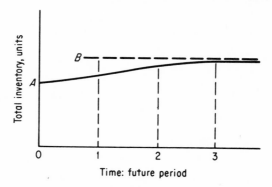

Time: future period

Figure 2

[2] $C(I_T, Q)$ is assumed to be differentiable over the relevant ranges of I_T and Q.

on the average each product is produced in the factory about once every three months. In other words, the factory produces about one-third of the products each month. If our total inventory is currently at A (Figure 2), and we desire it, for smoothing reasons, to be at B by the end of the month, by using the method above, we shall raise the triggers and lot-sizes for all products. However, only a portion of the products will actually be triggered for production during the month, so that our actual month's end inventory will rise only a part of the way from A to B, and in this way we have not accomplished the desired production. If we make no further changes in triggers and lot-sizes, we shall approach level B after some months. Unfortunately, in the meantime, we shall try to set out on some new course, which we can reach only in the long run, and so on. It is the transient that we must be concerned with, and not the steady state.

3. AGGREGATE PRODUCTION CONSTRAINT

Another way of attacking the problem is to minimize total inventory cost while constraining the production triggered during the month to equal desired aggregate production, P^*.[3] The constraint is

$$\sum_{p \in P} Q_p = P^*$$

where $p \varepsilon P$ means that we should include lot-sizes for products we expect to trigger during the month. The Lagrangian function is

$$L = \sum_i C(I_{Ti}, Q_i) + \lambda (\sum_{p \in P} Q_P - P^*). \qquad (1)$$

At the beginning of the process we do not know which products will be triggered, so we shall include all of them tentatively. The first-order conditions for a minimum are

$$\frac{\partial L}{\partial I_{Ti}} = 0$$
$$i = 1, 2, \ldots, N. \qquad (2)$$
$$\frac{\partial L}{\partial Q_i} = 0$$

We can solve Equations (2) pair by pair, for $I_{Ti}(\lambda)$ and $Q_i(\lambda)$. Then we
  1. Select a value of λ.
  2. Compute $I_{Ti}(\lambda)$ and $Q_i(\lambda)$.
  3. See if the ith product is expected to trigger during the month by computing

[3] The desired aggregate production, P^*, can be obtained by a number of different methods, including the linear decision rules of Holt, Modigliani, Muth, Simon [1], other methods given in the last chapter of that book, seat-of-the-pants, etc.

$$p_i = \frac{I_{Ti}(\lambda)}{I_i^0 - S_i}$$

(3)

where I_i^0 is the current inventory of the product and S_i is expected sales during the month. If $p_i \geq 1$, we expect the product to trigger and to be produced, and thus we shall include $Q_i(\lambda)$ in the accumulated production (i.e., it is one of the Q_p's). After repeating this process for all products, we can plot one point on a λ, P graph (an example is given in Figure 3). Several selections of λ would let us determine λ^* for the desired P^*; then we can redetermine $I_{Ti}^*(\lambda^*)$ and $Q_i^*(\lambda^*)$. In this way the inventory decisions will, on the average, generate desired total production.

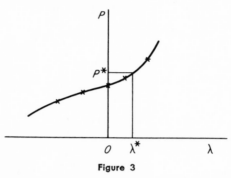

Figure 3

This method should give quite good results, although it is not strictly optimal, in the sense that we have interposed inventory rules (based on a model, $C(I_T, Q)$, designed for independent product control) between the inventory cost minimization and production decisions.[4] A more unfortunate problem is that the numerical calculations are quite lengthy:[5] we must solve the N pairs of nonlinear equations (2) (for N products) several times each month. These calculations are probably not feasible if the inventory is made up of very many products. This impasse led us to consider alternatives, described in the next section.

4. THE COST OF CONSTRAINTS

Because of the difficulties described above, we were led to wonder how much the optimally constrained triggers and lot-sizes vary from

---

[4] An attempt to work directly with individual product decisions and aggregate costs is given by A. Schild [3]. The difficulty with Schild's approach is that he has no way of insuring that set-ups (in the factory) are made in integral amounts.

[5] For example, for the model we have been using, which is of average complexity, the solution of Equations (2) for one product takes about a minute on the IBM 650, when index registers and core storage are used.

their unconstrained values. We investigated the variation by minimizing $C(I_T, Q)$ for a single product subject to a constraint on its
average inventory, I (suppressing the product subscript):

$$\phi = C(I_T, Q) + \lambda\left[\frac{Q}{2} + I_T - sT_L - I\right]. \tag{4}$$

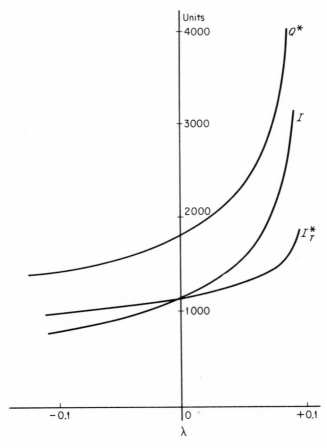

Note : $C_F = \$200$
$C_I = 0.1\$/(\text{units} \times \text{month})$
$D/C_I = 30$ (no units)
$T_L = 1.8$ months
$r = 3$ (no units)
$s = 500$ units/month

Figure 4 Variation of Q and I_T

The partial derivatives give the conditions for the minimum:[6]

$$\frac{\partial \phi}{\partial I_T} = 0$$

$$\frac{\partial \phi}{\partial Q} = 0.$$

(5)

We found that $Q^*(\lambda)$ varies substantially more than $I_T^*(\lambda)$, for a variety of levels of sales and costs. A typical outcome is shown in Figure 4.[7]

These results suggested the possibility of fixing I_T at its average, unconstrained value, and then accomplishing constrained changes in inventory solely through increasing and decreasing Q.[8] Such a practice would lead to some simplification in calculations.

Before settling on this plan, however, we decided to investigate the costs attached to constraining only Q, or only I_T, while maintaining various average inventory levels. This investigation was carried out as follows:

1. Set $\lambda = 0$, solve Equations (5) for (I_T, Q), the unconstrained values.

2. Choose a value of λ, solve equations (5) for (I_T^*, Q^*).

3. Compute $I(\lambda) = \dfrac{Q^*}{2} + I_T^* - sT_L$.

4. Constrain only Q to obtain the same $I(\lambda)$ as in 3, as

$$Q' = 2[I(\lambda) - I_T + sT_L].$$

5. Constrain only I_T to obtain the same $I(\lambda)$ as in 3, as

$$I_T' = I(\lambda) - \frac{Q}{2} + sT_L.$$

6. Compute the following costs:

   a. $C(I_T^*, Q^*)$—the cost of constraining "both."
   b. $C(I_T, Q')$—the cost of constraining only Q.
   c. $C(I_T', Q)$—the cost of constraining only I_T.

7. Return to 2, to choose another λ.

A typical set of results is given in Figure 5.[9] The results were

---

[6] Details of the cost model and these equations are given in the Appendix.

[7] See the Appendix for a complete definition of notation.

[8] Expressing the possibility as a rule to obtain desired total production, we would make the same set of products during a month for any level of P^*, and then get P^* by making more or less of each product in this set.

[9] See the Appendix for a complete definition of the notation.

not at all what we expected, and they show that the conclusion above is entirely wrong. When average inventory is above its unconstrained level, the three costs (6a, 6b, 6c) are very similar; in this situation,

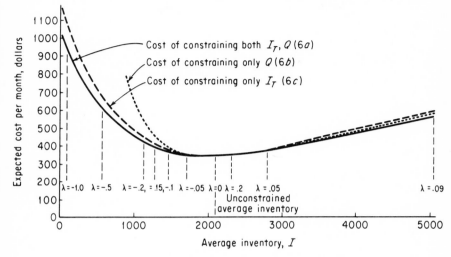

Note: $s = 1000$ units/month; see note, Figure 4 for other values.

Figure 5 Cost of constraints.

as long as I_T and Q are at least as great as their unconstrained optimal values $(\boldsymbol{I_T}, \boldsymbol{Q})$ it hardly matters at all how the average inventory is obtained, at least from a cost standpoint. On the low side, however, it makes a great deal of difference: if Q is set at $\boldsymbol{Q}$, and I_T is reduced to get lower average inventory, the costs (6c) are not much higher than the best selection of I_T and Q (6a); if, on the other hand, I_T is fixed at $\boldsymbol{I_T}$, and Q is reduced, the costs (6b) rise much more rapidly.

Consequently, the better "reduced constraint" rule is to fix the lot-size Q at its long-run, unconstrained value, and raise and lower the trigger to achieve desired inventories. From the production side, this means that the lot-sizes should be fixed, and more or fewer products produced to make up the month's desired production P^*.

5. COMPUTATIONALLY SIMPLE APPROXIMATIONS FOR APPLICATION

The results of the cost comparisons of Section 4 indicate that, from an inventory cost standpoint, constraint on only the trigger is the better alternative. If we pursue the problem as we have been we would seek to minimize L, as given in Equation (1), but with the lot-sizes fixed at $\boldsymbol{Q}_i$

$$L = \sum_i C(I_{Ti}, \boldsymbol{Q}_i) + \lambda (\sum_{p \in P} \boldsymbol{Q}_p - P^*).$$

Note that derivatives with respect to the remaining decision variables do not contain λ:

$$\frac{\partial L}{\partial I_{Ti}} = \frac{dC(I_{Ti}, \boldsymbol{Q}_i)}{dI_{Ti}} = 0. \tag{6}$$

and hence we are unable to use this technique to solve the problem as stated. One approach would be to choose from the set of all Q_i's subsets that satisfy

$$\sum_{p \in P'} Q_p = P^*$$

(at least approximately) and then select that subset which will minimize expected total inventory costs. In so doing, we would usurp the function of the triggers (except perhaps for priority ranking) and would have to restructure the entire problem.

As an alternative, the following approximate method is appealing:

1. Determine the unconstrained triggers from Equation (2) (with $\lambda = 0$).[10]

2. Compute the "priority" indexes

$$p_i = \frac{I_{Ti}}{I_i^0 - S_i}$$

for all products.

3. Rank the products in descending order by p_i.

4. Go down this list, accumulating $\boldsymbol{Q}_i$'s until the desired total P^* is reached.

These, then, would be the set of products that we would manufacture during the month. The priority of manufacture would be given by the p_i's. Since we ignored manufacturing costs in determining these, it would be possible to alter the order to obtain more efficient schedules.

This method would provide the factory at the begining of the month with information about the expected production for the month, in detail. Such information would be useful not only in setting schedules, but also in determining manpower requirements department by department, and so on. Also, having fixed and foreseeable production lots (the $\boldsymbol{Q}_i$'s) is useful when materials are ordered in exact quantities for particular runs. This advantage is lost when the $\boldsymbol{Q}_i$'s are constrained and changed. In addition, the unconstrained triggers could be used as secondary protection against run-out of products not on the original list.

[10] It would be possible to use an approximation $\hat{I}_T = a + b\boldsymbol{s}$, as described in the Appendix.

APPENDIX

The inventory cost model used to make the calculations in the paper is described in detail in Appendix E of [2], and in Chapters 12 and 13 of [1]. The costs represented by the model include: a fixed lot cost, inventory holding cost, and run-out cost proportional to the number of units out times the length of time out. The notation[11] for the model is

C_F = fixed lot cost; \$.
C_I = inventory holding cost coefficient; \$/unit/month.
D = depletion cost coefficient; \$/unit/month.
T_L = lead time; months.
s = sales rate during the lead time; units/month.

s is a random variable, subject to

$f(s)$ = probability distribution of s.
s = expected sales rate; units/month.

and the decision variables:

Q = lot-size; units.
I_T = trigger level; units.

The cost function gives the expected cost per period of the inventory system for a single product:

$$C(I_T, Q) = \frac{C_F s}{Q} + C_I\left(\frac{Q}{2} + I_T - sT_L\right)$$
$$+ \frac{s(D + C_I)}{2Q} \int_{I_T/T_L}^{\infty} \frac{(sT_L - I_T)^2}{s} f(s)ds. \qquad (A1)$$

The derivatives of the cost function are

$$\frac{\partial C}{\partial I_T} = -\frac{s(D + C_I)}{Q} \int_{I_T/T_L}^{\infty} \frac{sT_L - I_T}{s} f(s)ds + C_I = 0 \qquad (A2)$$

$$\frac{\partial C}{\partial Q} = -\frac{s}{Q^2}\left[C_F + \frac{D + C_I}{2} \int_{I_T/T_L}^{\infty} \frac{(sT_L - I_T)^2}{s} f(s)ds\right] + \frac{C_I}{2} = 0. \qquad (A3)$$

Equations (A2) and (A3) can be solved in the following way:

1. Choose a value for $Q^{(1)}$ for Equation (A2) (the standard lot-size formula gives a satisfactory initial selection).

2. Using $Q^{(1)}$, solve Equation (A2) for I_T; Newton's method of successive approximations brings rapid convergence.

3. Use the value of I_T from Equation (A2) in Equation (A3); solve Equation (A3) for $Q^{(2)}$.

4. Compare $Q^{(1)}$ with $Q^{(2)}$; if the difference is small enough, the

[11] The period used for the model is a month; other periods could be used. In any event, the period used for the inventory model is independent from the planning period for $P*$.

equations are solved; if not, replace $Q^{(1)}$ with $Q^{(2)}$, return to step 2, and repeat.

The probability distribution $f(s)$ that was used was the gamma. Several studies of sales data (see Chapter 15 of [1]) indicate that the gamma distribution fits very well; this distribution also makes the mathematics of Equations (A2) and (A3) tractable.

The gamma density function can be written as

$$f(s) = \frac{q^r}{(r-1)!}e^{-qs}s^{r-1}$$

and its cumulative distribution is

$$F(S) = \int_0^s f(s)ds.$$

The two parameters of the distribution are q and r, which are related to the mean s and variance σ_s^2 as

$$r = \frac{s^2}{\sigma_s^2}$$

$$q = \frac{s}{\sigma_s^2} = \frac{r}{s}.$$

All of the integrals of Equations (A2) and (A3) can easily be transformed into the class of cumulative probability distributions:

$$F_i\left(\frac{I_T}{T_L}\right) = I\left(\frac{qI_T}{T_L}, r-i\right) = \int_0^{I_T/T_L} \frac{q^{r-i+1}}{(r-i)!}e^{-qs}s^{r-i}ds \qquad (A4)$$

which may be written as

$$I\left(\frac{qI_T}{T_L}, r-i\right) = \int_0^{qI_T/T_L} \frac{1}{(r-i)!}e^{-s}s^{r-i}ds. \qquad (A5)$$

The latter expression (A5) is an incomplete gamma function and is in a form suitable for computation on electronic computers. Flow charts for this computation are given on pp. 255 and 256 in [1].

Further investigation of sales data has shown that $r = s^2/\sigma_s^2$ is nearly constant for wide ranges of sales data. This assumption, of course, greatly reduces the extent of investigation of past sales data, from all the products to a sample of them.

A further assumption that reduces the amount of necessary computation is that the ratio D/C_I is constant for large groups of products. Both D and C_I are intimately and directly related to the value of a unit of the product, and the assumption seems quite justified.

Graphs of I_T^* vs. s and Q^* vs. s are given in Chapter 13 of [1] for various values of r and D/C_I.

For practical applications the following suggestions are made:

1. By using the groupings of products by r and D/C_I noted above,

it is possible to solve the unconstrained minimum cost equations (A2) and (A3) for a few sets of $(r, D/C_I)$ vs. s for selected values of C_F and C_I, which would represent all products within the each set.

2. Simple approximations can be made for I_T^* and Q^* as functions of s for each of these subclasses of products. For example, the straight line approximation $\hat{I}_T = a + bs$ gives very good results.

3. These approximations can be used each month, as sales forecasts of s are made for the near future, to get $\hat{I}_T$ and $\hat{Q}$ to respond to changes in sales levels.

4. The work above in steps 1 and 2 would have to be revised only occasionally, when there are substantial changes in costs or predictability.

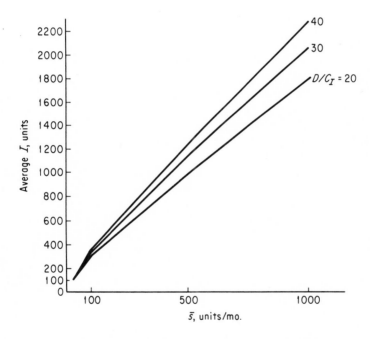

Note: D/C_I indicated on graph; see note, Figure 4 for other values.

Figure 6 Average inventory as a function of expected sales.

Finally, Figure 6 shows the relationship of the unconstrained, optimal inventory level I for a single product. The graph shows that I is nearly a linear function of s, when both lot-size and buffer are considered, and not the square-root relationship that has long been indicated when only the lot-size is used.

REFERENCES

1. Holt, C. C., F. Modigliani, J. F. Muth, and H. A. Simon, *Planning Production, Inventories and Workforce*, Englewood Cliffs, N. J.: Prentice-Hall, Inc., 1960.

2. Winters, P. R., "Inventory Control in a Multiple Warehouse System," GSIA, Carnegie Institute of Technology, 1958.

3. Schild, A., "On Inventory, Production and Employment Scheduling," *Management Science* (January 1959).

9

Simulation Tests of Lot=size Programming

B. P. Dzielinski, C. T. Baker, A. S. Manne

INTERNATIONAL BUSINESS MACHINES CORPORATION

1. INTRODUCTION

We consider the following production planning problem. Given a forecast of the demand for each product over a finite horizon of discrete planning periods, determine, for all component parts, the optimum number of parts to make on each manufacturing order, and the planning period in which to place each order so that the total variable cost of operations is minimized. The planning procedure should take the following costs into account: set-up costs, inventory costs, shortage or stock-out costs, regular and overtime labor costs, and hiring and firing costs.

A paper presented at the Factory Scheduling Conference, Carnegie Institute of Technology, May 10–12, 1961. Reprinted from *Management Science* 9 (1963) 229–258. This work was performed at the IBM Research Center, Yorktown Heights, New York and was previously reported on in the IBM Research Report RC-489, June 30, 1961. The authors wish to acknowledge Dr. R. E. Gomory and Mr. R. E. Levitan who contributed comments and suggestions on the early development of the program, Messrs. J. M. Coombs, W. J. Constandse, and Dr. C. F. Kossack for their help and support, and finally to Messrs. Y. Wong and V. Van Ness for the programming of the simulation models. A. S. Manne is at Stanford University.

In the case of some metal parts fabricating industries, such production planning problems may become intractable because of the large number of different parts involved. Each part competes in different ways for the available production equipment and work force; also, each has future orders that are of a dynamic uncertain nature. Usually each part can satisfy requirements from one of several alternative production sequences, and here is where the difficulty arises: matching the sequences for individual items so as to remain within the over-all limitations on equipment and work force availability.

The purpose of this paper is to show how to adapt to this dynamic, uncertain environment through a deterministic programming method proposed by A. S. Manne [1]. The study involved a simulation test of a scaled-down metal fabrication plant, utilizing a linear programming model as the tool for planning production for the component parts over a multiperiod planning horizon. Because of the dynamic, uncertain environment, only the initial step of each programming solution was assumed to be implemented. At the end of each period newer information on orders, etc. was obtained; the simulation program reformulated the planning task so that newer solutions were computed and implemented as before. The planned activity was updated period by period; new information was used as it became available.

The linear programming model consists of making lot-size decisions simultaneously for each part, where each part could be produced from one of several production schedules. For realistically large numbers of parts, this resulted in a computational bottleneck as of 1960. Therefore, for this study, a small number of parts were defined from a sample of data collected in an actual manufacturing process. These data were used throughout the simulation tests.

As a bench mark for the method considered here, a standard economic order quantity model was also simulated. The standard EOQ formula assumes that no significant interactions exist between the choice of optimal lot size for the many items produced in a plant. This model was preferred for comparison purposes for the following reasons: (1) comparison with actual past operations would be difficult and expensive to obtain; (2) the EOQ system could inexpensively simulate the individual items so that in effect it provided a check on the parts aggregation developed for the linear programming model; (3) it is a familar technique in industrial engineering practice.

2. THE FACTORY MODEL

For our purpose, we regard this study as being comprised of a planning model for a scaled-down fabrication shop that was observed

in actual operation.   This plant supplied manufactured parts to an
inventory.   In turn, this inventory satisfied the demands of an assembly
shop; that is, it served as the buffer between the two shops.

The scaling down amounted to planning production for a sample
of products; the demands for component parts were determined directly
from the demands for the products.   Independent demands were not
part of these component part demands.   The machine facilities were
combined into a lesser number K of facility types, and finally the
adjustments on the plant capacities were made to conform with this
scaling procedure.

Therefore, we can discuss the simulation model in terms of the
block diagram of Figure 1.

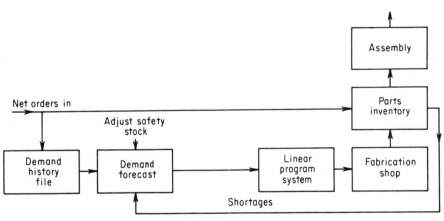

Figure 1

The net orders for each product were received and accumulated in
the order history file.   At the end of each period these data were
extrapolated to produce a forecast of net orders for each product for
each of several future time periods.   The inventory required for each
period was then augmented by a safety stock allowance, in recognition
of the dynamic, uncertain nature of the problem.   Furthermore, if
the forecasts revealed either an increasing or a decreasing trend, adjustments were made either to increase or to decrease the safety stock
allowance accordingly through the several future periods of the forecast.   If, for example, the forecast for one product in some month
was for nine net orders and the policy was to hold a one-month
safety stock allowance, then the inventory requirement consisted of
18 net orders altogether.   In addition to the safety stock allowance,

the inventory requirements were augmented by the amount of any backlogs carried over from the preceding period.

The forecast was made by extrapolating the past data on the net orders received; the following method, described by Brown [2, 3], was used.

$\hat{S}(t + \tau)$, the forecast of the net orders received at a time τ units in the future, is given by

$$\hat{S}(t + \tau) = S(t) + b(t)\left[\frac{1}{\alpha} + \tau - 1\right], \qquad 0 < \alpha < 1 \qquad (1)$$

where $\hat{S}(t)$ and $b(t)$ are the estimates at time t of the average of the net orders received and the trend in these orders, respectively. $S(t)$ and $b(t)$ are obtained from the following relations:

$$S(t) = \alpha S(t) + (1 - \alpha)S(t - 1) \qquad (2)$$

and

$$b(t) = \alpha[S(t) - S(t - 1)] + (1 - \alpha)b(t - 1) \qquad (3)$$

Where $S(t)$ is the number of net orders actually received in period t.

Several values of α were tested with net order data taken from an operating firm for 1954 and 1955. The analysis showed that a value of $\alpha = 0.1$ provided the minimum forecasting error, when one is forecasting one month into the future. In order to avoid the benefit of hindsight, no direct use was made of the 1954–1955 data in the subsequent experiments.

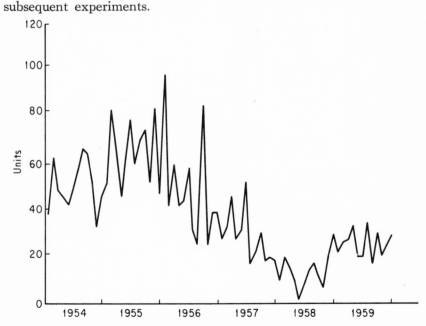

Figure 2. Net orders received by months for six years.

More explicitly, the adjusted net requirements for the ith part at time $t + \tau$ could be expressed directly from the product forecasts as follows:

$$\left. \begin{array}{ll} r_{i1} = (1 + \lambda)\hat{S}_i(t + 1) - y_i(t + 1), & \tau = 1 \\ r_{i\tau} = \hat{S}_i(t + \tau), & \tau = 2, 3, \ldots, T \end{array} \right\} \quad (4)$$

Where $r_{i\tau}$ are the net requirements; $\hat{S}_i(t + \tau)$ is the basic forecast; λ is the safety stock factor; and $y_i(t + 1)$ is the initial inventory (or backlog, if negative) for period $t + 1$.

3. THE LINEAR PROGRAMMING SYSTEM

The formulation of this production planning problem in linear programming terms is similar to that given by Manne in [1]. However, certain variations and approximations were made in order to gain computing feasibility with the linear programming codes in existence as of 1960. These differences are described later.

One important aspect of the formulation in [1] is its ability to take set-up costs into account. By their very nature, these costs appear to preclude the use of linear programming. However, set-up costs may be taken into account through the use of activities related to alternative possible *production sequences*. A *production sequence* for one part over a planning horizon of T periods is a sequence of T non-negative integers that specify the quantities of that part which are to be produced in each of the T periods. (A zero quantity may be specified in some of these periods.) The specified requirements for the part during T periods can be satisfied by a number of different set-up sequences, i.e., lot-splitting plans. However, because of certain "dominance" considerations, not all possible sequences need be considered (see [1] and [4]). The function of the linear programming computations is to select the optimal combination of production sequences for all of the parts in the system over the entire planning period.

The $r_{i\tau}$ coefficients defined in the preceding section constituted the inputs to the lot-size programming computations. From their values the set-up sequences were generated according to the rules in Appendix A, Section A.3.

The output of the linear programming computations is a set of production orders for the parts to be fabricated in order to satisfy the inventory and sales requirements. This computation indicates whether the required number of pieces for a part should be made in one batch, two batches, or more. It also determines the batch size(s) and the period in which the batch(es) should be made. These decisions are

made so that the total *discounted* cost of future operations is minimized. The minimand used in the computation was composed of all
cost elements previously mentioned, with just one exception—the
shortage costs. These costs were not recognized explicitly within the
linear programming model. However, the dollar value of these shortages was recorded separately, once each period, as the simulation
progressed.

The simulation was conducted as though the linear programming
solution for the immediate planning period were actually released to
the fabrication shop as a set of orders for production during that
period. The remainder of the solution that pertained to the subsequent periods was ignored, and a new linear programming computation
using the revised sales information was performed between each
period's operation. It was assumed that all orders released for production at the start of a period were completed by the end of that
period and sent immediately to the parts inventory and were available
at the end of that period to satisfy the demand for them. Thus the
problem of detailed scheduling or optimum sequencing of the jobs
through the various facilities was not considered in this experiment.
Finally, backlogs were regarded as occurring only when an insufficient
number of parts were on hand to satisfy completely all the current
demands and prior backlogs.

The unknowns, coefficients, and constants for the linear programming formulation were defined as follows.

1. Unknowns

$\theta_{ij} =$ fraction of the total requirement for the ith part produced
with the jth alternative set-up sequence.

$$(i = 1, 2, \ldots, I), (j = 1, 2, \ldots, J).$$

$W_{k\tau}^1 =$ number of workers assigned to first-shift operations on
facility k during period $(t + \tau)$; *no overtime*.

$$(k = 1, 2, \ldots, K), (\tau = 1, 2, \ldots, T).$$

$W_{k\tau}^2 =$ number of workers assigned to first-shift *overtime* operations on facility k during period $(t + \tau)$; each of these
workers works a fixed number of straight-time and overtime hours during the period.

$W_{k\tau}^3 =$ number of workers assigned to second-shift operations on
facility k during period $(t + \tau)$; *no overtime*.

$W_{k\tau}^4 =$ number of workers assigned to second-shift *overtime*
operations on facility k during period $(t + \tau)$; each of these
workers works a fixed number of straight-time and overtime hours during the period.

$D^+W_{k\tau}$ = increase in the total number of workers employed at facility k from period $(t + \tau - 1)$ to period $(t + \tau)$.

$D^-W_{k\tau}$ = decrease in the total number of workers employed at facility k from period $(t + \tau - 1)$ to period $(t + \tau)$.

2. Parameters recalculated each period

$L_{ijk\tau}$ = labor input required during period $(t + \tau)$ to carry out the jth alternative set-up sequence on the kth facility for part i.

$$L_{ijk\tau} = \begin{Bmatrix} 0 \\ a_{ik} + b_{ik}x_{ij\tau} \end{Bmatrix} \quad \text{when } x_{ij\tau} \begin{Bmatrix} = 0 \\ > 0 \end{Bmatrix}$$

where a_{ik} and b_{ik} refer, respectively, to the standard labor set-up time and the standard unit running time for the ith part on the kth facility. The numbers $x_{ij\tau}$ refer to the amount of part i required by sequence j during period τ. These numbers define the alternative production sequences. They are generated from the requirement forecasts $r_{i\tau}$ according to the rules given in Appendix A, Section A.3.

3. Constants

W_k = maximum number of workers that can be assigned to facility k during a single shift.

H^1 = total number of first-shift hours per period, excluding overtime.

H^2 = total number of first-shift hours per period, including a fixed amount of overtime.

H^3 = total number of second-shift per period, excluding overtime.

H^4 = total number of second-shift hours per period, including a fixed amount of overtime.

$R^1_{k\tau}$ = first-shift wage for facility k, no overtime; discounted over τ periods.

$R^2_{k\tau}$ = first-shift wage for facility k, with overtime; discounted over τ periods.

$R^3_{k\tau}$ = second-shift wage for facility k, no overtime; discounted over τ periods.

$R^4_{k\tau}$ = second-shift wage for facility k, with overtime; discounted over τ periods.

$\Gamma_{o\tau}$ = cost of laying off one worker; discounted over τ periods.

$\Gamma_{h\tau}$ = cost of hiring one worker; discounted over τ periods.

$c_{i\tau}$ = unit material cost of part i; discounted over τ periods.

The linear programming problem was stated as follows:

$$\text{Min} \sum_{i, k, \tau} \left\{ \sum_{r=1}^{4} [R^r_{k\tau} W^r_{k\tau} + \Gamma_{o\tau} D^- W_{k\tau} + \Gamma_{h\tau} D^+ W_{k\tau}] + \sum_j \theta_{ij} c_{i\tau} x_{ij\tau} \right\}$$

subject to

$$\sum_{j} \theta_{ij} = 1, \qquad\qquad\qquad i = 1, \ldots, I \qquad (A)$$

$$\sum_{i,j} L_{ijk\tau} \theta_{ij} \leq \sum_{\tau=1}^{4} H^{\tau} W_{k\tau}^{\tau}, \qquad \begin{cases} k = 1, \ldots, K \\ \tau = 1, \ldots, T \end{cases} \qquad (B)$$

$$\sum_{\tau=1}^{4} W_{k\tau}^{\tau} = \sum_{\tau=1}^{4} W_{k,\tau-1}^{\tau} + D^{+}W_{k\tau} - D^{-}W_{k\tau} \qquad \begin{cases} k = 1, \ldots, K \\ \tau = 1, \ldots, T \end{cases} \qquad (C)$$

$$W_{k\tau}^{1} + W_{k\tau}^{2} \leq W_{k}, \qquad\qquad k = 1, \ldots, K$$

$$W_{k\tau}^{3} + W_{k\tau}^{4} \leq W_{k}, \qquad\qquad \tau = 1, \ldots, T \qquad (D)$$

and

$$\theta_{ij}, W_{k\tau}^{\tau}, D^{+}W_{k\tau}, D^{-}W_{k\tau}, \text{ all} \geq 0.$$

There are I equations in group (A). These restrictions specify that the total planned requirements for each part must be satisfied by a convex combination of the admissible production sequences. Values for the unknowns θ_{ij} usually turn out to be either 0 or 1. Manne in [1] proves that there will be no more than a small number of instances—here, KT items—for which the θ_{ij} may take on proper fractional values. The fractional θ_{ij} were given the following physical interpretation in this simulation experiment where a solution was assumed with just two such proper fractions, θ_{i1} and θ_{i2}:

period τ	1	2	3	
requirements $r_{i\tau}$	10	8	9	
production sequence 1	18	0	9	$\theta_{i1} = .40$
production sequence 2	10	17	0	$\theta_{i2} = .60$
.40 production sequence 1	7.2	0	3.6	
.60 production sequence 2	6	10.2	0	
Total (rounded)	13	10	4	

The resulting sequence, (13, 10, 4), although a physically feasible one, could not have been generated by the rules given in Appendix A, Section A.3. In fact, this sequence violates a "dominance theorem" which states that the only sequences that need to be considered within a lot-size programming model are as follows: those in which the delivery requirements are fully satisfied out of production from the *nearest* preceding period in which set-up costs for that item are incurred [1, 4].

There are KT inequations in group (B). These inequations ensure that the total capacity of machine group k during period τ will be sufficient to produce the assigned work load.

There are KT equations in group (C). These are simply the balance equations that relate the size of the work force from one period

to the next.   Note that the initial work force availability is predetermined prior to each lot-size programming calculation.

There are $2\,KT$ inequations in group (D).   These inequations limit
the number of workers who can be assigned to machine group k in
period τ for both the first and second shifts.

The linear programming model was formulated for carrying inventories for anticipated usage beyond the stated planning horizon.   However, this feature was not tested in these experiments.   The effects
of inventory holding costs were not considered explicitly in the
minimand of the programming formulation, but they entered through
the discounting of labor and purchased raw material costs.

3.1. Approximations in the Linear Programming System

There are a total of $I + 4KT$ constraining equations in the linear programming formulation.   The sample of data on four final products gathered from the metal fabricating plant was composed of 950 fabricated
component parts.   There were thirteen groups of machine tools in
the plant's fabrication shop.   Thus, with $I = 950$ and $K = 13$, there
were far more constraining equations than could be accommodated
within any currently available linear programming code.   It was
apparent that further reductions and approximations would be required
in order to reduce the number of restraining equations to a manageable level.

The first step was to restrict the planning horizon to three periods.
Then the thirteen machine groups were combined into two larger
groups.   A correlation analysis of the manufacturing data for the 950
fabricated component parts revealed a high positive correlation in the
use of machine groups, and this provided the basis for defining just
two major machine groups.   These changes gave a value of $4KT =
24$, to which the I equations for the component parts had to be added.

In order to make these simulation tests, it was desirable to simulate
many months of sales history.   Since one- and two-month planning
periods were used, this required making dozens of linear programming
computations within a reasonable amount of computing time.   From
these considerations, it appeared that a system with 60 to 70 restraining equations should be employed.   We obtained such a system
by defining a set of 35 aggregate parts which were used in place of
the original 950 fabricated component parts.   This put $I = 35$ which,
with $4KT = 24$, gave a 59 equation system.   One further consideration added somewhat to the size of the linear programming matrix.
Although the model was set up in terms of a two-shift maximum
operation,   a "third shift"   with   higher   costs   and with unlimited

machining capacity was also defined. This "third shift" provided a safety valve to bypass the total infeasibility that could have arisen from large upswings in the requirements during certain peak demand periods. In order to provide a bookkeeping record of this factor, twelve more restraint equations were occasionally added to the model.

Since the defined aggregate parts consisted of two or more component parts, there arose a problem with regard to the component parts that were used in more than one distinct product. Unless this physical aspect of the problem was recognized, difficulties would arise in deriving the demand for the aggregate parts from the demands for the products. Also, other difficulties could arise in relating the quantities of the aggregate part to the quantities of the individual parts in the inventories.

In order to avoid the difficulties of common usage of component parts, a set of pseudo-products were defined as follows: Consider the four basic products A, B, C, D, and every possible combination of them—AB, AC, AD, BC, BD, CD, ABC, ABD, BCD, ACD, $ABCD$. These defined every possible way that an individual part could be used in common among four products. Each such possibility was called a pseudoproduct. We then computed the number of labor hours needed for each pseudoproduct in order to produce one unit of each parent product. It was found that only two of the eleven possible pseudoproducts were of any significant magnitude. Therefore, the system was regarded as being comprised of six products: four actual and two pseudo. The individual parts for the four final products were separated into these size categories and within each category, a number of aggregate parts were defined.

In defining the aggregate parts, three attributes of the component parts were taken into consideration: set-up time, unit running time, and the unit raw material cost. These attributes appeared important because of their role in the linear programming computations. An aggregate part was defined as a collection of component parts entering into the identical final product and having similar values for their machining times and material costs.

The number of aggregate parts categories assigned to each product was determined by the relative production volume of the product, based upon a ten-month sample of the actual sales data. Thus, more categories were assigned to products having relatively high volumes of production. The number of categories was assigned as follows:

product A	11
product B	6
product C	6
product D	5

pseudo I   4

pseudo II   3

For each aggregate part, the standard set-up time for each machine group was the sum of the set-up times in that machine group for all of the individual parts. Similarly, the standard unit running times per machine group and the unit raw material costs were the sums of the unit running times and unit costs for all of the individual parts in the aggregate part. The two latter sums reflected any multiple use of a part on a product. In other words, the simulation proceeded as though the production rates and inventory levels were identical for each individual part belonging to a given aggregate.

4. THE EOQ SYSTEM

The use of the typical EOQ formula as a tool to control production and inventories is well documented [5, 6]. The formula balances set-up costs against inventory carrying costs in order to determine the economic order quantity. The balance point between the two costs is then determined by classical calculus methods; a constant rate of future demand is assumed. This procedure usually ignores any effects of the lot-size decision upon the plant's labor costs, overtime premium, shift pay differentials, and hiring and firing costs (see Appendix A, Section A.2).

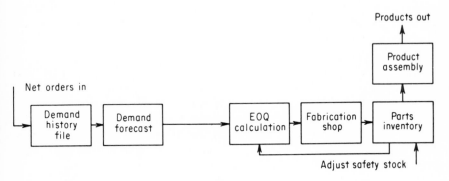

Figure 3

As in the LP system, the EOQ system may be described with the aid of Figure 3. The net orders received accumulate in the historical file. Once each period these data are used to prepare a forecast of sales for each product for one period in the future. (This was the same forecasting method as was used in the linear programming tests.) The forecast of each products was, in turn, a forecast for each component part of that product. The forecasts for period $t + 1$

were then used as the constant rates of demand, r_i, for the component parts in the EOQ calculations.

At the beginning of each period, if the inventory level for the ith part was forecast to be less than the safety stock allowance at the end of period t, an EOQi was computed for the ith part. This EOQi was augmented to produce the final order size, q_i for the ith part:

$$q_i = \text{EOQ}_i + \lambda r_i - y_i(t + 1)$$

where λ is the safety stock control parameter $(0 \leq \lambda)$, r_i is interpreted as a constant future demand rate, and $y_i(t + 1)$ is the inventory on hand (or the backlog) for the ith part. The fabrication shop was then instructed to produce a batch of size q_i for the ith part in period $t + 1$. At the end of each period, all of the parts needed to fill the current orders on hand plus any backlog orders from the previous period were subtracted from the current production and the previous inventory, and a new inventory (or backlog) level was calculated. The inventory levels of all the component parts were then tested to see if the current safety stock level had been reached. If so, the part was listed for production in the following period.

In these EOQ tests, we assumed that the size of the work force was readjusted each period according to the production requirments. Overtime costs, extra shift payments, and hiring and layoff costs were incurred—in descending order of preference—as required by the production load and the machine capacities.

5. MEASURES OF PERFORMANCE

Since the EOQ system was used as a basis for appraising the linear programming system, the same measures of performance were recorded in the simulation tests for both systems. The several summary measures recorded for this purpose were the total undiscounted operating costs, which included inventory holding costs and all labor costs (straight, overtime, and shift premium, and change-over costs). No dollar cost was imputed to shortages. However, the total dollar volume of the individual part shortages was recorded. In addition, the dollar amount of the inventory on hand at the end of each period was recorded, along with the size of the work force at each facility.

5.1 Discussion of the Results

Four tests were conducted with the linear programming (LP) and EOQ systems. The LP problem, as formulated in this paper, was solved each time by the SCROL system available on the IBM 704. The EOQ system was also simulated on the 704.

A general LP problem matrix is shown in Appendix B.

The parameters in the four tests are as follows:

T = maximum number of planning periods = 3.
λ = safety stock factor = 0 or 1.
m = production months in each planning period = 1 or 2.

<table>
<tr><td>Test One</td><td>Test Two</td></tr>
<tr><td>$T = 3$</td><td>$T = 3$</td></tr>
<tr><td>$\lambda = 0$</td><td>$\lambda = 1$</td></tr>
<tr><td>$m = 1$</td><td>$m = 1$</td></tr>
<tr><td>Test Three</td><td>Test Four</td></tr>
<tr><td>$T = 3$</td><td>$T = 3$</td></tr>
<tr><td>$\lambda = 0$</td><td>$\lambda = 1$</td></tr>
<tr><td>$m = 2$</td><td>$m = 2$</td></tr>
</table>

The simulation tests were conducted over the late 1956 and complete 1957 demand history of the firm. The total demand pattern

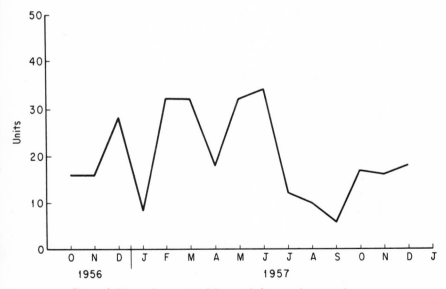

Figure 4. Net orders received by month—four products, total.

for this period on the four final products is shown in Figure 4. Each test was started with identical initial inventories and initial work force levels related to the average demand from previous periods. The cost data recorded for comparison here include the effect of these initial conditions.

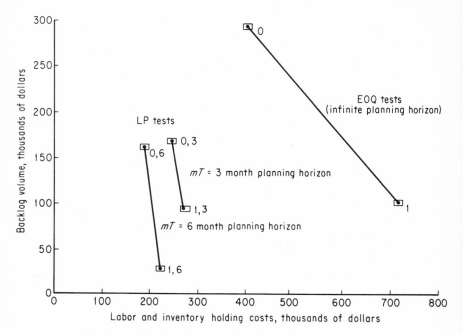

Note: 0 = no safety stock: 1 = one-month safety stock.

Figure 5. Relationship backween backlogs and dollar volume of labor and inventory costs.

Figure 5 summarizes the difference between the two systems for three and six production months in the planning horizon and for two safety stock levels. Two measures of performance are plotted here : the dollar volume of backlogs and the undiscounted operating costs. These data indicate a substantial advantage for the LP over the EOQ system, a two-to-one difference in total cost at comparable backlog volumes.

As might be expected, increasing the safety stock increases the operating costs but decreases the backlog dollar volume, and increasing the number of production months in each planning period has a favorable effect on total operating costs for the LP system.

Figures 6, 7, and 8 show the detailed comparison of undiscounted operating costs, inventory levels, and undiscounted labor costs between the two systems. The undiscounted operating costs are plotted as an accumulated time series over the simulated test period. Figure 7 indicates that most of the savings obtained by the LP system come from the inventory cost component.

It must be remembered that the LP system, like the EOQ system,

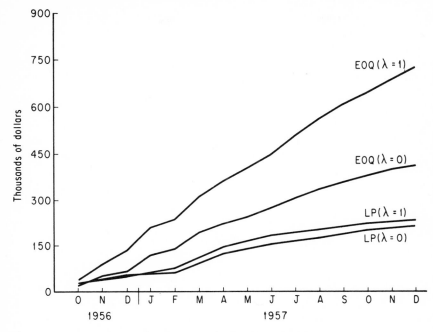

Note: $\lambda = 0$ (no safety stoc&); $\lambda = 1$ (one-month safety stock).

Figure 6. Accumulated total operating costs (labor and inventory) for EOQ and LP systems with two production months per planning period.

is making lot-size decisions, but that these decisions are performed in a different context. For instance, the ordinary EOQ formula states:

$$EOQ = \sqrt{\frac{2(\text{usage rate})\ (\text{hours per set-up})\ (\text{wage rate})}{\rho\,(\text{hours/unit})(\text{wage rate}) + \rho\,(\text{material cost/unit})}}$$

$$= \sqrt{\frac{2(\text{usage rate})\ (\text{hours/set-up})}{\rho\,(\text{hours/unit}) + \rho\,(\text{material cost/unit})/(\text{wage rate})}}$$

where ρ represents the cost per unit of capital for one period.

Note how the EOQ decision rule is based upon the assumption of a constant wage rate from period to period. On the other hand, when the LP system makes its decision, the implicit labor cost varies with the relative scarcity, and this, in turn, affects the choice of lot-sizes for the parts. For instance, during the upswing in the business cycle, implicit labor costs are higher, and hence the batch-size will be increased in order to save on labor costs. During the downswing of the business cycle the implicit labor costs are lower, and hence shorter batches are produced. The LP system then tends to produce on a hand-to-mouth basis. Thus, because of the consideration of hiring and firing costs within the linear programming model, large lots are produced during the upswings and small ones during downswings. These lot-size adjustments tend to reduce fluctuations in the plant's own work force, but accentuate the fluctuations in demand for

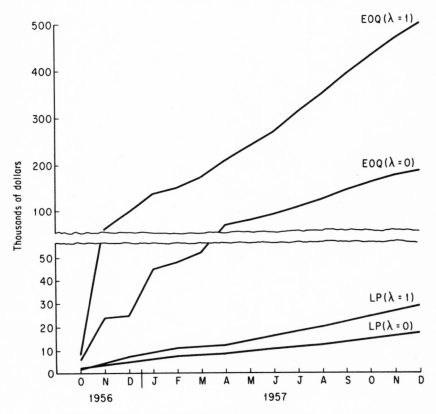

Note: See note, Figure 6. Note change of scale.

Figure 7. Accumulated inventory holding costs for EOQ and LP systems with two production months per period.

materials produced by the plant's suppliers. What is best for the individual plant is not inevitably the best policy from the viewpoint of the economy taken as a whole.

Figure 8 shows the accumulated total labor costs, that is, the sum of straight-time labor, overtime and shift premium labor, and changeover costs. In the EOQ system the safety stock policy had little effect upon these costs, but in the LP system when the one-month safety stock factor was introduced, the labor costs were increased about eight percent.

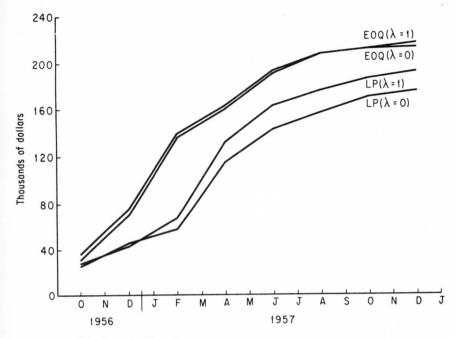

Note: See note, Figure 6.

Figure 8. Accumulated labor costs for the EOQ and LP systems by months with two production months per period.

This figure indicates a labor cost advantage for the LP system of from 12 to 18 percent over the EOQ system, depending upon whether costs are compared to the higher or lower accumulated cost line.

Note from Figure 8 that the labor costs for the LP system did not accumulate as rapidly in time as they did for the EOQ system. If the present values of these operating systems were computed by applying a present worth factor to these costs, a still more favorable comparison with the LP system would be evident.

In Figure 9, the accumulated dollar volume of parts shortages is plotted over the same test period. In this measure, the effect of the safety stock factor is obvious—regardless of the system making lot-size decisions. However, in the LP system the movement from a zero safety stock to a safety stock equal to one month's expected demand caused a reduction in accumulated shortages by a factor of 5 to 1. By employing the same change in the EOQ system, the accumulated shortages were reduced by a factor 2.8 to 1. (This result was unexpected and may be the result of sampling only a short time series of backlogs.)

In summary, when the LP system was employed to make lot-size decisions for six production months within the three-period planning horizon, and when it is compared to a similar EOQ system without any safety stocks, the LP system is favored by a factor of 11 to 1 with respect to inventory holding costs; accumulated labor costs are approximately twelve percent lower; accumulated dollar volume of parts shortages is lower by a factor of 1.7 to 1.   When the safety stock factor is set equivalent to a month's expected demand, the inventory holding costs are lower by a factor of 17 to 1; accumulated labor costs are lower by 21 percent; the accumulated dollar volume of parts shortages is lower by a factor of 3 to 1 for the LP system over the 15-month simulation test period.

A companion set of tests was performed when a single production month was assigned to a planning period.   That is, reviews and decisions were made each month, and production was planned over only three months in the future.   These tests still indicate a favorable performance for the LP system when inventory holding costs and dollar volume of parts shortages are compared, but not so when ac-

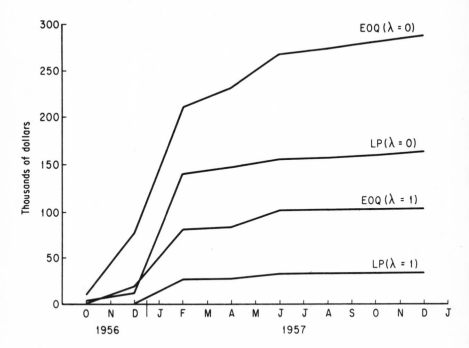

Note: See note, Figure 6.

Figure 9. Accumulated dollar volume of parts backlogs for the EOQ and LP systems by months with two production months per planning period.

cumulated labor costs are compared.   Figure 10 shows cumulative labor costs for the LP system when three and six production months are considered in the planning horizon, and compares these with a single EOQ system measure of accumulated labor costs.

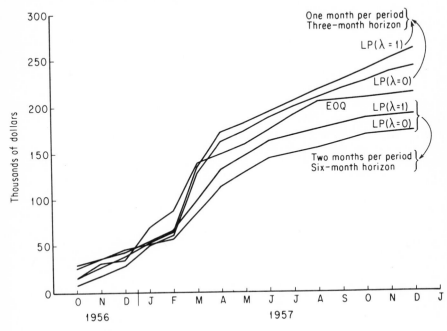

Note: See note, Figure 6.

Figure 10. Accumulated labor costs for the EOQ and LP systems by months with one and two production months per planning period for the LP system.

This figure indicates that restricting the length of the planning horizon from six to three months increased the accumulated labor costs of the LP system from 36 to 38 percent.   Even if the savings in inventory holding costs resulting from the restricted time horizon are credited, the difference in accumulated net labor cost amounts to approximately 30 percent.

6. A COMMENT

These results emerge from a single set of simulation experiments. Although extreme care was taken to eliminate all possible sources of numerical errors, there is no guarantee that the same favorable experience will be repeated in other tests.   The authors feel that the basic theoretical framework of lot-size programming appears sound—

even in a dynamic, uncertain environment.   At the practical level, there are many difficulties with the parts aggregation scheme designed to overcome the computing restrictions operative as of 1960.   In attempting to gain computing feasibility through aggregation, there is always a possibility of major distortions.

APPENDIX A :   OUTLINE OF THE TWO SIMULTATION MODELS

A.1 General Assumptions

The two alternative lot-size planning models are described in some detail : the *single-item economic order quantity* (EOQ) and the *multi-item linear programming of lot sizes* (LP) models.

Briefly, the over-all framework of the system under study is that of a manufacturing plant fabricating metal items in lot sizes on production facilities, and the items, therefore, compete with each other for service by these facilities.

The completed items are received into an inventory.   The demands on the inventory represent the result of assembly schedules for final end products demanded by some customer of the firm.   The control of inventory and production in the plant is performed by a lot-size and reorder level determination on each item.

Other assumptions for the system are

1. Maximum straight-time work force levels are specified for each facility group.

2. Maximum overtime hours are specified for each facility group.

3. Overtime and second-shift wage costs are specified multiples of straight-time labor rates.

4. Labor hiring and firing cost factors are also specified.

5. A lot-size or production run of an item started in a production period is completed within that period.

The demand for each item is estimated by means of exponential smoothing of past actual demands for the item.

Neither of the two control techniques to be described take explicit account of uncertainty in forecasting future demands.   The chief object of computer simulation is to determine whether—in the presence of substantial forecasting errors—there remains any significant difference in the over-all effectiveness of these two control techniques.

Two measures of performance will be used to evaluate the alternative control techniques.   One measure will consist of the *total variable costs*.   This total will consist of the following components :
    a. *Straight-time and premium labor costs*. These costs are asso-

ciated with the labor hours expended as straight-time and overtime labor at each facility group; they are obtained by knowing the labor force size, labor rates, and the capacity of each facility group.

b. *Labor change-over costs.* These are costs associated with increases or decreases in work force levels at any facility group, and they are proportional to the number of units of labor varied in the period.

c. *Carrying costs.* These are costs that are proportional to the amount of inventory on hand at the beginning of each period. The value of inventory on hand is measured as the value of material purchased to manufacture these on-hand units. (In the EOQ formula, the inventory cost component consists of *both* labor and material costs.)

d. *Ordering costs.* These are fixed costs incurred each time an order is placed. They are primarily office clerical costs associated with preparing the order for factory production.

The second measure of performance associated with operating the production process is the value of any parts shortages *not* available to satisfy demand schedules. These shortages will be satisfied in the coming periods; i.e., no demands are lost. No numerical value as to the cost of incurring these backlogs will be specified.

A.2 Single Item Economic Order Quantity Determination

The use of the economic order quantity (EOQ) as a tool to control production and inventories is widely documented [5], [6]. This method assumed that there are no significant interactions between the choice of production run length for each of the many items produced for stock within a typical batch-type manufacturing plant. With this zero interaction assumption, the average monthly cost of producing and stocking each item will then consist of two major components. The first cost components are those that increase as lot-size increases, and the second cost components are those that decrease.

Interest on average invested capital + average monthly cost of each production run is then

$$\rho\left[\frac{ap + (bp + c)x}{2}\right] + \frac{r}{x}[ap + (bp + c)x] \tag{A1}$$

where x = number of units in each production run.

   ρ = one-period interest rate on money.

   a = total set-up hours (plant labor plus clerical).

   b = hours to produce one unit of the item.

   c = material cost of one unit of the item.

r = one-period expected demand rate per item.

p = hourly wage rate of factory workers.

The problem is to choose x in order to minimize the sum of these costs. To find the minimum of (A1) with respect to x, we equate the derivative to zero, and obtain the conventional square root formula for x^*, the economic order quantity (EOQ):

$$\text{EOQ} = x^* = \sqrt{\frac{2ar}{\rho b + \rho\left(\dfrac{c}{p}\right)}} \tag{A2}$$

Note that the zero-interaction assumption for the cost expression (A1) and for the derived square root formula (A2) is fully justified under steady-state conditions. With demand rates constant over time and with the aggregate work force adjusted to equilibrium requirements, it is quite reasonable, in calculating the cost data in the formula, to assume that p represents the straight-time labor costs.

The simulation program A computer simulation program is developed to study ordering decisions, that is, determining lot sizes and reorder levels in order to satisfy the expected demands on the items. Lot-size and reorder levels, denoted as q and z respectively, will be calculated for each production period by means of a set of equations. The procedure for calculating the values is as follows: the first task is to set the initial conditions, after which simulation proceeds from the set of equations. The initial conditions needing specification are:

1. $y_i(0)$, assumed initial inventory for the initial period of the ith item.

2. $r_i(0)$, assumed demand rate for the initial period of the ith item.

3. $z_i(0)$, an assumed reorder level in the initial period of the ith item.

4.
$$\left(\sqrt{\frac{2a_i}{b_i + \left(\dfrac{c_i}{p}\right)}}\right)$$

a constant term for the ith item required for the EOQ calculation.

5. Initial total number of workers available for assignments on facility k.

6. α, a specified value for the parameter in the demand smoothing equation, where $0 < \alpha < 1$.

At the beginning of a specified period t, the primary task is to determine how much positive production on any item i needs to be ordered. It will be determined in the following manner:

$$q_i = \begin{cases} 0, & \text{if } y_i(t) > z_{it} \\ x_i^* + \{z_{it} - y_i(t)\}, & \text{if } y_i(t) \le z_{it} \end{cases} \quad t = (1, 2, \ldots, T). \tag{A3}$$

where

$$x_i^* = \left(\sqrt{\frac{2a_i}{\left(b_i + \frac{c_i}{p} \right)}} \right) \left(\sqrt{\frac{r_{it}}{\rho}} \right) \tag{A2a}$$

and
$$z_{it} = (\lambda)(r_{it}) \qquad (\lambda \geq 0). \tag{A4}$$

Equation (A2 a) calculates the economic order quantity; Equation (A4) determines the reorder level z which is a function of the current expected demand rate r, and λ is treated as a parameter which may be varied to represent the different levels of stock protection. The inventory level (y_i) of the ith item may take on positive or negative values. Negative values of (y_i) will represent backlogs of demand for the item in any period. The actual order quantity issued to the factory for production of the ith item is q_i.

This means that q_i, or the lot-size for an item, is composed of the EOQ plus any deficiency between the inventory on hand and the current reorder level. The addition of the stated quantities to the EOQ brings the inventories for the coming period up to a level to (1) satisfy expected demands for the coming period, and (2) replenish the safety stock to a specified level.

At the end of the period t the actual demand for each item is computed from the demands of end products recorded for the period by

$$d_i = \sum_{l=1}^{L} g_{it} \times S_l \qquad l = (1, 2, \ldots, L) \tag{A5}$$

where g_{it} is the number of units of item i per unit of end product l, and S_l is the actual demand of end product l in period t.

The subtraction of actual demands from available stocks results in a new inventory balance for the subsequent production period. We previously mentioned that inventories may take on positive or negative values; positive inventories incur a carrying cost, and negative inventories are listed as a backlog for them.

Inventories (or backlogs) at the start of the $(t + 1)$th period will be calculated as follows:

$$y_i(t + 1) = y_i(t) + q_i - d_i \tag{A6}$$

Once this record-keeping for the tth period is completed, it becomes possible to compute certain other quantities that are required for planning production in the $(t + 1)$th period. For instance, $r_i(t + 1)$, the new expected demand rate, needs to be calculated, as described in the main body of this report.

Once $r_i(t+1)$ is calculated and $y_i(t+1)$ is known, it then becomes possible to determine if the reorder level has been reached for any of the i items. This process is repeated for each of the periods included in the simulation experiment.

Calculating Total Variable Costs for Period t. After all the q_i's are known, it becomes possible to compute the labor requirements for each item i and for each facility group k,

$$L_{ikt} = \begin{cases} 0 & \text{if } q_i(t) = 0. \\ a_{ik} + b_{ik} \cdot q_i(t) \end{cases}, \quad \begin{aligned} & \text{if } q_i(t) = 0. \\ & \text{if } q_i(t) > 0. \end{aligned}$$

$$(i = 1, \ldots, I; \; k = 1, \ldots, K). \quad (A7)$$

Next we compute the amount of straight-time plus overtime man-hours and changes in workforce levels from the preceding period.

The amount of straight-time plus overtime man-hours provided on both shifts during each time period must be sufficient to cover the labor requirements generated by the calculation of the production quantities (20 weekdays and four Saturdays in an average month; 1.6 hours per day on the first shift and 1.52 hours on the second shift):

$$[m][32W_{kt}^1 + 38.4W_{kt}^2 + 30.4W_{kt}^3 + 36.5W_{kt}^4] \geq \sum_i^I L_{ikt} \quad (A8)$$

where m refers to the number of months included within planning period t. Also,

$$\begin{aligned} W_{kt}^1 + W_{kt}^2 &\leq W_k, \\ W_{kt}^3 + W_{kt}^4 &\leq W_k, \end{aligned} \quad \text{(all } k, t\text{).}$$

That is, the number of workers assigned to the first shift on both straight time and overtime cannot exceed a maximum number, denoted as W_k for each facility group k. The same holds true the second shift. In the event the $\sum_i^I L_{ikt}$ is greater than W_k $(38.4 + 36.5)$, a safety valve is provided in the form of a third shift. That is, excess workers required are supposedly assigned to a third shift at a double-time penalty cost.

Once the man-hour requirements are known, the rule for determining the values of W_k^1, W_k^2, W_k^3, and W_k^4 within the EOQ model is as follows:

1. Assign all work to first shift if it can be so done by straight time only or by straight-time and overtime work.

2. If the requirements are greater than the first-shift capacity at full overtime, then assign a full straight-time shift (only on the first shift), and put the remaining hours on a straight-time second shift.

3. If the requirements are greater than the assignments of hours, as in (A2), the excess is assigned to overtime on the first shift. Any

excess beyond that point is assigned to the second-shift overtime.

4. If both shifts have labor hours assigned to them at a full straight-time and overtime basis, and there still remains some required manpower, this excess is assigned to the "third shift."

Finally, the changes in the work force levels on each of the facilities needs to be computed. This computation is accomplished by the equations that link the size of the work force of period t to the preceding period:

$$W_{kt}^1 + W_{kt}^2 + W_{kt}^3 + W_{kt}^4 - (W_{k,t-1}^1 + W_{k,t-1}^2 + W_{k,t-1}^3 + W_{k,t-1}^4)$$
$$= D^+ W_{kt} - D^- W_{kt} \quad (A9)$$

A.3 Multi-item Linear Programming of Lot-sizes[1]

The linear programming model described below is explicitly designed to handle the transient phenomena associated with nonequilibrium initial conditions, i.e., unbalanced inventory and work force levels. If it is plausible to suppose that negligible change-over costs are involved in any transition from initial to equilibrium conditions, and if labor premium costs are negligible, there would be little point in investigating the lot-size model described below.

Calculation of Alternative Labor Input Sequences Here, a maximum of T periods will be stipulated for the transition from initial to equilibrium conditions. Let each possible sequence of set-up combinations during the transition phase be denoted by the subscript j. ($j = 1,$ $2, \ldots, J; J = 2^T$). Each such sequence consists of a vector, Δ_j, whose components $\delta_{j\tau}$ take on the value of zero or one:

$$\Delta_j = \begin{pmatrix} \delta_{j1} \\ \cdot \\ \cdot \\ \cdot \\ \delta_{j\tau} \\ \cdot \\ \cdot \\ \cdot \\ \delta_{jT} \end{pmatrix}.$$

Requirements for item i in period τ are denoted by $r_{i\tau}$.

The terminal inventory of item i is to be sufficient to last for n periods beyond $T (n \geq 0)$[2]. Then for each value of i, j, and n, we are to construct the time-phased production vector, X_{ijn}:

---

[1] These notes should be supplemented by referring to [1] and [4].

[2] In the simulation experiments, no allowance was made for carry-overs beyond T; i. e., n was set at zero.

$$X_{ijn} = \begin{pmatrix} x_{ijn,\,1} \\ \cdot \\ \cdot \\ \cdot \\ x_{ijn,\,\tau} \\ \cdot \\ \cdot \\ \cdot \\ x_{ijn,\,T} \end{pmatrix}.$$

The output levels $x_{ijn\tau}$ are determined according to Equations (A 10), (A11a), or to Equation (A11b) below. These conditions are equivalent to the rule that each period's demand requirement first be satisfied out of any remaining initial inventory and then out of production during the most recent period in which set-up costs have been incurred. The following rules generate a "dominant" set of vectors:

If $$\delta_{j\tau} = 0, \qquad x_{ijn\tau} = 0. \tag{A10}$$

Definition of $f(j, \tau)$:

$$f(j, \tau) = \left\{ \begin{matrix} 0 \\ 1 \end{matrix} \right\} \qquad \text{according as} \quad \sum_{p=1}^{\tau-1} \delta_{jp} \left\{ \begin{matrix} \geq 1 \\ = 0 \end{matrix} \right\}.$$

Definition of y_i:

$$y_i = y_i(1) = \text{initial inventory of item } i.$$

Definition of $g(j, \tau)$:

$$g(j, \tau) = \max \{ p : \tau \leq p \leq T; \quad \text{and} \quad \sum_{s=\tau}^{p} \delta_{js} = 1 \}.$$

If $\delta_{j\tau} = 1$ and $g(j, \tau) < T$,

$$x_{ijn\tau} = \sum_{p=\tau}^{g(j,\tau)} r_{ip} - f(j, \tau)[y_i - \sum_{p=1}^{\tau-1} r_{ip}]. \tag{A11a}$$

If $\delta_{j\tau} = 1$ and $g(j, \tau) = T$,

$$x_{ijn\tau} = [\sum_{p=\tau}^{T} r_{ip} - nr_{i\tau}] - f(j, \tau)[y_i - \sum_{p=1}^{\tau-1} r_{ip}]. \tag{A11b}$$

A production vector X_{ijn} is ruled out as "infeasible" if, for the value of τ such that $f(j, \tau) = \delta_{j\tau} = 1$, then either Equation (A12a) or Equation (A12b) holds: [3]

$$x_{ijn\tau} < 0 \tag{A12a}$$

$$y_i < \sum_{p=1}^{\tau-1} r_{ip}. \tag{A12b}$$

[3] To reduce problems of machine interference, it might be desirable at this point also to rule out any production vectors implying run lengths which would tie up individual facilities for excessive periods of time, e. g., two weeks to four weeks.

Finally, from among those production vectors that are feasible, we generate the labor input coefficients $L_{ijkn\tau}$ for each of the parts i and the facility groups k $(i = 1, \ldots, I; \ k = 1, \ldots, K)$.

$$L_{ijkn\tau} = \begin{Bmatrix} 0 \\ a_{ik} + b_{ik} \cdot x_{ijn\tau} \end{Bmatrix} \tag{A13}$$

according as

$$x_{ijn\tau} \begin{Bmatrix} = 0 \\ > 0 \end{Bmatrix}$$

and where a_{ik} and b_{ik} refer, respectively, to the labor set-up and running time for the item i on facility k.

The *maximum* number of positive coefficients $L_{ijkn\tau}$ to be generated for each simplex problem equals:

$$\begin{pmatrix} \text{number} \\ \text{of items} \end{pmatrix} \begin{pmatrix} \text{number of} \\ \text{possible} \\ \text{sequences} \end{pmatrix} \begin{pmatrix} \text{number of} \\ \text{facilities} \end{pmatrix} \begin{pmatrix} \text{number of} \\ \text{carry-over} \\ \text{possibilities} \end{pmatrix} \begin{pmatrix} \text{average number of} \\ \text{time periods with} \\ \text{positive production} \end{pmatrix}$$

$$(=)\ (I) \quad (J = 2^T) \quad (K) \quad (N) \quad \left(\frac{T}{2}\right)$$

$$\approx (35) \quad\quad (2^3) \quad\quad (2) \quad\quad (1) \quad\quad (3/2) = 840$$

Equations of the Linear Programming Model The first group of equations specify that the requirement for each item be satisfied by means of some convex combination of the stipulated sequence for that item:

$$\sum_{j,\,n} \theta_{ijn} = 1, \quad (\text{all } i). \tag{A}$$

The next group says that the amount of straight-time plus overtime man-hours provided on both shifts during each time period must be at least sufficient to cover the labor requirements generated by the production sequences employed (20 weekdays and four Saturdays in an average month; 1.6 hours per day on first shift and 1.52 hours on second shift):

$$[m][32W_{k\tau}^1 + 38.4W_{k\tau}^2 + 30.4W_{k\tau}^3 + 36.54W_{k\tau}^4] \geq \sum_{i,\,j,\,n} L_{ijkn\tau}\theta_{ijkn\tau};$$
$$(\text{all } k, \tau) \tag{B}$$

Next come the equations that link the size of the work force of each period to the preceding one: [4]

$$W_{k\tau}^1 + W_{k\tau}^2 + W_{k\tau}^3 + W_{k\tau}^4 = W_{k,\tau-1}^1 + W_{k,\tau-1}^2 + W_{k,\tau-1}^3 + W_{k,\tau-1}^4$$
$$+ D^+ W_{k\tau} - D^- W_{k\tau}, \quad (\text{all } k; \ \tau = 1, \ldots, T). \tag{C}$$

And finally come the equations specifying that during each shift

---

[4] If the model were to prescribe that the work force be at equilibrium levels at the end of period T, this restriction would require K extra equations.

the number of workers assigned to each facility group must not exceed the capacity of that group:

$$W_{k\tau}^1 + W_{k\tau}^2 \leq W_k,$$
$$W_{k\tau}^3 + W_{k\tau}^4 \leq W_k, \quad \text{(all } k, \tau).$$

(D)

The total number of equations in each simplex problem would be as follows:

Number of equations in (A) $= I$ $\qquad = 35$
Number of equations in (B) $= KT$ $\qquad = 6$
Number of equations in (C) $= KT$ $\qquad = 6$
Number of equations in (D) $= 2KT$ $\qquad = 12$
$\qquad\qquad\qquad\qquad\qquad = I + 4KT \quad 59$

Calculation of the payoff coefficients The total variable costs to be minimized by means of the linear programming model consists of the *present value* of each of the following components:

(P1)   Straight-time and premium labor costs.
(P2)   Labor change-over costs.
(P3)   Carrying costs.
(P4)   Ordering costs.
(P5)   Carry-over credits for the terminal inventory at time T.

In order to calculate the present-worth factor period τ, it will be convenient to assume that all costs incurred during period τ are due for payment at the end of that period. Then, if we denote by ρ the one-period interest rate on money, the present worth factor for τ periods would be $e^{-\rho\tau}$.

The calculation of the first two cost components, (P1) and (P2), is straightforward, and will not be described in detail here. These costs are all proportional to the work force variables: $W_{k\tau}$ and $DW_{k\tau}$. The remaining three components are associated with the unknowns θ_{ijn}, and for each value of i, j, and n must be summed together in order to form the payoff coefficient P_{ijn}.

Material costs are directly proportional to the quantity produced in each time period, $x_{ijn\tau}$. Let c_i denote the unit cost of material required for item i. Then, for a given value of i, j, and n:

$$(P3) = \sum_{\tau=1}^{T} [e^{-\rho\tau}][x_{ijn\tau}][c_i].$$

The clerical cost component is determined by the number and the timing of individual orders released. Let w_i denote the clerical cost associated with each run of item i, and recall from Section 3 the definition of the zero-one variables $\delta_{j\tau}$. Then, for a given value of i and j:

$$(P4) = \sum_{\tau=1}^{T} [e^{-\rho\tau}][\delta_{j\tau}][w_i]$$

Finally, a carry-over credit is to be assigned to any inventory carried forward from period T into the equilibrium phase. If this inventory is estimated to be sufficient to last n months beyond T, the carry-over credit for the item is based upon the difference in present value obtained by deferment of the onset of the steady-state cost level, as follows:

$$P(5) = \text{credit for } n \text{ periods' worth of terminal inventory}$$

$$= \{1 - e^{-\rho n}\} \begin{Bmatrix} \text{present value of all future labor and material costs incurred} \\ \text{during equilibrium phase see Eqs. (1) and (2), Section A.2.} \end{Bmatrix}$$

$$= e^{-\rho\tau}\{1 - e^{-\rho n}\}\left\{\left(\frac{r_{i1}}{x_i^*}\right)[a_i p + (b_i p + c_i)x_i^*]\left(\frac{1}{\rho}\right)\right\}.$$

Concluding Remarks

1. The number of periods worth of carry-over, n, may be specified arbitrarily for all set-up sequences other than the one in which $\delta_1 = \ldots \delta_\tau = \ldots \delta_T = 0$. In this one exceptional case,

$$n = \frac{y_i}{r_i} - \sum_{\tau=1}^{T} r_{i\tau} = \frac{y_i - \sum_{\tau=1}^{T} r_{i\tau}}{r_{i1}}.$$

2. Three convenient values for n are 0, $x^*/2r$, x^*/r.

3. The order quantites, x, given by Equation (2a) in Section A. 2, are needed not only for the EOQ simulation itself, but also for the calculation of the carry-over credits and of the $W_{k,T+1}$ within the linear programming model.

4. Each "feasible" sequence vector for the unknowns θ_{ijn} will contain KT labor input coefficients, $L_{ijn\tau}$; a payoff row coefficient, P_{ijn}, consisting of material costs, clerical costs, and carry-over credits; and also a coefficient of $+1$ in the appropriate requirement row of equation group (A).

APPENDIX B: GENERAL PROBLEM MATRIX OF LP MODEL

Equations / Unknowns		The J alternative set-up sequences for the I parts	Work force and change in work force variables — Shift one—three periods—two facilities	Shift two—etc.		Slack variables	Right-hand side
Cost coefficients		P P P P P P P P P P P P P P .... P P P P P P P	R^1 R^2 Γ_h Γ_o R^1 R^2 Γ_h Γ_o R^1 R^2 Γ_h Γ_o R^1 R^2 Γ_h Γ_o R^1 R^2 Γ_h Γ_o	R^3 R^4 Γ_h Γ_o ... R^3 R^4 Γ_h Γ_o		. .	
Equation group A	$i=1$	1 1 1 1 1 1 1	...		. .	1
	$i=2$	1 1 1 1 1 1 1	...		. .	1
	...	. . . .	...		. .	. .
	...	. . . .				
	...	. . . .				
	...	. . . .				
	...	. . . .				
	$i=35$	.... 1 1 1 1 1 1 1	...		. .	1
Group B	$\tau=1, k=1$	L LL LL LL L........L LL L	$-H$ $-H$ $-H$ $-H$	...	1	. .	0
	$\tau=1, k=2$	L LL LL LL L........L LL L	$-H$ $-H$	...	.	. .	0
	$\tau=2, k=1$	L L LL L L LL........L L LL	$-H$ $-H$	...	.	. .	0
	$\tau=2, k=2$	L L LL L L LL........L L LL	$-H$ $-H$	...	.	. .	0
	$\tau=3, k=1$	L LLL L LLL........L LLL	$-H$ $-H$	...	.	. .	0
	$\tau=3, k=2$	L LLL L LLL........L LLL	$-H$ $-H$ $-H$ $-H$	... $-H$ $-H$	1	. .	0
Group C	$k=1, \tau=1$	....	1 1 -1 1 1 1 -1 1	...		. . W_k^1 . . . . W_k^4	
	$k=1, \tau=2$	....	-1 -1 1 1 -1 1 -1 -1	...		. .	0
	$k=1, \tau=3$	....	-1 -1 1 1 -1 1	...		. .	0
	$k=2, \tau=1$	....	1 1 -1 1	...		. . W_k^1 . . . . W_k^4	
	$k=2, \tau=2$	....	-1 -1 1 1 -1 1	...		. .	0
	$k=2, \tau=3$	....	-1 -1 1 1 -1 1	... 1 1 -1 1		. .	0
Group D Shift 1	$\tau=1, k=1$	....	1 1 1 1	...	1	. .	W
	$\tau=1, k=2$	....		...	.	. .	W
	$\tau=2, k=1$	....	1 1	...	.	. .	W
	$\tau=2, k=2$	....	1 1	...	.	. .	W
	$\tau=3, k=1$	....	1 1	...	.	. .	W
	$\tau=3, k=2$	....	1 1	...	1	. .	W
Group D Shift 2	$\tau=1, k=1$	....		1 1 ...		1 .	W
	. . . . .	. . . .		...		. .	. .
	. . . . .						
	. . . . .						
	$\tau=3, k=2$	....		... 1 1 . .		1	W

APPENDIX C GLOSSARY OF TERMS

The following is a list of mathematical symbols used in this paper. Any symbols defined below and used without indices in special cases are omitted from this list.

I = the number of items manufactured by the plant and controlled by the two simulation models $(i = 1, 2, \ldots, I)$.

J = the number of possible production sequences by which each item can be produced $(j = 1, 2, \ldots, J)$.

n = number of months' worth of inventory beyond the planning horizon $(n = 1, 2, \ldots, N)$.

T = number of planning periods in the planning horizon $(\tau = 1, 2, \ldots, T)$.

K = number of different facility groups in the plant $(k = 1, 2, \ldots, K)$.

m = number of production months included in each planning period $(m = 1, 2, \ldots)$.

$\hat{S}(t+\tau)$ = the forecast of net orders received at a time τ units in the future.

$S(t)$ = the estimate of the average of the net orders received as of time interval t.

$b(t)$ = the trend estimate of the net orders received as of time interval t.

α = smoothing parameter in forecasting equations.

r_{i1} = the adjusted net requirements for the ith part for period τ, when $\tau = 1$.

$r_{i\tau}$ = the net requirements for the ith part for period τ when $\tau = 2, 3, \ldots, T$.

λ = arbitrary safety stock level parameter.

θ_{ij} = fraction of the total requirements for the ith part produced with the jth alternative set-up sequence $(i = 1, 2, \ldots, I; j = 1, 2, \ldots, J)$.

$W_{k\tau}^1$ = number of workers assigned to first-shift operations on facility k during period $(t + \tau)$; no overtime $(k = 1, 2, \ldots, K; \tau = 1, 2, \ldots, T)$.

$W_{k\tau}^2$ = number of workers assigned to first-shift *overtime* operations on facility k during $(t + \tau)$; each of these workers works a fixed number of straight-time and overtime hours during the period.

$W_{k\tau}^3$ = number of workers assigned to record-shift operations on facility k during period $(t + \tau)$; *no overtime.*

$W_{k\tau}^4$ = number of workers assigned to record-shift *overtime* operations on facility k during period $(t + \tau)$; each of these workers works a fixed number of straight-time hours and a fixed number of straight-time and overtime hours during the period.

$D^+W_{k\tau}$ = increase in the total number of workers employed at facility k from period $(t + \tau - 1)$ to period $(t + \tau)$.

$D^-W_{k\tau}$ = decrease in the total number of workers employed at facility k period $(t + \tau - 1)$ to period $(t + \tau)$.

$L_{ijk\tau}$ = labor input required during period $(t + \tau)$ to carry out the jth alternative set-up sequence on the kth facility for part i.

$x_{ij\tau}$ = the amount of part i produced by the sequence j during the period $(t + \tau)$; these numbers define the alternative production sequences.

W_k = maximum number of workers that can be assigned to facility k.

H^1 = total number of first-shift hours per period, excluding overtime.

H^2 = total number of first-shift hours per period, including a fixed amount of overtime.

H^3 = total number of second-shift hours per period, excluding overtime.

H^4 = total number of second-shift hours periond, including a fixed amount of overtime.

b_{1k} = hours required to manufacture one unit of the ith item independent of set-up time on facility k.

z_{it} = the reorder level of the ith item in period t.

$R^1_{k\tau}$ = first-shift wage for facility k, no overtime; discounted over τ periods.

$R^2_{k\tau}$ = first-shift wage for facility k, with overtime; discounted over τ periods.

$R^3_{k\tau}$ = second-shift wage for facility k, no overtime; discounted over τ periods.

$R^4_{k\tau}$ = second-shift wage for facility k, with overtime; discounted over τ periods.

$\Gamma_{o\tau}$ = cost of laying off one worker; discounted over τ periods.

$\Gamma_{h\tau}$ = cost of hiring one worker; discounted over τ periods.

$c_{i\tau}$ = unit material cost of part i; discounted over τ periods.

q_i = augmented final order size on the ith item as calculated in the economic order quantity simulation program.

$x_i^* = \mathrm{EOQ}_i$ = economic order quantity calculated for the ith item by the standard formula balancing set-up costs versus inventory carrying costs.

$y_i(\tau)$ = inventory on hand for the ith item at the beginning of the τth period, if $y_i(\tau) < 0$; it is interpreted as a shortage.

$\rho =$ one-period interest rate on money.

$a_{ik} =$ the number of hours required to set-up and place a lot-size order for manufacture (plant labor plus clerical) for the ith item on facility k.

$\delta_{j\tau} =$ Kronecker delta, takes on the value of 0 or 1 in the jth possible production sequence at τ.

$\Delta_j =$ a column vector whose components $\delta_{i\tau}$ take on values of zero or one.

$X_{ij} =$ a time-phased production vector whose $x_{ij\tau}$ components are the amount of production of part i produced by the sequence j.

$e^{-\rho\tau} =$ the present worth factor for τ periods to compute the *present value* of the several cost components explicitly expressed in the LP minimand.

$w_i =$ the clerical cost associated with each run of item i.

REFFERENCES

1. Manne, A. S., "Programming of Economic Lot Sizes," *Management Science* **4**, 2 (1958), 115–135.
2. Brown, R. G., *Statistical Forecasting for Inventory Control*, New York: McGraw-Hill Book Company, Inc., 1959.
3. Brown, R. G., "Exponential Smoothing for Predicting Demand," *ORSA*, November 16, 1956, San Francisco, California.
4. Levitan, R. E., "A Note on Professor Manne's 'Dominance' Theorem," *Management Science* **5**, 3 (1959), 332–334.
5. Magee, J. F., *Production Planning and Inventory Control*, New York: McGraw-Hill Book Company, Inc., 1957.
6. Whitin, T., *The Theory of Inventory Control*, Princeton, N. J.: Princeton University Press, 1953.
7. Beach, F. E., *Economic Models*, New York: John Wiley & Sons, Inc., 1957.
8. Baumol, W. J., *Economic Dynamics*, New York: The Macmillan Company, 1951.
9. *SCROL, A Comprehensive Operating System for Linear Programming on the IBM 704*, C. E. I. R., Inc., 1200 Jefferson Davis Highway, Arlington 2, Va.
10. Vazsonyi, A., *Scientific Programming in Business and Industry*, New York: John Wiley & Sons, Inc., 1958.

10

Optimization of a Total Production and Distribution System

K. H. Ishler, R. M. Sharp, W. W. Staley, Jr.

UNITED STATES STEEL CORPORATION
and
WESTINGHOUSE ELECTRIC CORPORATION

The problem-solving technique that follows demonstrates a linear programming approach to the optimization of a total system. This approach achieves a minimization of the total costs associated with an integrated production and distribution system by the use of linear programming and certain techniques of partitioning and parametric variation. The purpose of this paper is to present a method of handling a problem that, because of the size and complexity of its multistage production and distribution system, would ordinarily be unacceptable to a linear programming study.

1. THE SYSTEM

The hypothetical system includes an extraction stage, a multistage processing operation, and a fabricating stage, followed by distribution

This paper is an abstract of a paper written while the authors were attending the Graduate School of Industrial Administration, Carnegie Institute of Technology. The authors are indebted to Professor W. W. Cooper for his valuable assistance during the writing of the original paper. K. H. Ishler and W. W. Staley, Jr. are now affiliated with the United States Steel Corporation, and R. M. Sharp with the Westinghouse Electric Corporation.

of the final product to the consumer.   Raw materials and semifinished goods flow through this system, and the finished goods are transported to the final consumer.

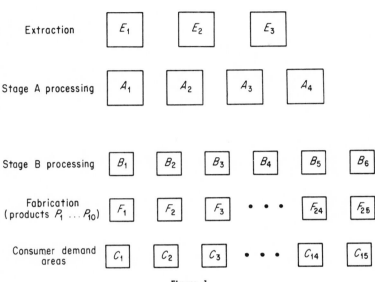

Figure 1

The system is depicted graphically in Figure 1.   Raw material is extracted at three separate extraction locations (E_1, E_2, E_3).   Following extraction, the raw material is first sent for stage A processing to any one of four locations (A_1, A_2, A_3, A_4).   The material, now in a semifinished form, is next processed in stage B at any one of six locations (B_1, B_2, . . ., B_6).   The output of this process is a homogeneous product that is used in fabricating the final product.

In the final stage, fabrication, the semifinished material is converted into the final product at one of 25 fabricating locations (F_1, . . ., F_{25}). For our purposes, the fabricated product can be classified into ten unique product groupings (P_1, . . ., P_{10}).   This differentiation of the products into unique product groupings is made almost entirely on the basis of the final form of the product.   Additionally, it should be noted that each of the ten products is fabricated at several, but in no case all, of the fabricating locations.   For example, P_1 can be produced at F_{16}, F_{17}, and F_{18}; P_2 can be fabricated at F_1, F_2, F_5, and F_{16}.

Finally, to reduce the problem to manageable proportions, the total marketing area for the system can be divided into 15 areas of consumer demand (C_1, . . ., C_{15}) which are to be supplied with each product in the desired quantity. Such a separation of the market into consumer demand centers is made on the basis of plant location and geographical population centers.

2. OPTIMIZING THE SYSTEM

In Figure 1 it can be seen that the system is composed of a number of directed links between the various processing stages. Associated with each link are certain processing and transportation costs which apply if that link is used. Certain of these links, in sequence, determine a path or route for the flow of products through the system to the consumer. For example, if the customer demand in location C_2 for product P_1 is X units, some or all of this demand could be supplied via the following path: raw material extracted at unit 1, processed at stage A processing unit 3, further processed at stage B processing unit 4, fabricated at fabricating unit 17, and thence shipped to customer area 2. Symbolically, we can refer to this path as $E_1 A_3 B_4 F_{17} C_2$. Another path for supplying all or part of the same demand might be $E_2 A_4 B_6 F_{16} C_2$.

In the following section, this path-type approach to optimizing a total system will be discussed under the heading, "Direct Approach." Following this, the difficulties of treating such a system by this method will be pointed out and a suitable model for approximating the system optimization will be presented. It must be pointed out, however, that the purpose of presenting such an approximation to the optimum solution is to demonstrate a method that is both reasonably accurate and computationally feasible. In an actual situation, once such an approximation is obtained, further refinements would allow the firm to approach more closely the true optimum.

3. DIRECT APPROACH

The direct appoach to optimizing this total system consists of identifying and enumerating all of the paths that can *potentially* supply some or all of the demand for the required products. If we then allow each potential path to be a separate variable in the system and add appropriate constraints so that capacity limits of the various facilities are not exceeded, we can represent this system by a linear programming model. For example, we would first identify all of the potential paths for supplying each demand area with the required products. These paths could be enumerated symbolically as in the previous example ($E_1 A_3 B_4 F_{17} C_2$). Then, we would enumerate the two general classes of constraints required for this system as follows:

1. The summation of product flow for all paths through each processing unit must be less than or equal to the maximum capacity of this unit (and equal to or greater than its minimum capacity, if such a constraint exists). This requires one or two constraint equations for each processing unit in the system.

2. The summation of product flow for all paths through all product X producing facilities and ending in customer demand area Y must be equal to the demand for the product in that area. This requires ten constraint equations (one for each product) for each of the fifteen demand areas.

The total of the variable production and transportation costs associated with each path constitute the cost (c_j) that is assigned to that variable in the formulation.

In the previous section, there were listed two paths that could potentially supply product 1 to area 2, and many more potential paths could also be listed. Since the total problem involves considering the demand for ten separate products in fifteen consumer demand areas, there will exist 149 other *sets* of paths similar to the set of potential paths for supplying product 1 to area 2. If all of the possible paths through this system were included in the suggested linear programming model, there would be approximately 27,000 variables and from 53 to 91 constraints. Such a problem would necessitate the use of very large computing facilities and, in fact, it must be noted that the enumeration and identification of these paths would itself be a tedious task. Consequently, the following approach can be used to reduce the problem to more manageable proportions while, at the same time, approximating the optimization of the system.

4. RECOMMENDED APPROXIMATION APPROACH

4.1. Suboptimization Model

In this approximation approach, the total system can be divided into three separate subsystems. Each of these three subsystems can then be optimized with respect to total production and shipping costs relevant to that subsystem, and the results tied together will form a suboptimum solution for the total system.

Subsystem 1 includes fabricating facilities and all of the customer demand areas. The optimum solution to this subsystem provides a production and shipping schedule that minimizes the total costs associated with fabricating the products and shipping them to the demand areas. Subsystem 2 includes all stage B processing units and all fabricating facilities. Here, the optimization problem involves minimizing the total costs of processing through stage B and shipping the stage B output in the desired quantities to the fabricating plants. The third of these subsystems, subsystem 3, includes all of the firm's extraction, stage A, and stage B facilities. An optimum solution to this subsystem is one that minimizes the total production and shipping costs involved in the extracting and stage A processing of the product and shipping it to stage B in the desired quantities.

A solution to subsystem 1 may be obtained by solving ten allocation problems by the transportation method [1, 2, 3] of linear programming (one for each of the ten products). The demand requirements for the general form of these ten allocation problems will be stated as the demand (or sales) estimate for fabricated product group X at each of the 15 demand centers. The costs (c_{ij}) associated with this allocation model are the variable fabricating costs per unit of X at facility i, plus the shipping costs per unit of X from the designated facility (i) to the corresponding demand area (j). Each of these transportation matrices will be of the general form shown in Figure 2.

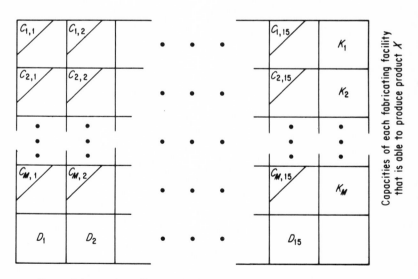

Demand for product X at each of the demand centers

Figure 2

By solving such a transportation model for each of the ten product groups, we can determine the amount of production to be scheduled at each of the fabricating facilities, and where and in what quantity each facility should ship its output. This solution represents the optimization of subsystem 1. The solutions as provided by these ten allocation problems are then aggregated; demand for the output of stage B at the 25 fabricating facilities can then be determined by converting total fabricated production (solution to subsystem 1) at the plants to required input (stage B production).

The optimum solution to subsystem 2 can be obtained by solving the transportation model of Figure 3.

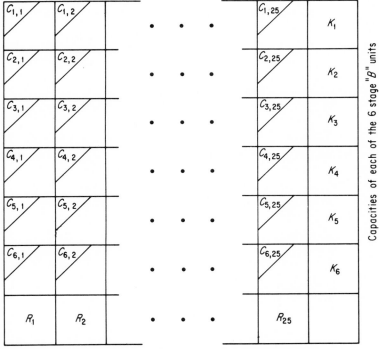

Demand for stage "B" output at each of the 25 plant locations
(from sub-system #1)

Figure 3

Again, the costs (c_{ij}) represent the various variable production and shipping costs per unit associated with processing the product through stage B and shipping it to the fabricating units. The solution to this transportation problem provides us with an allocation schedule for stage B production among the six stage B processing units, and a shipping schedule for distributing this output to the various fabricating units. The production schedule for the stage B units then enables a determination to be made of the demand for stage A output at the stage B processing units. These figures then become the demand for stage A output at the stage B processing units in subsystem 3.

Finally, we obtain an optimum production and shipping schedule

for subsystem 3.   Here, we make use of the same linear programming
"path-type" approach as was described in the section pertaining to
the direct model.   The only difference in this case is that this subsystem will involve fewer variables and constraints than the two
previous subsystems.

Various possible "paths" can be traced through this subsystem from
the extraction units to the stage B processing units.   In this system,
there will be 72 variables and from 13 to 26 constraint equations.
The costs to be associated with each variable (or "path") are the
total unit costs of extraction and stage A processing of the product,
plus the total shipping costs per unit from the extraction unit to the
stage A operation and from the stage A operation to the stage B
processing unit.   To illustrate, one possible path would be $E_1A_3B_6$.
The cost figure to be associated with this variable would be the summation of the following costs:

1. Variable cost per unit of output of extraction unit 1.
2. Variable cost per unit of output of stage A processing unit 3.
3. Cost per unit to ship from E_1 to A_3.
4. Cost per unit to ship from A_3 to B_6.

The summation of product flow for all possible paths originating
at a particular extraction location must not exceed its maximum
capacity, nor fail to meet minimum required output if such constraints
exist.   Likewise, the summation of product flow for all paths through
a stage A unit must be less than or equal to the maximum capacity
and equal to or greater than minimum capacity of the unit.   For example, the constraint to be associated with stage A processing unit
1 would be

$$\sum_{x=1}^{3} \sum_{z=1}^{6} E_x A_1 B_z$$

is equal to or less than the maximum capacity of A_1 and equal to
or greater than the minimum capacity of A_1.   Similar constraints
can be devised for each of the extraction and stage A units in the
system.   The material flows through all paths ending at one particular stage B unit must be equal to the amount of stage B output
scheduled for that unit in the solution to subsystem 2.   Such a constraint for B_1 would be

$$\sum_{x=1}^{3} \sum_{y=1}^{4} E_x A_y B_1$$

is equal to scheduled production for B_1 (from subsystem 2 solution).
Proper constraints for each facility in the system should be formulated
and the problem solved by the simplex method [1 and 2].

The suboptimum solution technique is not yet complete.   The solution to subsystem 1 will yield a production schedule for the various fabricating facilities and a shipping schedule from the fabricating plants to the demand centers. The solution to subsystem 2 will yield an allocation to stage B production among the stage B producing units, and a shipping schedule from stage B units to fabricating plants in accordance with the allocation established in subsystem 1. Finally, the solution to subsystem 3 will yield an allocation of volume among the three extracting units and an allocation of stage A operations among the four stage A units. It will also yield a shipping schedule from the extracting units to stage A units, and from the stage A units to the stage B units.

Thus, we have scheduled production at all of the facilities and have scheduled shipments of goods between the various stages of the total system. Subsections of the total system have thus been optimized with respect to the production and shipping costs relevant to that subsystem. *This, however, will not guarantee an over-all optimum.* Therefore, our next task is to develop a method whereby we will be able to approach the true optimum for the total system.

4.2. Analysis of Shadow Costs

Shadow costs are the $z_j - C_j$ values under the structural vectors of an optimum simplex tableau. These values represent the additional cost per unit that would be incurred if that particular vector were brought into the basis. Shadow costs also indicate the additional cost per unit that would be incurred by choosing to make use of a non-optimum shipping route, as determined by the transportation model.

From the suboptimization models just described, it is easy to determine which of the potential paths through the system are "active," that is, which paths have nonzero (and, of course, nonnegative) material flows in the suboptimum solution. This set of active paths may not, however, be the exact subset of paths that would become "active" if the total system were solved by the direct approach. To insure the accuracy of the final optimization model, we must consider the possible entry of some additional paths into our present set of active paths. The problem here is to determine which of the currently inactive paths should be added to the set of active paths.

By observing the shadow prices of the optimum transportation matrices and of the optimum simplex tableau of the suboptimization model previously described, we can determine which inactive "links" in the system come closest to being active. (A link is a path through one of the three subsystems. For example, $F_{10}C_{12}$, B_3F_{10}, and $E_1A_2B_3$ are each links drawn from subsystems 1, 2, and 3, respectively.) We shall assume that the closer a particular shadow price approaches zero, the more likely it is that the corresponding variable (or link) will have a nonzero value in the true optimum solution. This is not always true, but is a reasonable heuristic rule for choosing new paths. Judgment must be employed to determine how many additional links from each subsystem should be allowed to enter the final optimization model. Such a judgment will depend on (1) the closeness of each individual shadow price to zero, and (2) the number of additional paths that can be added to the optimization model before computational limits are violated (see Chapter 9 of [1]).

Once it has been decided what links should be activated, the next step is to determine what new active paths through the *total system* must be added to include all newly activated links in the final optimization model. These new links must be combined with other new links, as well as with existing active links, to form all possible new paths through the total system. These new paths should then be included in the total set of active paths that will constitute the variables in the final optimization model.

4.3. Optimization of Total System—Optimization Model

Hopefully, we now have a technique for identifying all "active" paths, or paths that might possibly enter into an optimum solution to the total system. The final step in the entire procedure is to optimize the total system; only these "active" paths are to be considered to be variables. By eliminating all paths that, because of cost considerations, would not be likely to enter an optimum solution, it is probable that the number of variables to be considered can be reduced from 27,000 to less than 500.

The linear programming model to be employed will be very similar to the method described in the "direct approach" section of this paper. The only difference is that there will be significantly fewer variables involved, and thus, the problem will be computationally feasible.

Constraints in this model will be of the following general form:

1. Summation of product flow for all *active* paths through facility X is less than or equal to the maximum capacity of facility X, and greater than or equal to the minimum capacity of facility X.

2. Summation of product flow for all *active* paths through any facility producing product X and ending at demand center Y must equal estimated demand for product X in area Y.

Costs associated with each variable will be the total of all variable production and shipping costs per unit for that particular path.

This problem can be solved by making use of the simplex method of solving linear programming problems. Most of the available computational routines for computer solution could be employed to arrive at a solution. The solution will provide a production and shipping schedule for the total distribution system that will minimize the cost directly incurred by these activities.

5. ALTERNATE APPROACH—OPTIMIZATION OF TOTAL SYSTEM

An alternate method for analyzing inactive paths to determine whether they should be included in the final optimization model is as follows:

1. Solve by the simplex method *the total system* optimization problem, considering as active paths only those paths that contain material flow in the suboptimization solution.

2. Apply the previously described "shadow cost analysis" to the *suboptimization models* to determine all other potentially active paths.

3. To determine whether any of these potentially active paths would be included (i.e., enter the basis) in an optimum solution, proceed as follows, the notation being that of [1]:

   a. Let P_j equal the column vector representing the path to be tested as it would have appeared in the initial tableau if, in fact, it had been included.

   b. Let $\omega' =$ the $z_j - c_j$ row of the basis inverse (i.e., the $z_j - c_j$ row under the slack vectors) of the optimum tableau.

   c. The (vector) product $\omega' \cdot P_j$ will be the $z_j - c_j$ value for this P_j vector in the optimum tableau.

   d. If $\omega' \cdot P_j$ is positive, P_j (this path) should be brought into the basis of the optimum tableau, and a new optimum should be obtained by applying the simplex algorithm.

   e. If $\omega' \cdot P_j$ is negative, discard this particular P_j and test another P_j; i.e., another possible path that is presently "inactive."

By this method, it is possible to determine which "inactive" paths should enter the optimal solution and thus lower the total cost. This method, however, will not directly evaluate the total incremental savings associated with using this path. To determine the total savings associated with bringing any P_j into the basis, it is necessary to determine θ, (where $\theta = \min_i P_{i0}/X_{ik}$) which is the number of units of P_j that will enter the system. Thus $\theta(z_j - c_j)$ are the total realizable savings associated with bringing P_j into the basis.

Because of the size of this problem, it will be necessary to solve the total system optimization by use of a machine code. It should be noted that certain commercially available codes employ partitioning and curtaining procedures which will readily enable the investigation of numerous P_j vectors (paths).

6. LIMITATIONS OF THE MODEL

There are certain limitations to the use of this technique. Some of the important limitations are:

1. The use of this model is limited to long-range planning. The techniques are designed to obtain the optimal allocation of products for a time period with a given demand. It does not, however, show the optimal response of the system for seasonal or other changes in demand.

2. The approach chosen is one of minimizing costs. Therefore, the model will always choose to allocate capacity to the lowest cost product. These tools make no attempt to maximize the profitability, which, in situations where demand exceeds capacity, can introduce serious errors in the solution.

7. ADDITIONAL APPLICATIONS OF THE MODEL

Besides serving as a long-range planning guide, this optimization technique offers potential for other applications:

1. It provides information on the cost of capacity and operating limitations at certain facilities and thus aids in capital budgeting for alterations and additions to existing facilities.

2. It aids in determining the optimal placement of new facilities by showing which alternatives would provide the greatest cost savings.

3. It points out the sensitivity of the system to changes in related costs and other parameters.

4. It allows the determination of the costs associated with meeting high-priority or rush orders.

REFERENCES

1. Charnes, A., and W. W. Cooper, *Management Models and Industrial Applications of Linear Programming*, Vol. I. New York: John Wiley & Sons, Inc., 1961.

2. Churchman, C. W., R. L. Ackhoff, and E. L. Arnoff, *Introduction to Operations Research*, New York: John Wiley & Sons, Inc., 1958.

3. Reinfeld, N. V. and W. R. Vogel, *Mathematical Programming*, Englewood Cliffs, N. J.: Prentice-Hall, Inc., 1958.

11

Average Cost Method
of Scheduling

C. Bachovzeff, J. Corrigan
UNITED STEEL CORPORATION, LTD.
and
ARTHUR ANDERSON & COMPANY

1. INTRODUCTION

The scheduling technique, using the average cost method to be described in this paper, is applicable to a specific type of scheduling problem. This is a common problem, especially in utility companies, and deals with scheduling machines meeting a cyclic load. The machines produce an identical product such as electric power which, unfortunately, cannot be stored. Therefore, the production must equal the demand load at any time. The load schedule that varies with time might look like the one shown in Figure 1. Such a schedule would require some of the machines to be shut down and started up periodically to meet the peaks and valleys in the load requirements. The machines that must meet the load can have various capacities and efficiencies. They may have decreasing, constant, or increasing

This method was developed for a project undertaken in an "Operation Research" course taught by Professor W. W. Cooper at the Graduate School of Industrial Administration, Carnegie Institute of Technology. The project was a consulting job for Duquesne Light Company, and it was through their co-operation that the project was made possible.

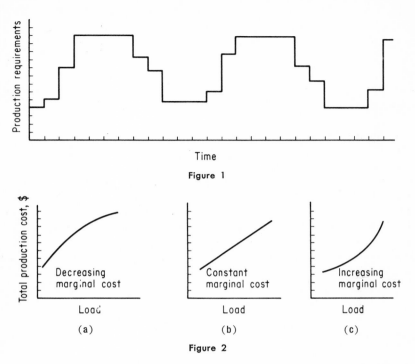

Figure 1

Figure 2

marginal costs, as shown in Figure 2. They may even have combinations of these types of marginal costs. The machines cannot be operated at zero load, and each machine must be shut down when its load is reduced below a given minimum amount. Inclusion of this last requirement makes the scheduling difficult, since it is impossible to reduce the load on a given machine to zero and keep the machine just idling until the load is again needed. Instead, the machine must be shut down and thus incur a shut-down and start-up cost. Such costs can be substantial.

The average cost method was originally developed for an electrical utility company but can be applied to parallel problems, such as gas and water pumping, machines manufacturing identical items, and can even be extended to consideration of multiplant operations. The technique is easy to apply, requiring few rules and at most three tables. Although the method does not guarantee an optimum schedule, it closely approaches such an optimum.

Linear programming and dynamic programming were investigated as alternative techniques to the scheduling problem outlined. In order to describe the problem as a linear program, too many constraints had to be applied for practical computation, even when approximations were made. The application of linear programming is discussed in an unpublished report by the authors using methods outlined in reference [1]. Dynamic programming is discussed in references [2] and [3]. It was found that in a problem involving 17 machines, too many combinations had to be investigated before a near optimum was obtained. The average cost method was then developed to reach a near optimum in a short time.

2. AVERAGE COST METHOD

In order to explain the average cost method, a simple example will be discussed. Consider two machines with characteristics as shown in Figure 3. Machine 1 has a starting-up cost of m dollars and a shut-down cost of n dollars. When operated at a theoretical no-load, it has a fixed cost of b dollars per hour. However, the machine must be shut-down when the production is lower than 1 unit per hour. Its shut-down cost is n dollars. Also, when the machine is started up again, a further start-up cost of m dollars is incurred.

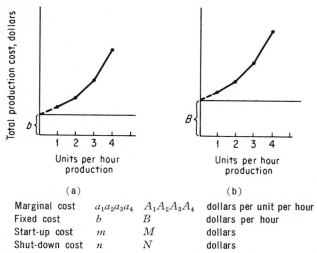

	(a)	(b)	
Marginal cost	$a_1 a_2 a_3 a_4$	$A_1 A_2 A_3 A_4$	dollars per unit per hour
Fixed cost	b	B	dollars per hour
Start-up cost	m	M	dollars
Shut-down cost	n	N	dollars

Note: Machines are to be shut down if production is less than one unit per hour.

Figure 3

The marginal cost of production for machine 1 varies as shown in Figure 3(a). The first unit per hour is produced at a_1 dollars. The second unit is produced at a_2 dollars per hour; the third at a_3, and the fourth at a_4. With this machine the marginal cost increases as additional units per hour are produced, i.e.,

$$a_1 < a_2 < a_3 < a_4.$$

An increasing marginal cost is the most difficult to schedule and is used in the example to illustrate the difficulty. Constant or decreasing marginal costs are easier to handle and will be discussed later.

Machine 2 has characteristics similar to machine 1. Upper-case letters are used to designate its relevant costs.

Assume that the two machines are required to produce according to the schedule shown in Figure 4. Suppose that machine 1 was operating from x_0 hours to x_1 hours producing two units per hour.

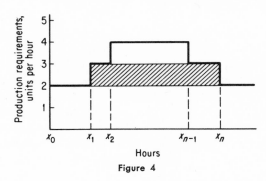

Figure 4

During this period machine 2 was shut down. The assumption is made that previous to time x_1, scheduling decisions have been made which have tried to minimize total cost of production. At hour x_1 the production must be increased to three units per hour until hour x_n, when the production again has to be reduced to two units per hour. At hour x_2 the production must be increased to four units per hour and again reduced at hour x_{n-1} to three units per hour. A decision must be made at hour x_1 whether to start up machine 2, which has a low marginal cost for producing one additional unit per hour, or to produce the one additional unit per hour on machine 1, if it is known that in hour x_n this unit will no longer be required.

In deciding how to schedule the additional unit per hour at x_1, the length of time this increase is required is considered (shown hatched in Figure 4). The fact that there is a further increase to four units per hour at hour x_2 is neglected, for the time being, until the initial decision for increasing the production to three units per per hour is made. When it has been completed, the next production increase (i.e., to four units per hour) will be considered.

If the third unit per hour (which must be produced from hour x_1 to hour x_n) is scheduled for machine 1, then the additional cost of this production would be the marginal cost of producing the third unit on machine 1, i.e., a_3, multiplied by the number of units produced (one in this case) and also by the number of hours the unit is required, which is $(x_n - x_1)$. Briefly, the cost is

$$a_3(x_n - x_1).$$

If the third unit per hour is to be produced on machine 2, then the total additional cost incurred is the start-up cost (M), plus the fixed cost (B) multiplied by the time $(x_n - x_1)$, plus the marginal cost of producing one unit on machine 2 (A_1), multiplied by the hours $(x_n - x_1)$ plus the shut-down cost N. This is, briefly,

$$M + B(x_n - x_1) + A_1(x_n - x_1) + N.$$

The machine that should be scheduled is the one which produces the third unit at the lowest total additional cost over the period x_1 to x_n. If machine 1 is scheduled, then it must be true that

$$a_3(x_n - x_1) < N + B(x_n - x_1) + A_1(x_n - x_1) + N. \qquad (1)$$

Although this calculation can be easily done for two machines, it presents a considerable amount of work if a large number of machines are to be evaluated. A fast and simple means of deciding which machine to schedule is then desirable. Such a method will now be developed.

Dividing Equation (1) through by $(x_n - x_1)$, we obtain

$$a_3 < \frac{M}{(x_n - x_1)} + B + A_1 + \frac{N}{(x_n - x_1)} = C(x_n - x_1). \qquad (2)$$

Thus the marginal cost of producing the third unit on machine 1 must be less than the start-up and shut-down cost averaged over $x_n - x_1$ hours, plus the fixed cost B plus the marginal cost of producing one unit on machine 2. We call the second expression the *average cost*. Specifically, it represents the cost of producing one unit per hour on machine 2 during a period of $x_n - x_1$ hours, if it is given that machine 2 is started up at the beginning and shut down at the end of this period.

The symbol for the average cost will be denoted by $C(x_n - x_1)$, as indicated in Equation (2).

To facilitate decision-making, tables can be compiled of average costs for each increment that each machine is normally increased in production and the number of time units which normally represent a complete cycle of operation. In the case of machine 2, the increments would be one, two, three, and four units per hour increase of production.

If production increments are not constant, then both the average and the marginal cost should be calculated—based on a common unit that will enable comparison between the average and marginal cost. In the example just discussed, this comparison presents no problem, but with electrical generators it was necessary to use a base of dollars per megawatt-hour. This problem is discussed later. For a utility company with loads fluctuating over 24 hours, the average costs could be calculated from 1 to 24 hours.

In the above example, if the decision to be made was whether to schedule the third unit for hours x_1 to x_n, then the marginal cost of producing the third unit on machine 1 (i.e., a_3) would be compared with average cost of producing one unit on machine 2 over a period of $(x_n - x_1)$ hours, [i.e., $C(x_n - x_1)$]. The machine with the lower cost would then be scheduled. After the decision for scheduling the third unit per hour is complete, then the next increment is considered, i.e., the fourth unit per hour and so on, until the schedule for the increasing cycle in the production is finished.

If machine 2 is not scheduled in hours x_1 and x_2, it may happen that taking only one-unit increments at a time, the marginal cost of machine 1 will always exceed the average cost of machine 2. However, if the average cost, when two units are scheduled on machine 2 from x_2 to x_{n-1}, is found to be lower than the marginal costs of scheduling the third and fourth units on machine 1, then machine 2 would be scheduled for this period. Thus it may be found that it is necessary to consider average costs for incremental increases of two or more units per hour. If such is the case in the schedule in Figure 4, then there is a problem of the time period x_1 to x_2 when there is only an increase of one unit per hour. Should machine 1 be increased in production to three units per hour and then decreased in time x_2 when machine 2 is started? Or should machine 2 be started in hour x_1? If only the pertinent costs are considered, machine 2 would be started in hour x_1 if the marginal cost of the first unit per hour for machine 1 (i.e., A_1) plus the fixed running cost B is less than the marginal cost of producing the third unit on machine 1 (i.e., a_3). Briefly, then,

$$A_1 + B < a_1 .$$

The start-up and shut-down costs are not included here, since they occur just once, and have been justified for the period $x_2 - x_{n-1}$.

However, although such comparisons could be made, they are unnecessary when there is a large number of machines and there is a cyclic load pattern with high peaks and valleys. The load would increase in fairly large steps compared with the individual machine capacities. This was the case with the demands of the utility company which we were considering and so allowed just the simple average cost method to be applied.

If the starting-up, shut-down, and operating fixed costs are high, then the average costs of the machines might prove to be always greater than the marginal costs. In such a case, scheduling is greatly simplified, since machines operating are increased in load to their maximum before a machine not already operating is considered for production. The average cost method is, therefore, unnecessary.

The above gives a description of the basic ideas involved in the average cost method. However, in order to be able to complete a schedule for the type of problem considered above, additional rules must be used with the average cost method. The rules will be given in the next section.

3. SUPPLEMENTARY RULES FOR THE AVERAGE COST METHOD

3.1 Marginal Cost Comparison

If machines 1 and 2 are both operating at x_1 hours (in Figure 4), then the machine to schedule when the load increases from two to three units per hour would be the one with the lowest marginal cost for the next available unit that can be produced. Similarly, when loads are decreased when both machines are operating, machines with the highest marginal cost are decreased first. This is done until one of the machines is at its minimum load and must be shut down. We discuss machine shut-downs next.

3.2 Machine Shut-downs

To develop rules for shutting down machines, consider the first case in which machines 1 and 2 are both operating. They are producing at four units per hour. Three of the units are produced on machine 1 and only one on machine 2. The load is decreased in hour x_n from four to three units per hour, and the load again increased to four units per hour in hour x_{22}, as shown in Figure 5. There is a

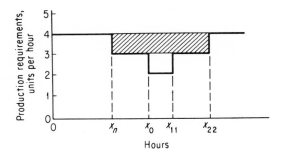

Figure 5

further decrease in load in hour x_0 to two units per hour and then an increase in load to three units per hour in hour x_{11}. In considering the decrease in load in hour x_n from four units to three units per hour, the length of time this decrease will last is taken into account. This time is from x_n to x_{22} hours and is shown hatched in Figure 5. The further decrease to two units per hour is considered after the first decision has been made.

In hour x_n a decision must be made either to (1) shut down machine 2 and produce the three units on machine 1, or (2) reduce the load on machine 1 by one unit per hour. It will be assumed that in hour x_{22}, machine 2 will be returned to production when four units per hour are required again. Also, the assumption is made that, previous to hour x_n, machines have been scheduled so as to try to minimize total costs. The decision to be made now must be the one that minimizes total production costs over the period x_n to x_{22}.

The additional cost of the first alternative would be the shut-down and start-up cost of machine 2, plus the cost of producing the third item on machine 1. Thus,

$$\text{Cost of alternative } (1) = M + N + a_3(x_{22} - x_n).$$

The additional cost of alternative (2) would be the cost of producing one unit per hour on machine 2 for $(x_{22} - x_n)$ hours.

$$\text{Cost of alternative } (2) = A_1(x_{22} - x_n) + B(x_{22} - x_n)$$
$$= (A_1 + B)(x_{22} - x_n).$$

If machine 2 is shut down, then cost of alternative (2) must be greater than cost of alternative (1). Thus,

$$(A_1 + B)(x_{22} - x_n) > M + N + a_3(x_{22} - x_n). \qquad (3)$$

If the expression $a_3(x_{22} - x_n)$ is transferred to the left-hand side of the inequality, then

$$(A_1 + B - a_3)(x_{22} - x_n) > M + N. \qquad (4)$$

Therefore, in order to shut down machine 2, the amount that can be saved by just producing on machine 1 (i.e, the difference in producing on machines 1 and 2) must be greater than the start-up and shut-down cost of machine 2. This calculation might take some time to complete if there were quite a number of machines to consider. An approximate method is suggested and should be quite sufficient for most scheduling decisions. If expression (4) is divided by $(A_1 + B - a_3)$, then

$$x_{22} - x_n > \frac{M + N}{(A_1 + B - a_3)}. \qquad (5)$$

The quantity $(M + N)/(A_1 + B - a_3)$ is called the *critical shut-down time.* If machine 2 is not required for more than the critical shut-down time, then it should be shut-down. The question to be answered using the critical shut-down time method is what value of marginal cost should be used for machine 1. Marginal costs a_2, a_3, and a_4 each might be used at various times. In the two-machine problem, it is not too much trouble to tabulate critical times for each marginal cost of machine 1. However, in a case where there are many machines, this becomes a long tabulation. To simplify this problem, we suggest an approximation which, in most cases, will not give a decision different from the optimum one. Namely, the machines which are usually shut down when the load is decreased can be compared with an average marginal cost of the more efficient machines at loads at which the less efficient machines are usually shut down. A table of such critical shut-down times can be compiled to assist in scheduling.

We now discuss a second shut-down rule that is to be applied when both machines 1 and 2 are operating at the lowest possible load and there is a further load decrease. This implies that one of the machines be shut down. Consider a forecast schedule, as shown in Figure 6. If machine 1 is shut down in hour x_p, the saving in op-

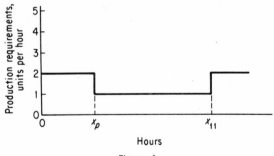

Figure 6

erating cost would be the cost of producing the one unit on machine 1 for the hours the machine is shut down, less the start-up and shut-down cost. This would be

$$a_1(x_{11} - x_p) - (m + n).$$

It is assumed that machine 1 will be returned to production in hour x_{11}, when load is increased to two units per hour. Similarly, if machine 2 were shut down, the production saving would be

$$A_1(x_{11} - x_p) - (M + N).$$

The machine with the greatest saving should be shut down. A table of priority for shutting down machines in these circumstances can be drawn up for the times that are commonly observed when machines are at minimum loads.

This completes all the rules that are necessary for scheduling the original problem outlined. A summary of these rules is given in the next section.

4. SUMMARY OF SCHEDULING RULES

Given the projected load curve, starting from the first hour (or suitable time period), and taking each subsequent hour in turn, determine the machines to be scheduled and the rate at which they are scheduled as follows:

4.1 When Load is Increasing

a. All available machines are in operation. Schedule the machines with the lowest available marginal cost. Repeat until load is satisfied.

b. Some machines are operating and others are shut down.
1. Determine number of hours the load increase is required.
2. Of the machines operating, find the one with the lowest available marginal cost. Of the machines shut down, find the one with the lowest available average cost for the number of hours the load increase is required. Schedule the machine with the lowest of the two available costs. Repeat this procedure till the load increment is satisfied.

4.2 When Load is Decreasing

a. No machines at minimum load. Decrease load on units with the highest marginal cost until the given load decrease is attained.

b. Some machines are operating at minimum load.
1. Determine the number of hours the load decrease is required.
2. Shut down machines operating at minimum load, if the hours the machine is not required are greater than the critical shutdown times.
3. Decrease load further, if necessary, on machines which have the highest marginal costs at specific loads and which are operating above base load.
c. All machines are at minimum load. Shut down machines with the highest value for total cost of operation for specific hours of shutdown, less start-up and shut-down cost.

5. APPLICATION OF AVERAGE COST METHOD

The average cost method outlined above was applied to 17 electrical steam-generating units which were coal fired. The daily load charts that had to be generated Mondays to Fridays look like that shown in Figure 7. The Saturday and Sunday chart was like that shown in Figure 8.

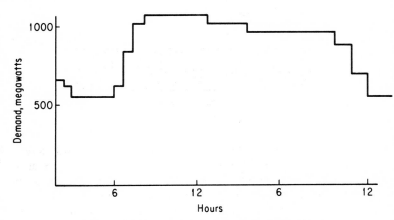

Figure 7 Typical weekly schedule, Monday to Friday.

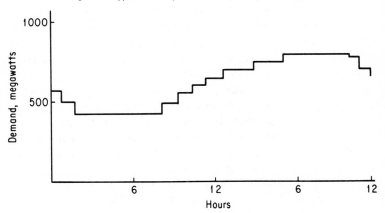

Figure 8 Typical Saturday-Sunday schedule.

The typical generator characteristic is shown in Figure 9. Each generator had a start-up and shut-down cost which amounted to a fairly large sum. The spinning cost was the fixed portion of the generating cost being incurred when the generator was operating, but stopped as soon as the generator was shut down. It can be looked upon as the theoretical cost of operating the generator at no load.

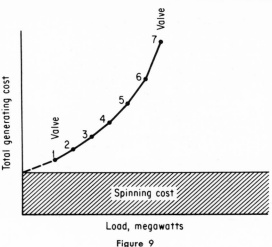

Figure 9

However, the generators could not be operated at no load, since that was an unstable operating condition. The minimum load was called the base load. It was about 30 percent of the maximum load of the generators. There were seven valves on the generators which were opened in turn as the load was raised. Marginal cost of operation was calculated for each valve and represented the increase in cost of operation from one valve opening to another. The amount of load generated by each valve's opening varied from valve to valve and generator to generator. To make comparison possible, marginal costs for each valve were brought to a common base by calculating them in dollars per megawatt-hour. Tables were compiled, listing the marginal costs in numerical order, with the lowest first for each valve of each generator. Marginal costs with these generators increased with load. If the generators had straight-line or decreasing marginal costs, the generators were scheduled up to their maximum load before generators not operating would be started up. In these cases, the average cost method was not necessary.

This describes the basic factors that must be taken into account in the generating problem. There were other factors which also had to be considered, but initially the utility company wanted a solution to the basic problem before all these other factors were incorporated. Prior to the average cost method, the generating company scheduled their generators by a marginal cost method for generators on the line, and a set of rules for starting and stopping generators as loads were increased or decreased. These rules were mostly developed by trial and error by studying the effect of certain scheduling changes on the total cost. For instance, it was found that starting

generators in a certain order próduced the lowest cost up to that date.
However, the generator company did not have a direct way of taking
into account spinning, start-up and shut-down costs into their scheduling.   The average cost method made it possible for them to consider these costs in a logical and easy way.

To facilitate the use of the average cost method, tables from one
hour to 24 hours were compiled of average costs for each valve opening.   These costs were calculated in dollars per megawatt-hour to
make comparison easy with marginal costs. A computer program was
written to do these calculations, from existing marginal cost values.
This saved clerical time that would have been used to make about
3,000 calculations which were required.   Also, it enabled easy updat-
ing of the tables as better cost data became available.

Critical shut-down times (i.e., the number of hours above which
a generator could be shut down if its load was not required) were
calculated by comparing the marginal costs at base loads of the less
efficient generators with the marginal cost of the two most efficient
generators.   These two efficient units were never shut down except
for maintenance.   The error in scheduling by this approximation was
not significant.   Since the load on the system never decreased to the
point where all the units on the line would be operating at base load,
an order of priority for shutting down generators at base loads was
not necessary.

With the tables, it was possible to schedule the generators fairly
quickly when the forecast for the load requirement of the day was
given.   With practice, it was possible to make a 24-hour schedule in
less than 30 minutes.   For instance, in making the schedule shown
in Figure 7, the forecast curve was divided into sections, as shown

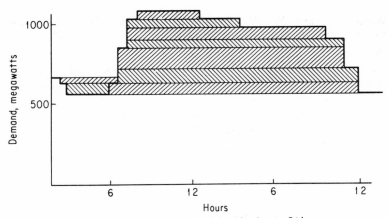

Figure 10 Typical weekly schedule, Monday to Friday.

hatched in Figure 10. Each section is considered in time sequence until the schedule is complete.

A comparison was made between the existing method of scheduling and the average cost method. It was found that there was no significant difference between the two methods. Because both methods used marginal costs to schedule generators once they were on the line—and the characteristics of the generators were such that the choice of selection was fairly limited—the fact that both methods produced identical schedules was not that unusual. However, the average cost method was an approach that enabled the evaluation of costs in a schedule that before could not be considered directly. It was a step in a direction which would enable better scheduling to be done, since all the other operating restrictions were incorporated with the basic method.

6. CONCLUSION

The average cost method is a technique which enables the consideration of marginal, fixed running, shut-down and start-up costs of a number of machines producing identical items. The method is simple and rapid in application, being not much more complicated to use than the marginal cost method of scheduling. Because a person is required to apply the method, restrictions and changes to the scheduling can be easily incorporated, as opposed to a purely mechanical method. Up to the time of writing, the average cost method was found computationally superior to more complex methods of linear programming and dynamic programming.

REFERENCES

1. Charnes, A. and W. W. Cooper, *Management Models and Industrial Application of Linear Programming*, New York: John Wiley & Sons, 1961. Two volumes.

2. Dale, K. M., *Dynamic Scheduling of Generating Units in the Daily Dispatch of Load on an Electric Utility System* (Master's thesis, University of Pittsburgh, July 1960).

3. Ostovlo, W. H. and others, "Computer Selection of Generating Units to be Operated: Part 1," *Economic Evaluation of Small Computor*, AIEE Publication CP-60-1398.

III

Integer Programming
Models in Scheduling

In the job-shop scheduling problem, a job cannot be scheduled to start until all of its immediate predecessors have been finished. Hence, some device is needed to signal when each job is finished. The obvious mechanism for this is a variable that is equal to one if the given job is finished and equal to zero otherwise. Using this idea and variants of it, one can formulate the job-shop scheduling problem as an integer linear programming problem, as shown by Alan Manne in Chapter 12, "On the Job-Shop Scheduling Problem." There have been at least three such formulations of the problem, and these are mentioned in the paper. One of the difficulties of formulation is that it is very wasteful of variables, as Manne's estimates show. However, his formulation seems to be the the most compact of the ones presently proposed. Besides the difficulties of the initial statement of the problem, the use of integer linear programming codes have so far not lead to uniformly good results. These problems are discussed in the next two papers.

Ralph Gomory's announcement in 1958 of the first algorithm for solving integer programming problems stimulated a great deal of work on problems that can be started within this framework. Many practical linear programming problems by nature demand integer-valued solutions. This is because activities and resources, such as machines and people, are frequently indivisible. Of course, such problems can be solved as ordinary linear programming problems, and attempts can then be made to "round" the answers obtained to give integer solutions. However, simple examples show that straightforward rules for rounding, such as the ordinary "scientific rounding" procedures, do not give optimal results. Hence, integer linear programming algorithms are absolutely necessary. In the "All-Integer Integer Programming Algorithm" (Chapter 13), Gomory presents one of his recent algorithms for this case. Here it is assumed that the initial data are integral-valued, and then the tableaux constructed in the course of working the all-integer algorithm always contain integers. Integer programming algorithms differ from the ordinary linear programming algorithms in that new constraints are created and added to the tableau as the algorithm proceeds. The all-integer algorithm has the advantage that each new constraint is added, immediately used as a pivot, and then discarded. Hence, the memory demands of the algorithm do not expand with time as was the case for some of the previous algorithms. Although the algorithm is proved to terminate in a finite number of steps, the experiments reported on by Gomory show that the actual number of steps required is highly variable and unpredictable. For this reason, only experimental use has so far been made of the various integer linear programming algorithms for solving actual problems. Many different research efforts are presently being made by Gomory and others to improve these algorithms.

In Chapter 14, "Computational Experience with Integer Programming for Job-Shop Scheduling," Alfred E. Story and Harvey M. Wagner report on the application of Gomory's algorithms to Wagner's formulation of the job-shop sheduling problem. Their approach is frankly experimental, using the computer as a research device to perform experiments with various ideas for solving the job-shop scheduling problem. They first describe some simple heuristic rules which they tried out before abandoning them in favor of the the integer linear programming formulation. Their results are quite variable and show promise, but, as the authors remark, "We have not yet found an integer programming method that can be relied upon to solve most machine sequencing problems rapidly."

In spite of the rather limited number of positive results reported by the authors of this part of the volume, the integer programming approach remains one of the highly promising directions for further research on the job-shop scheduling problem.

12

On the Job=shop Scheduling Problem

Alan S. Manne
STANFORD UNIVERSITY

It will be assumed that this sequencing problem involves the performance of n 'tasks'—each task being defined in such a way as to require the services of a single machine for an integral number of time units. (For concreteness, we may refer to the unit of time as a "day.") Any one end product will, in general, necessitate the performance of several tasks in sequence. The scheduling problem consists of drawing up a plan for time-phasing the individual jobs so as to satisfy : (1) sequencing requirements—e.g., the children must be washed before they are dried—and (2) equipment interference problems—e.g., the one-year-old and the three-year-old cannot occupy the bathtub at the same time. (All parents will devoutly hope that each of *these* tasks can be performed in less than a day.)

Research undertaken by the Cowles Commission for Research in Economics under Contract Nonr–358 (01), NR 047–066 with the Office of Naval Research. Reprinted from *Operations Research* 8 (1960), 219–223. This paper was stimulated by a paper of E. H. Bowman [1]. Bowman's ideas have led directly to the model formulated here.

The integer-valued unknowns x_j are to indicate the day on which task j is to be begun $(x_j = 0, 1, \ldots, T)$.[1] Just as in Selmer Johnson's formulation, [6], the schedule is to be drawn up so as to minimize the "make-span," i.e., the elapsed calendar time for the performance of all jobs—subject, of course, to the constraints upon sequencing and machine interference, and also subject to any delivery date requirements on individual items.

1. NONINTERFERENCE RESTRICTIONS

Suppose that jobs j and k require a_j and a_k consecutive days respectively.[2] Then if they are to be prevented from occupying the same machine at the same time, we must require that one of the two must precede the other by sufficient time so that the first one can be completed before the second is begun : either

$$x_j - x_k \geq a_k \quad \text{or else} \quad x_k - x_j \geq a_j. \tag{1}$$

In order to convert this condition into a linear inequality in integer unknowns, it will be convenient to define a new integer-valued variable y_{jk}, and to write down the following restrictions:

$$0 \leq y_{jk} \leq 1 \tag{2}$$

$$(T + a_k)y_{jk} + (x_j - x_k) \geq a_k \tag{3}$$

$$(T + a_j)(1 - y_{jk}) + (x_k - x_j) \geq a_j. \tag{4}$$

Condition (2) ensures that y_{jk} equals either zero or else unity. We already know that $|x_j - x_k| \leq T$. The effect of Conditions (3) and (4) may therefore be summarized as follows : if

$$(x_j - x_k) \begin{cases} > 0 \\ = 0 \\ < 0 \end{cases}$$

then

$$y_{jk} = \begin{cases} 0, 1 \\ 1 \\ 1 \end{cases} \quad \text{and} \quad y_{jk} = \begin{cases} 0 \\ 0 \\ 0, 1 \end{cases}$$

where the first set of values for y_{jk} is implied by Condition (3) and the second set by Condition (4).

Hence, if $(x_j - x_k) = 0$, there is no value that can be assigned to y_{jk} so as to satisfy both (3) and (4). If, on the other hand, $(x_j - x_k) \neq$

[1] For purposes that will shortly become evident, it will be convenient to suppose that we have sufficient a priori knowledge to be able to select a (large) integer T that will constitute a *redundant* upper bound upon the unknowns x_j.

[2] In a somewhat more complex model, one could allow for the possibility of "hereditary" effects—i. e., dependence of the processing time of one item upon the machine setting employed for the previous one.

0, y_{jk} will be set at a value of either zero or unity depending upon which job is to precede the other. Equations (3) and (4) then ensure that the first job will be initiated in sufficient time to be completed before the beginning of the second one. Note that with the classical form of linear programming, it would have been impossible to specify such an either-or condition as (1). This noninterference restriction leads directly to a nonconvex set of restraints upon the unknowns. It is little wonder that Gomory's discovery of integer programming [4] has led to a revival of interest in the machine interference problem.

2. SEQUENCING RESTRICTIONS

Once the noninterference stipulations have been written down, the remainder of the formulation becomes virtually automatic. If job j is to precede k, this means that job k is to be performed at least a_j days later than j. The integer programming condition becomes

$$x_j + a_j \leq x_k. \tag{5a}$$

"Weak" precedence relations may be written in an analogous fashion. For example, in order to specify that both jobs i and j precede k, but that there is no precedence restriction affecting the performance of i and j, we would have

$$x_i + a_i \leq x_k \qquad x_j + a_j \leq x_k. \tag{5b}$$

Still another possibility might be that there be a delay of exactly Θ_{jk} days between the performance of jobs j and k. Such a restriction would be indicated by

$$x_j + a_j + \Theta_{jk} = x_k. \tag{5c}$$

3. SPECIFIC DELIVERY REQUIREMENTS

It may happen that the shop is committed to the delivery of an individual job no later than a specified date. If task j is the last task which the shop is to perform upon the item, and if the item is to be available on day d_j, this form of requirement may be written

$$x_j + a_j \leq d_j. \tag{6}$$

4. OVER-ALL DELIVERY REQUIREMENTS

Following Johnson [6], we shall employ as our minimand the "makespan," or total calender time needed for the performance of all prospective jobs. If this calendar time is denoted by t, the problem now consists of the minimization of t with respect to the nonnegative integers x_j and y_{jk}, subject to constraints (2) to (6), and also subject to

$$x_j + a_j \leq t. \qquad (j = 1, \ldots, n) \qquad (7)$$

The economist, conditioned as he is to take a dim view of any minimand other than dollar costs, will find it difficult to be altogether happy with Johnson's criterion, the minimization of t, the make-span. In defending this choice of minimand, however, it should be pointed out that t is likely to be correlated with dollar costs. In minimizing t we may conceivably also obtain the following cost and profit benefits: (1) a lowered amount of inventory tied up in work in process, (2) a shorter *average* customer delay time, and (3) a lower amount of idle time incurred prior to the performance of all currently booked jobs— i.e., a greater capacity to take on additional work as new orders materialize. To the extent that all of these factors work in the same direction, calendar time might constitute a reasonable proxy variable for economic cost. The job sequence that serves to minimize the make-span might also be one that scores quite well on the criterion of dollar costs.

5. COMPUTATIONAL ASPECTS

If all of the slack variables and also the minimand t are excluded, the number of unknowns here is equal to the total number of the x_j plus the y_{jk}. If, then, there are n tasks and if also there are m possible conflicting pairs of machine assignments, the total number of unknowns would come to $n + m$. For example, with five machines and with ten tasks to be performed on each machine, we would have $n = 50$, and $m = \frac{1}{2}(5)(10)(10 - 1) = 225$. The total number of integer-valued unknowns x_j and y_{jk} would come, therefore, to 275—an impressive computational load but by no means an impossible one.[3]

It is worth pointing out that if an algorithm were available to handle "mixed" integer programming problems—problems in which some of the unknowns are constrained to take on integer values and others are permitted to be continuous—this scheduling model would fit very

---

[3] By contrast, if the formulation discussed in Part II of Wagner's paper [7] is used, the total number of unknowns would come to 600—again, slack variables and also the make-span minimand are neglected. In general, Wagner's formulation will require slightly more than twice the number of unknowns in the current proposal. [Because of the large number of inequalities implied by his condition (8), the current proposal is bound to be advantageous in terms of the number of inequality restraints.]

Why concentrate upon the number of nonslack variables, and why ignore the number of constraints in estimating computation requirements? Because with Gomory's method for integer programming, one is repeatedly applying the dual

naturally into the category of such a "mixed" problem.   The y_{jk} unknowns here are necessarily of a discrete nature. [Otherwise, it would be impossible to impose Condition (1).]   However, it might be more efficient and possibly more realistic to regard the start-dates x_j as continuous variables, and not to constrain these to be integers.   The success of this kind of modification would hinge ·entirely upon the computational costs of any algorithms designed to handle "mixed" problems.

In further work along these lines, one of the most important avenues to be explored would be the possibility of reducing the number of unknowns y_{jk}.   Aside from the upper bound constraints (2), these unknowns are involved only in connection with the machine-interference conditions (3) and (4).   Since many of these restrictions will inevitably turn out to be redundant in any particular numerical problem, it might be quite feasible to apply here a computer code designed around Dantzig's principle of "secondary constraints" [3].[4]   In the traveling-salesman problem, for example, one does not write down explicitly all conceivable "loop constraints," but only those that have been violated during the course of previous iterations [2].   By applying the identical principle to the machine-scheduling problem, this suggestion may conceivably make it economical to obtain specific solutions to realistic examples.

In weighing the benefits from exact optimization of large systems via integer programming, the investigator ought not to permit himself to ignore the likelihood that Monte Carlo methods for *approximate* optimization will entail lower computing costs.   A very promising start along these lines has recently been reported by Heller [5].

REFERENCES

1. Bowman, E. H., "The Schedule-Sequencing Problem," *Opns. Res.* **7**, 621–624 (1959).

2. Dantzig, G. B., et al., "Solution of a Large-Scale Traveling-Salesman Problem," *Opns. Res.* **2**, 393–410 (1954).

simplex algorithm—an algorithm in which the original number of nonbasis variables is apparently the critical factor. Needless to say, with the limited amount of computing experience currently available in the area of integer programming, one cannot afford to be too dogmatic with such predictions.

One further comment: I feel that the real advantage of Wagner's formulation over this one lies in the case where it is known that the order position of each end product is the same from one machine in the processing sequence to the next (Part IV of his paper). This is a really important case, and I suspect that his approach will turn out to be quite practical there.

[4] Richard Levitan is in the process of writing an integer-programming computer code in which this principle is being applied.

3. ———, "Upper Bounds, Secondary Constraints, and Block Triangularity in Linear Programming," *Econometrica* (April 1955).

4. Gomory, R., "Outline of an Algorithm for Integer Solutions to Linear Programs," *Bulletin of the American Mathematical Society* (September 1958).

5. Heller, J., "Some Numerical Experiments for an $M \times J$ Flow Shop and Its Decision-Theoretical Aspects," *Opns Res.* 8, 178–184 (1960).

6. Johnson, S. M., "Optimal Two and Three Stage Production Schedules and Setup Times Included," *Naval Res. Log. Quart.* (March 1954). Reprinted as Chapter 2 of this volume.

7. Wagner, H., "An Integer Linear-Programming Model for Machine Scheduling," *Naval Res. Log. Quart.* (June 1959).

13

An All=integer Integer Programming Algorithm

Ralph E. Gomory

INTERNATIONAL BUSINESS MACHINES CORPORATION

The purpose of this paper is to describe a new method of integer programming which differs from its predecessors in two main points:

1. It is an all-integer method; that is, if the coefficients in the original matrix are integers, all coefficients remain integral during the whole calculation.

2. It is a uniform procedure closely resembling the ordinary dual simplex method, with the difference that the pivot element is always − 1. The cycle of maximizing, adding an inequality, etc. characteristic of [2] has been eliminated.[1]

We shall use the notation of [2] so that we regard the linear programming problem as the problem of maximizing in nonnegative variables.

[1] I should like to acknowledge the stimulus of some ideas advanced by M. D. McIlroy of the Bell Telephone Laboratories.

This work was performed at the IBM Research Center, Yorktown Heights, New York and was previously reported in the *IBM Research Report* RC-189, January 29, 1960.

$$z = a_{0,0} + \sum_{j=1}^{j=n} a_{0,i}(-t_j) \qquad (1)$$

subject to the restrictions

$$x_1 = a_{1,0} + \sum_{j=1}^{j=n} a_{i,j}(-t_j)$$

.

.

.

$$x_m = a_{m,0} + \sum_{j=1}^{j=n} a_{m,j}(-t_j) \qquad (2)$$

$$t_1 = -1(-t_1)$$

.   .

.   .

.   .

$$t_n = \qquad -1(-t_n)$$

or in matrix form to maximize z subject to

$$X = A^0 T^0 \qquad A^0 = (\alpha_0, \alpha_1, \cdots, \alpha_n)$$

$$X = \begin{bmatrix} z \\ x_1 \\ x_2 \\ . \\ . \\ . \\ t_1 \\ . \\ . \\ . \\ t_n \end{bmatrix} \qquad T_0 = \begin{bmatrix} 1 \\ -t_1 \\ -t_2 \\ . \\ . \\ . \\ . \\ . \\ -t_n \end{bmatrix}. \qquad (3)$$

We shall assume throughout that the columns α_j, $j \neq 0$ are lexico-graphically positive, i.e., that the problem is dual feasible. If they are not, this can easily be arranged; see, for example, [3].

In the ordinary dual simplex method, we would perform a series of Gaussian eliminations on the matrix A^0 appearing in (3) in order to introduce new sets of nonbasic variables. By doing this we con-tinually form new expressions such as

$$X = AT \qquad (4)$$

where the vector T is the vector of the new nonbasic variables, and A is the result of transforming A^0 by Gaussian eliminations. The pivot element in these steps is chosen by the dual simplex rule with the result that the columns of the matrices always remain lexico-graphically positive. When α_0, the column of constants, has only nonnegative entries (except possibly in the first position), the solution to the ordinary linear programming problem has been obtained.

The procedure we shall describe is very close to this. However, instead of constantly introducing new nonbasic variables from among the original variables of the problem, new ones are created as we go along. These new variables will be added by introducing them first as basic variables in a new equation adjoined to the bottom of the matrix A appearing in (4) and then doing Gaussian elimination to make the new variable nonbasic.

We now turn to the derivation of these new relations. We give a derivation which includes the relations used in [1] and [2], as well as those used here.

Let us consider a typical equation

$$x = a_0 + \sum_{j=1}^{j=n} a_j(-t_j) \qquad (5)$$

or

$$0 = a_0 + \sum_{j=1}^{j=n} a_j(-t_j) + 1(-x)$$

which is one of the equations appearing in (4). We shall represent every coefficient a_j appearing in (5), as well as the 1, in the form $b_j\lambda + r_j$, where b_j is an integer, r_j is a remainder, and λ is a positive number to be determined later. That is,

$$a_j = b_j\lambda + r_j = [a_j/\lambda]\lambda + r_j, \qquad j = 0, \ldots, n$$
$$1 = [1/\lambda] + r$$
$$0 \le r_j < \lambda, \qquad 0 \le r < \lambda$$
$$0 < \lambda \qquad (6)$$

where square brackets indicate integer part of. Substituting the expressions in (6) into (5) and assembling all the remainder terms except r_0 on the left gives

$$\sum_{j=i}^{j=n} r_jt_j + rx = r_0 + \lambda \left\{ [a_0/\lambda] + \sum_{j=1}^{j=n} [a_j/\lambda](-t_j) + [1/\lambda](-x) \right\}. \qquad (7)$$

Any nonnegative integer values for x and the t_j which satisfy (5) will also satisfy (7) and will make the left-hand side of (7) a non-negative number, since the r_j are nonnegative. Let us now look at the right-hand side and especially at the contents of the curly bracket, which we can write separately as s,

$$s = [a_0/\lambda] + \sum_{j=1}^{j=n} [a_j/\lambda](-t_j) + [1/\lambda](-x). \qquad (8)$$

Clearly, the value obtained by substituting the same x and t_j into (8) will be an integer, since all the coefficients appearing are integers (though of any sign). However, s is not only integer but in fact nonnegative, for suppose s were a negative integer such as -1, -2, etc. Since $r_0 < \lambda$, a negative integer s would make the entire right-hand side of (7) negative. However, we know that the left side is non-negative, so this is a contradiction. Thus the s introduced by equation (8) is a new nonnegative integer variable.

Let us examine this first for the case $\lambda = 1$. Here $[1/\lambda] = 1$, so on substituting (5) into (8) we have

$$s = [a_0] + \sum_{j=1}^{j=n} [a_j](-t_j) - \left\{ a_0 + \sum_{j=1}^{j=n} a_j(-t_j) \right\}$$

or

$$s = -f_0 - \sum_{j=1}^{j=n} f_j(-t_j) \qquad (9)$$

where f_j denotes the fractional part of a_j. This equation was the starting point for the algorithm described in [1] and [2]. Its relation to the new method is described at the end of this paper.

We will now consider the case $\lambda > 1$. Here we have $[1/\lambda] = 0$, and (8) becomes

$$s = [a_0/\lambda] + \sum_{j=1}^{j=n} [a_j/\lambda](-t_j)$$

or

$$s = b_0 + \sum_{j=1}^{j=n} b_j(-t_j). \qquad (10)$$

Equation (10) represents a new equation which must be satisfied (with nonnegative s) by any integer solution to the original linear programming problem. Thus, we can adjoin (10) to the bottom of (4) and consider it as a possible row in which to pivot. Before proceeding any further, we must assemble certain facts needed for using (10).

In the dual simplex method the only equations, or rows, in which one may pivot are those in which the constant term is negative (this means an unsatisfied inequality). Furthermore, in our notation, only negative elements are eligible pivot elements. Thus, a row is eligible for pivoting only if it starts with a negative constant and contains other negative elements. Clearly, we have

$$a_j < 0 \Rightarrow b_j = [a_j/\lambda] < 0$$

so if the row appearing in (5) is eligible, so is the row in (10) which is derived from it.

We are thus assured that if there are any eligible rows left in (4) we can create from any one of them a new eligible row (10). If there are no eligible rows, the problem has been completed or has no solution.

We shall now try to adjust the new row so that the pivot element will become -1. That this is possible can be seen from the fact that for λ sufficiently large, all negative b_j's become -1's, and all others vanish. So for sufficiently large λ the pivot element can only be -1.

However, as we shall see, we can do better than this. We need one observation.

Let J be the set of indices j, $j \neq 0$, for which $a_j < 0$. Then if the dual simplex rule applied to (10) gives a pivot element $b_{j'} = -1$, we must have

$$\alpha_{j'} = \min_{j \in J} \alpha_j. \tag{11}$$

That is to say, if the pivot does turn out to be -1, the pivot column can only be the (lexicographically) smallest column having a negative entry in the row (5). To see this, we simply apply the usual pivot selection rule, which says that the pivot column is that column $a_{j'}$ for which

$$\left(\frac{-1}{b_{j'}}\right)\alpha_{j'} = \min_{j \in J}\left(\frac{-1}{b_j}\right)\alpha_j.$$

Hence,

$$\frac{-1}{b_{j'}}\alpha_{j'} \leq \frac{-1}{b_j}\alpha_j, \qquad \text{all } j \in J \tag{12}$$

If $b_{j'} = -1$, and b_j is a negative integer,

$$\alpha_{j'} \leq \frac{-1}{b_j}\alpha_j \leq \alpha_j$$

so

$$\alpha_{j'} = \min_{j \in J} \alpha_j.$$

Since the b_j do not enter into the choice of pivot column, the same column will be chosen as pivot column for all those λ which have the property that they produce from (5) a row (10) with pivot element -1. Let us consider two such λ's, λ_1 and λ_2. The result of pivoting on the rows of type (10) will be to add $[b_0/\lambda_1]\,\alpha_{j'}$ or $[b_0/\lambda_2]\,\alpha_{j'}$ to the column of constants (the zero column). Clearly, the zero column, and hence the objective function, will be decreased more if the smaller λ is used, since the pivot column is the same in both cases and only the coefficient is changed. We can summarize this by saying that the requirements for choosing λ are (1) it should produce a pivot of -1, and (2) the λ used should be as small as possible.[2]

Using these two requirements, we shall now select λ. If $\alpha_{j'}$ is the smallest column α_j with $j \in J$, and α_j is another column of the same set, then if $\alpha_{j'}$ is to have a -1 in the new row and be chosen by the simplex rule as pivot column, we must have, for all $j \in J$, $(-1/b_j)\ \alpha_j \geq \alpha_{j'}$. Here b_j is a negative integer. Let μ_j be the largest integer for which $(1/\mu_j)\alpha_j \geq \alpha_{j'}$. (That there are some integers fulfilling this last inequality is clear, since it is satisfied by 1.)[3] In order for $\alpha_{j'}$ to be our pivot column, then, we must have

$$-b_j = -\left[\frac{a_j}{\lambda}\right] \leq \mu_j \tag{13}$$

and the smallest λ fulfilling (13) is

$$\lambda_j = \frac{-a_j}{\mu_j}. \tag{14}$$

We note that λ_j is not necessarily an integer.

In order to fulfill conditions such as the above for all columns α_j, $j \in J$, we must have λ at least as great as

$$\lambda_{\min} = \max_{j \in J} \lambda_j. \tag{15}$$

This choice of λ leads to the selection of $\alpha_{j'}$ as pivot, and for $\alpha_{j'}$ we have $\mu_{j'} = 1$;   hence,

$$\lambda_{\min} \geq \frac{-a_{j'}}{\mu_{j'}} \geq -a_{j'}$$

so

$$\left[\frac{a_{j'}}{\lambda_{\min}}\right] = b_{j'} = -1.$$

We can summarize the procedure for obtaining the minimal λ in these four steps:

1. Select the smallest α_j with $j \in J$; this will be the pivot column α_{j_0}.
2. For each α_j, $j \in J$, find the largest integer μ_j such that

$$\left(\frac{1}{\mu_j}\right)\alpha_j \geq \alpha_{j_0}.$$

[2] This choice of λ is the one which, subject to requirement (1), produces the biggest change in the zero column. It does not necessarily result in replacing the original row (5) by a derived row (10) that is as strong an inequality as is possible or is necessarily either stronger or weaker than the original. For example, from $x = -4 - 3(-t_1) - 5(-t_2)$, we derive for $\lambda = 2$, $s = -2 - 2(-t_1) - 3(-t_2)$; for $\lambda = 3$, $s = -2 - 1(-t_1) - 2(-t_2)$; for $\lambda = 4$, $s = -1 - 1(-t_1) - 2(-t_2)$. Since the variables on the left are required to be nonnegative, these represent the inequalities $3t_1 + 5t_2 \geq 4$, $2t_1 + 3t_2 \geq 2$, $t_1 + 2t_2 \geq 2$, $t_1 + 2t_2 \geq 1$. The second of these is weaker than the first, the third stronger, the last weaker again.

[3] If the relation is satisfied for all integers, the α_j will never be chosen in preference to $\alpha_{j'}$ and the λ_j of (14) may be taken as zero.

3. Set $\lambda_j = \dfrac{-a_j}{\mu_j}$.

4. Find $\lambda_{\min} = \max\limits_{j \in J} \lambda_j$.

Step 2 can usually be accomplished for each column by a single division.[4]

We are now in a position to describe the algorithm.

Assume an all-integer starting matrix A^0 which is dual feasible. We choose a row having a negative constant term (if there are none, the problem has been solved); for this row we choose $\lambda_{\min}$ and the pivot column by the four steps given above. We create a new row of type (10) using this $\lambda_{\min}$ and adjoin this row to the bottom of the matrix A. We now perform Gaussian elimination on the new row; i.e., we introduce s as a new nonbasic variable, we drop the new row, and then repeat this process. Because this pivot element is -1, the matrix remains in integers. A numerical example is attached as an appendix.

We shall next show that for certain rules of choice of row this process is a finite one.

We shall assume that the problem has some integer solution X' which gives the objective function a value z_0.

At any stage of the calculation we have the variables x represented as a constant column plus a sum of nonnegative columns times nonnegative variables (preceded by minus signs).

$$X = \alpha_o + \sum_{j=1}^{j=n} \alpha_j(-t_j). \tag{16}$$

Since any solution must give the t_j nonnegative values, we see that any solution X is lexicographically equal or less than α_0. Furthermore, α_0 is decreased lexicographically after each step, since a negative multiple of one of the columns is added to it. Thus, we have a descending sequence of α_0's

$$\alpha_0 > \alpha_0^1 > \alpha_0^2 \dots > X' \tag{17}$$

bounded below by the assumed solution X'. Let us suppose that we have an infinite sequence of this sort. Since we are dealing with all-integer vectors $\alpha_0, \alpha_0^1, \alpha_0^2, \dots$, the components of the vectors change by integer amounts. Let us consider the first component (the ob-

---

[4] If α_j and α_{jo} both begin with nonzero terms $a_{0,j}$ and $a_{0,jo}$, then if $a_{0,jo}$ does not divide $a_{0,j}$, $\mu_j = [a_{0,j} / a_{0,jo}]$. If $a_{0,jo}$ does divide $a_{0,j}$, then $\mu_j = a_{0,j} / a_{0,jo}$ if $\alpha_j > (a_{0,j} / a_{0,jo}) a_{jo}$, and $\mu_j = (a_{0,j} / a_{0,jo}) - 1$ otherwise. If the two columns begin with unequal numbers of zeros (α_{jo} must have more), μ_j is arbitrarily large and $\lambda_j = 0$. If both columns have p zeros, the procedure is as above with $a_{p,j}$ and $a_{p,jo}$ substituted for $a_{0,jo}$ and $a_{0,jo}$. Also, it is worth noting that μ_{jo} is always 1.

jective function). If this decreased indefinitely, it would eventually get below z_0, the first component of X'. This is a contradiction. Consequently, the first component can only decrease strictly for a finite number of steps and then must remain stationary thereafter at some fixed value $z' \geq z_0$. From this point on, the second component must be nonincreasing. There are now two possibilities: (1) the second component may reach some final value and remain fixed thereafter, or (2) it might decrease indefinitely.

If (1) occurs, we can move on to the third component, which presents the same two alternatives. If alternative (1) occurs for each component, we shall have a fixed α_0 after a finite number of steps. Since α_0 will decrease strictly as long as there are negative elements in the constant column, this means that there are no more such elements and that the problem has been solved. A rule that will guarantee finiteness, then, is one that can exclude possibility (2).

Let us consider the first component for which alternative (2) occurs. After a certain point, the component becomes negative and remains negative. Thus its row is eligible for selection as a row (5). However, it is never selected, for if it were selected, and a row of type (10) generated from it, the pivot column $\alpha_{j'}$ would have a strictly negative coefficient $a_{j'}$ in the row in question, and, upon pivoting, the constant term of the row would be strictly increased. This would contradict the assumed nonincreasing character. Thus any rule which, if the constant term of a row goes negative and remains negative, will sooner or later select that row, will exclude possibility (2), and give a finite algorithm.

Examples of such rules are

1. Always select the first row (from the top) having a negative element.

2. Select the rows by a cyclic process; i.e., on the first step look at the first row, and then, if it does not have a negative constant, look at its successors; on the second step, look at the second row and then its successors, etc.

3. If the rows are chosen at random, a finite process will result with probability 1.

As an example of a rule not covered by this finiteness proof, we cite the ordinary simplex selection rule; that is, choose the row with the largest negative constant term.

The rules of choice we are currently using in computations have evolved partly through a trial-and-error process. Our first attempt was to use the old tried and true simplex rule of choice described above, even though we lacked a finiteness proof for it. We chose at each step the row with largest negative constant and formed the new row from it.   The idea, of course, was that a large negative constant in the original row would, most likely, lead to a reasonably large constant in the new row.   This approach was an almost complete failure. This rule did not seem to solve any but the very smallest problems. As an extreme example, we can cite one seven-variable, seven-inequality problem which we later solved in ten steps but which with this rule ran for 1200 pivots before being taken off the machine.

An approach which does seem to be effective, however, is to focus attention not on the rows but rather on the columns and to construct a new row to make the pivot column as large as possible.   There seem to be two reasons why a column criterion makes more sense here than a rule such as seeking a large negative constant.   One reason is that in this all-integer method an integer multiple of the pivot column is subtracted from the zero column.   Thus the amount of progress is at least as great as the size of the pivot column.   This is in contrast with the ordinary simplex method, where it is possible for a large new column to be brought in at a very small level. Second, when we deal with degeneracies, a common feature of integer programming problems, it is the degree of degeneracy of the columns that makes the essential difference.   That is, in considering any two columns such as

$$\alpha_1 = \begin{bmatrix} 0 \\ 0 \\ 7 \\ -3 \\ 2 \\ 1 \end{bmatrix} \qquad \alpha_2 = \begin{bmatrix} 0 \\ 2 \\ -1 \\ -4 \\ 2 \\ 4 \end{bmatrix}$$

any multiple of α_2 is to be preferred to any multiple of α_1, so here everything is determined by the column and the size of the constant term is secondary.   Consequently, the following approaches seem plausible for this form of integer programming.

First, rank the columns of the matrix as 1, 2, 3, 4, etc. in order of descending size; denote the rank of jth column by $C(j)$.   Then assign to each eligible row the rank

$$R(i) = \max_{j \in J} C(j).$$

This rank $R(i)$ is the rank of the column that would be chosen as pivot column if the ith row were used to generate a new row.   We then choose a row i_0 by

$$R(i_0) = \min_{\text{eligible } i} R(i).$$

A still stronger approach is the following, which we are currently programming. First obtain $R(i)$ values, not only for the eligible rows but for all rows. Then choose a row i_0, either as above or by some other rule such as the largest negative criterion, and form the appropriate new row (10). Next carry out the pivot operation only on the column of constants; i.e., more exactly compute (in a separate place) the numbers $a_{i,0} + b_0 a_{i,j_0}$. Consider the rows i for which this expression is negative. These are the rows whose constants would be negative after the pivot step. If among these rows there are some with rank strictly lower than $R(i_0)$, select one, say i_1. If a_{i_1,j_0} times the row of the b_j's is added to the i_1 row, a new row is formed with constant term $a_{i_1,0} + b_0 a_{i_1,j_0}$, which is negative. This new row has a rank strictly smaller than $R(i_0)$, since its entry in the j_0 column is zero and its entries in columns having rank $> R(i_0)$ are nonnegative. This last follows from the definition of rank, which shows that both rows involved have this property and from the fact that $a_{i_1,j_0} \geq 0$ because $R(i_1) < R(i_0)$. This process can now be iterated, with the newly created combined row playing the role of the original row i_0, and being used to create new b_j's, etc.[5] The basic idea here is to use the fact that in attempting to satisfy the inequality represented by the row i_0, we violate the inequality represented by the row i_1 to revise the new row and improve the rank of the pivot column.

Although one's first reaction to this sort of scheme is that the computation involved in these selection methods is excessive, a more detailed examination shows that the amount of work required can be expected to be much less than that required for a full pivot step. Thus, if the number of pivot steps is reduced substantially, these methods will be worthwhile.

The method we have used in our code so far has been only a very crude approximation of the above. The rule divides into two parts: (1) if all the relative cost coefficients, i.e., the $a_{0,j}$, $j \neq 0$, are nonzero, that is to say, if we are in a completely nondegenerate situation, we have used the old simplex rule choosing the row with the largest negative constant. (2) If some of the $a_{0,j}$ are zero, we form the function $N(j)$, which is a count of the number of zeros at the head of each column before a positive number is encountered. We then use $N(j)$, which is an approximation to the ranking of the columns, as the $C(j)$ of the first method described above.

Using this code, we have had irregular but interesting results. For example, we have a series of four 15-variable, 15-inequality problems

---

[5] In this process only the last row generated is actually used in pivoting. Thus, it is unnecessary to choose an optimal λ except in dealing with this last row. For all others $\lambda = -b_{j_0}$ will suffice to provide -1 somewhere in the smallest column.

arising from coding theory. The inequalities in the four problems are identical, except that the constant terms in the inequalities are increased by adding 2 to get from one problem to the next. All coefficients of the variables remain the same. Three of the problems are solved in 17, 21, and 23 pivot steps, respectively. Of the fourth we know only that it requires, with this code, over 400 pivot steps. A similar series of three 32×32 problems involved 23 and 156 iterations (this last took three minutes on the IBM 704), with a third problem unsolved after 200. Although in other sparser problems the results have been less irregular, there are still plenty of failures. There are indications that the procedures described above are worth investigating.

We shall now consider the relation of this all-integer method to the method of [1] and [2].

The derivation of the inequalities given earlier in this paper shows that both the algorithm described here and the algorithm of [1] and [2] are extreme cases. In [1] and [2] only inequalities of the $\lambda = 1$ type were used, whereas here only inequalities of the $\lambda > 1$ type were involved.[6] Inequalities of the $\lambda = 1$ type will give nontrivial eligible rows whenever there are nonintegers present in the zero column whether there are any negative elements there or not. However, these inequalities are not available if we have an all-integer matrix. On the other hand, the inequalities of $\lambda > 1$ type are available whenever there are negative elements in the zero column, but fail if the zero column is all nonnegative but possibly containing nonintegers.

The various states of the zero column with the corresponding available types of inequality are summarized in Table 1.

Table 1

	Negative constants	No negative constants
Some nonintegers	$\lambda = 1, \lambda > 1$	$\lambda = 1$
All integers	$\lambda > 1$	Solution

It is clearly possible to combine both classes of inequalities into algorithms having many interesting properties. For example, one could start by doing the regular simplex method to get somewhere near a solution or possibly to obtain a noninteger solution. Then from some point on, one could pivot only on additional rows generated either for $\lambda = 1$ or $\lambda > 1$. One type or the other is always available. Since the pivot element is either -1 or a proper fraction $-f_j$, the D–number described in [2] will now be monotone decreasing. Another approach would be to set in advance a bound for D

[6] Note that the derivation of the inequalities does not depend on the a_j being integers.

and to switch to additional rows whenever a pivot element of the ordinary simplex method would violate the bound on D. Operating with a fixed D means that round-off problems can be eliminated. There are obviously many combined algorithms that are possible, and we have no idea which are better than others.

APPENDIX

Example

Integer Programming

$$\min z' = 10x_1 + 14x_2 + 21x_3$$

or

$$\max z = (-10x_1 + 14x_2 + 21x_3)$$

subject to

$$8x_1 + 11x_2 + 9x_3 \geq 12$$
$$2x_1 + 2x_2 + 7x_3 \geq 14$$
$$9x_1 + 6x_2 + 3x_3 \geq 10.$$

The row marked with an arrow is used at each step.

$$j_0 = 1$$

$$\mu_1 = \left\lceil \frac{10}{10} \right\rceil = 1 \qquad \mu_2 = \left\lceil \frac{14}{10} \right\rceil = 1 \qquad \mu_3 = \left\lceil \frac{21}{10} \right\rceil = 2$$

$$\lambda_1 = \frac{2}{\mu_1} = 2 \qquad \lambda_2 = \frac{2}{\mu_2} = 2 \qquad \lambda_3 = \frac{7}{\mu_3} = \frac{7}{2}$$

$$\lambda_{\min} = \max\left(2, 2, \frac{7}{2}\right) = \frac{7}{2}$$

(1)

	1	$-x_1$	$-x_2$	$-x_3$
$z =$	0	10	14	21
$s_1 =$	-12	-8	-11	-9
$s_2 =$	-14	-2	-2	$-7\leftarrow$
$s_3 =$	-10	-9	-6	-3
$x_1 =$	0	-1	0	0
$x_2 =$	0	0	-1	0
$x_3 =$	0	0	0	-1
$\bar{s}_1 =$	-4	-1^*	-1	-2
$\lambda =$	$\frac{7}{2}$			

(2)

	1	$-\bar{s}_1$	$-x_2$	$-x_3$
$z =$	-40	10	4	1
$s_1 =$	20	-8	-3	7
$s_2 =$	-6	-2	0	$-3\leftarrow$
$s_3 =$	26	-9	3	15
$x_1 =$	4	-1	1	2
$x_2 =$	0	0	-1	0
$x_3 =$	0	0	0	-1
$\bar{s}_2 =$	-2	-1	0	-1^*
$\lambda =$	3			

(3)

	1	$-\bar{s}_1$	$-x_2$	$-\bar{s}_2$
$z =$	-42	9	4	1
$s_1 =$	6	-15	-3	7
$s_2 =$	0	1	0	-3
$s_3 =$	-4	-24	3	$15\leftarrow$
$x_1 =$	0	-3	1	2
$x_2 =$	0	0	-1	0
$x_3 =$	2	1	0	-1
$\bar{s}_3 =$	-1	-1^*	0	0
$\lambda =$	24			

(4)

	1	$-\bar{s}_3$	$-x_2$	$-\bar{s}_2$
$z =$	-51	9	4	1
$s_1 =$	21	-15	-3	7
$s_2 =$	-1	1	0	$-3\leftarrow$
$s_3 =$	20	-24	3	15
$x_1 =$	3	-3	1	2
$x_2 =$	0	0	-1	0
$x_3 =$	1	1	0	-1
$\bar{s}_4 =$	-1	0	0	-1^*
$\lambda =$	3			

(5)

	1	$-\bar{s}_3$	$-x_2$	$-\bar{s}_4$
$z =$	-52	9	4	1
$s_1 =$	14	-15	-3	7
$s_2 =$	2	1	0	-3
$s_3 =$	5	-24	3	15
$x_1 =$	1	-3	1	2
$x_2 =$	0	0	-1	0
$x_3 =$	2	1	0	-1

Solution $z' = 52$

$$x_1 = 1, \qquad x_2 = 0, \qquad x_3 = 2$$

Same Example Reworked by the Row Combination Method

(1) the first step is the same, since no higher-ranking inequalities are made negative by the pivot step.

(2)

Column Rank		1	2	3	
	1	$-\bar{s}_1$	$-x_2$	$-x_3$	Row
$z =$	-40	10	4	1	Rank
$s_1 =$	20	-8	-3	7	2
$s_2 =$	-6	-2	0	-3	$3\leftarrow$
$s_3 =$	26	-9	3	15	1
$x_1 =$	4	-1	1	2	1
$x_2 =$	0	0	-1	0	2
$x_3 =$	0	0	0	-1	3
$\bar{s}_2 =$	-1	-1^*	0	0	

Selecting the only negative row, we obtain, as before, the row $(-2, -1, 0, -1)$. However, its use would drive the lower-ranking s_3 row negative. Combining $15(-2, -1, 0, -1) + (26, -9, 3, 15) = (-4, -24, 3, 0)$, a row of rank 1. Applying $\lambda = 24$ gives $(-1, -1, 0, 0)$. No iteration of the process is possible, so this is used.

$$
\begin{array}{c}
(3) \\
\begin{array}{lrrrr}
 & 1 & -\bar{s}_3 & -x_2 & -x_3 \\
z = & -50 & 10 & 4 & 1 \\
s_1 = & 28 & -8 & -3 & 7 \\
s_2 = & -4 & -2 & 0 & -3\leftarrow \\
s_3 = & 35 & -9 & 3 & 15 \\
x_1 = & 5 & -1 & 1 & 2 \\
x_2 = & 0 & 0 & -1 & 0 \\
x_3 = & 0 & 0 & 0 & -1 \\
\hline
\bar{s}_3 = & -2 & -1 & 0 & -1^* \\
\lambda = & 3 & & &
\end{array}
\end{array}
\qquad
\begin{array}{c}
(4) \\
\begin{array}{lrrrr}
 & 1 & -\bar{s}_3 & -x_2 & -\bar{s}_4 \\
z = & -52 & 9 & 4 & 1 \\
s_1 = & 14 & -15 & -3 & 7 \\
s_2 = & 2 & 1 & 0 & -3 \\
s_3 = & 5 & -24 & 3 & 15 \\
x_1 = & 1 & -3 & 1 & 2 \\
x_2 = & 0 & 0 & -1 & 0 \\
x_3 = & 2 & 1 & 0 & -1
\end{array}
\end{array}
$$

REFERENCES

1. Gomory, Ralph E., "Outline of an Algorithm for Integer Solutions to Linear Programs," *Bulletin of the American Mathematical Society* **64**, 5 (1958).

2. Gomory, Ralph E., "An Algorithm for Integer Solutions to Linear Programs," Princeton-IBM Mathematics Research Project Technical Report No. 1 (Nov. 17, 1958).

3. Dantzig, G. B., L. R. Ford, Jr., and D. R. Fulkerson, "A Primal-Dual Algorithm for Linear Programs," in Annals Study 38, *Linear Inequalities and Related Systems*, Kuhn and Tucker, eds., Princeton N.J.: Princeton University Press, 1956.

14

Computational Experience with Integer Programming for Job=shop Scheduling

Alfred E. Story, Harvey M. Wagner

C. BREWER AND COMPANY, LTD.
and
STANFORD UNIVERSITY

1. INTRODUCTION

This paper reports on computational experience in solving a particular model of job-shop sequencing: n items are to be sequenced through each of three machines, I, II, and III; an item cannot proceed to machine II (III) before it has finished being processed on machine I (II); the processing time of each item on each machine is determinate; an optimal sequence is one which minimizes total elapsed time to complete all jobs on all machines.[1] The three-machine model is distinguished by the fact that no elementary algorithm exists giving a general solution, but it can be shown [3] that there always exists an optimal ordering for which the items are sequenced identically on each machine. This latter property of the three-machine model implies that if the items are numbered $1, 2, \ldots, n$, then we

[1] A comprehensive survey of general job-shop sequencing models is found in [3]; this reference includes a complete statement of the underlying assumptions.

A paper presented at the Factory Scheduling Conference, Carnegie Institute of Technology, May 10-12, 1961. This work has been supported in part by a grant from the Western Management Sciences Institute and in part by the Stanford Computation Center. The participation of Alfred E. Story was also sponsored in part by the National Science Foundation.

need only search for a permutation of the numbers 1, 2, . . ., n, out of the total $n!$ possible permutations. It has been shown elsewhere [3, 4] that the sequencing problem is mathematically equivalent to an integer linear programming model, and consequently the problem is potentially solvable by means of the recent developments in integer linear programming algorithms [1, 2].

In Section 2 we explore several simple heuristic techniques for obtaining trial permutations. The failures of these approaches lend insight to the inherent difficulties that must be overcome by a general method of solution. The integer linear programming model is summarized in Section 3. Experience in using integer programming codes is reported in Section 4; we comment on various modifications to accelerate the speed of obtaining solutions. Section 5 discusses work now in progress and anticipated.

2. FAILURES OF SIMPLE RULES

In order to place a proper focus on the need for as complex an algorithm as integer programming, we study a number of relatively simple rules for arriving at a trial solution permutation. Clearly, for n large, complete enumeration of the $n!$ permutations is out of the question; if $n=10$, the number of permutations is in excess of 3.6 million. By means of simple rules we can essentially restrict consideration to only a small subset of possible permutations, and select an ordering which is optimal within this subset.

The first simple rule we discuss might be termed a gradient procedure. Begin with a trial permutation. Then investigate "neighboring" permutations, and use a new trial ordering if an improvement is found. The procedure is repeated with the new permutation; i.e., the new set of neighboring permutations is investigated. Specifically, we tried sets of rules which investigated as neighboring permutations those that can be found by one of the following methods:

1. pairwise interchanges,
2. end around cycling,
3. order reversal,

of the items in a trial ordering. In Table 1 we give an example showing the inability of these rules to find a true optimal ordering. Observe that permutation 15 is optimal. If the initial trial solution is permutation 18, then by rule 1 it is possible to reach the neighboring orderings 5, 12, 13, 16, 17, and 24, all of which increase the elapsed time. By rule 2 it is possible to reach the neighboring orderings 4 and 21, both of which increase the elapsed time; a further repetition of rule 2 gives ordering 7, which also is not an improvement.

By rule 3 permutation 2 is found, and continued end around cycling yields permutations 12, 13, and 23, none showing any decrease in the elapsed time.

The second rule we tried might be termed a dynamic procedure. Select any two items and find the optimal ordering according to the criterion of minimum elapsed time. Arbitrarily select a third item, and, maintaining the precedence relation established for the initial two items, find the best ordering with the third item added—this means testing three possibilities, viz., placing the third item in front of, between, and following the previous two. Arbitrarily select a fourth item, and, maintaining the precedence relation established for the initial three items, find the best ordering with the fourth item added, and so forth. This method requires investigating $0.5(n-1)$

Table 1 Process times.

		Machine		
		I	II	III
Item	1	3	10	4
	2	4	1	5
	3	4	8	6
	4	6	4	1

Permutation number	Permutation	Elapsed time	
1	1234	29	
2	1243	32	
3	1324	33	
4	1342	33	
5	1423	32	
6	1432	36	
7	2134	32	
8	2143	35	
9	2314	31	
10	2341	34	
11	2413	38	
12	2431	36	
13	3124	32	
14	3142	32	
15	3214	28	Global optimum
16	3241	32	
17	3412	35	
18	3421	31	Local optimum
19	4123	35	
20	4132	39	
21	4213	37	
22	4231	36	
23	4312	37	
24	4321	33	

$(n + 2)$ precedence relations rather than $n!$. In Table 2 the rule is tested with the same example as in Table 1; items 1, 2, and 3 are used. If items 2 and 3 are first selected to be ordered, the optimal sequence is 2, 3. But the optimal sequence for all three items is 3, 2, 1, which reverses the previous ordering of items 2 and 3.

Table 2

Items 2 and 3			
Permutation number	Permutation	Elapsed time	
1	23	22	Optimal
2	32	23	

Items 1, 2, and 3			
Permutation number	Permutation	Elapsed time	
1	123	28	
2	213	31	
3	312	31	
4	132	32	
5	231	30	
6	321	27	Optimal

A word must be said about the methodology of testing simple rules. If the composite of simple rules includes many possibilities, then for small n, all permutations are likely to be enumerated. Consequently, in studying the efficacy of simple rules, one must either be modest in the number of rules encompassed in the composite or be sufficiently generous in the setting of n for the test examples. We found it helpful to have available a computer routine giving a complete listing of all permutations and their elapsed time values; by having such a listing for sample cases, it was possible to test rapidly whether a set of rules produced convergence to an optimal solution from an arbitrary initial permutation.

3. A LINEAR PROGRAMMING FORMULATION

In this section we indicate the statement of the job sequencing problem as a linear programming model [4] wherein the variables are constrained to be integer-valued. Let

$$x_{ij} = \begin{cases} 1, & \text{if item } i \text{ is scheduled in order-position } j \\ 0, & \text{if item } i \text{ is not scheduled in order-position } j. \end{cases}$$

For example, if $n=4$ and we wish to represent the permutation 3, 1, 4, 2, then we set $x_{12}=x_{24}=x_{31}=x_{43}=1$ and all other $x_{ij}=0$. Since in the three-machine case an optimal ordering exists in which

the items are sequenced identically on each machine, it is not necessary to add a superscript to x_{ij} to denote a machine.

The first set of constraints is identical to that for an assignment
problem.

$$\sum_i x_{ij} = 1, \quad \text{one of the items is assigned to order-position } j$$

$$\sum_j x_{ij} = 1, \quad \text{one of the order positions is assigned to item } i. \quad (1)$$

In addition to (1), we impose timing restrictions so that an item is
not processed on two machines at once and a machine is not processing two items at once. The nature of the constraints is illustrated
in Figure 1 for machines II and III. We translate the timing restrictions in Figure 1 into algebraic notation. We employ the designa-
tion "kth item" to mean that item which is in order-position k for
a given sequence.

Let s_k^h = time on machine h between the end of the kth item and
the start of the $k + 1$st item

u_k^h = time between end of the kth item on machine h and the
start of the kth item on machine $h + 1$

$X_{\cdot j} = [x_{1j}, x_{2j}, \ldots, x_{nj}]$

$[L]$ = row vector of processing times for items $1, 2, \ldots, n$ on
machine I

$[M]$ = row vector of processing times for items $1, 2, \ldots, n$ on
machine II

$[N]$ = row vector of processing times for items $1, 2, \ldots, n$ on
machine III.

Then we have for the constraint in Figure 1

$$s_k^{\mathrm{II}} + MX_{\cdot k+1} + u_{k+1}^{\mathrm{II}} = u_k^{\mathrm{II}} + NX_{\cdot k} + s_k^{\mathrm{III}}, \quad k = 1, 2, \ldots, n - 1. \quad (2)$$

In Table 3 we give a complete schematic tableau for the three machine
case with $n=6$. The criterion of minimal elapsed time is stated in
an equivalent form [3, 4] of minimal total idle time on machine III.

Interval letter			Interval letter
A	Time on machine II between end of kth item and start of $k+1$st item	Time between end of kth item on machine II and start of kth item on machine III	D
	+	+	
B	Time on machine II to process $k+1$st item	Time on machine III to process kth item	E
	+	+	
C	Time between end of $k+1$st item on machine II and start of $k+1$st item on machine III	Time on machine III between end of kth item and start of $k+1$st item	F

Figure 1

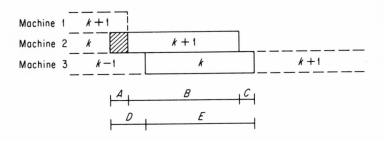

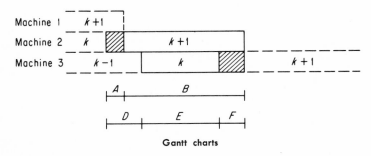

Gantt charts

Table 3 Tableau of detached coefficients.

		$X_{.1}$	$X_{.2}$	$X_{.3}$	$X_{.4}$	$X_{.5}$	$X_{.6}$	S^{II}	S^{III}	U^I		U^{II}	
	$\begin{cases}0\\0\\0\\0\\0\end{cases}$	M	$-L$					1		-1			
$n-1=5$			M	$-L$				1		1	-1		
				M	$-L$			1			1	-1	
					M	$-L$		1				1	-1
						M	$-L$	1					$1 -1$
	$\begin{cases}0\\0\\0\\0\\0\end{cases}$	N	$-M$					-1	1	-1			
$n-1=5$			N	$-M$				-1	1	1	-1		
				N	$-M$			-1	1		1	-1	
					N	$-M$		-1	1			1	-1
						N	$-M$	-1	1				$1 -1$
$\begin{matrix}2n-1\\=11\end{matrix}$	$\begin{cases}1\\1\\.\\.\\.\\1\end{cases}$	Assignment problem matrix							$4(n-1)=20$ variables				

$\underbrace{\qquad\qquad}_{n^2 = 36 \text{ variables}}$

Minimize

$$(L + M)X_{.1} + (1\ 1\ \ldots\ 1)S^{III}$$

where $X_{.j} = [x_{1j}, x_{2j}, \ldots, x_{6j}]; \ S^{(h)} = [s_1^h, s_2^h, \ldots, s_5^h]; \ U^{(h)} = [u_2^h, u_3^h, \ldots, u_6^h].$

A rule for obtaining a trial solution which is simple but somewhat more sophisticated than those discussed in Section 2 is to solve the linear programming model, the integer value constraints being ignored, and then to round the x_{ij} solution values to integers [starting, say, with the x_{ij} closest to 1 and maintaining feasibility in relations (1)]. In Table 4 we give a numerical example with its linear programming

Table 4 Process times

		Machines		
		I	II	III
Item	1	4	1	4
	2	5	8	20
	3	6	30	6
	4	30	4	5

Simplex solution

			Position		
		1st	2nd	3rd	4th
Item	1		.08	.11	.81
	2	1.00			
	3		.83	.08	.09
	4		.09	.81	.10

Rounded solution: 2, 3, 4, 1
Associated span: 58
Optimal solution: 2, 1, 3, 4
Associated span: 56

solution. The obvious rounded solution gives the ordering 2, 3, 4, 1 having elapsed time 58, whereas the optimal ordering is 2, 1, 3, 4 having elapsed time 56.

4. COMPUTATIONAL TESTS OF INTEGER PROGRAMMING ALGORITHMS

The integer programming algorithms we employed were based on approaches suggested by the publications of R. Gomory. Using an IBM 7090 computer, we attempted to solve with an "all-integer dual algorithm"[2] a number of test cases. At each iteration of the algorithm the current tableau contained all-integer coefficients; a trial solution was integer-valued but not necessarily nonnegative. Subsequently, using a Burroughs 220 computer, we explored variants on Gomory's first algorithm [1], which usually starts after an optimal simplex solution that is not all-integer-valued is obtained.

We performed our intensive tests of the IBM 7090 integer programming package IP03 with the set of problems listed in Tables 5A–5F. In each set we let the initial problem be a four-item model—items 1, 2, 3, and 4—and then constructed five more models by adding, one at a time, a new item to the previous list. For those models where we were able to obtain solutions, we indicate in Table 5 an optimal ordering and the associated time span. Our computational experience

[2] The program, written by IBM, is entitled IPO3.

using the IBM 7090 routine is summarized in Table 6. We show the size of each of the models, the total number of possible permutations, and the number of integer programming iterations at the termination of the computations. An iteration was logged for each pivot operation that occurred. In several of the cases, the symbol 1000* appears, and indicates that we terminated the computer run at 1000 iterations but had not yet obtained an optimal solution. With but one exception, the number of iterations increased with the number of items encompassed in a model. As a corollary, whenever a model required more than

Table 5 Process times and optimal sequence (if available).

A

Item	Machine			Optimal sequence of n items	Optimal idle time on machine III
	I	II	III		
1	5	8	20		
2	6	30	6		
3	30	4	5		
4	2	5	3	4123	22
5	3	10	4	41235	25
6	4	1	4	412365	22
7	8	7	2	4123567 (4123657)	25
8	16	10	4	not obtained	
9	2	4	12	not obtained	

B

Item	Machine			Optimal sequence of n items	Optimal idle time on machine III
	I	II	III		
1	9	13	6		
2	7	7	20		
3	6	4	8		
4	8	3	10	3421	10
5	20	7	2	32145	13
6	10	2	13	342165	10
7	7	10	7	3421675	10
8	2	8	5	34216785	10
9	6	13	6	not obtained	

C

Item	Machine			Optimal sequence of n items	Optimal idle time on machine III
	I	II	III		
1	6	7	3		
2	12	2	3		
3	4	6	8		
4	3	11	7	3412	13
5	6	8	10	35412	11
6	2	14	12	356241	14
7	19	1	6	not obtained	
8	9	9	3	not obtained	
9	10	9	8	not obtained	

D

Item	Machine			Optimal sequence of n items	Optimal idle time on machine III
	I	II	III		
1	4	5	5		
2	2	17	7		
3	2	10	4		
4	10	8	2	2134	26
5	7	15	6	21354	35
6	9	4	11	213654	28
7	1	12	6	7123654	33
8	2	3	8	71236854	28
9	7	6	6	712396854	28

E

Item	Machine			Optimal sequence of n items	Optimal idle time on machine III
	I	II	III		
1	9	1	5		
2	12	1	13		
3	8	6	7		
4	11	9	10	2413	19
5	5	13	6	not obtained	
6	12	3	9	not obtained	
7	9	3	13	not obtained	
8	8	14	6	not obtained	
9	1	1	7	not obtained	

F

Item	Machine			Optimal sequence of n items	Optimal idle time on machine III
	I	II	III		
1	15	5	14		
2	7	4	2		
3	9	14	18		
4	28	11	9	3412	30
5	1	17	4	31542	28
6	1	8	3	not obtained	
7	6	15	10	not obtained	
8	11	8	12	not obtained	
9	6	15	3	not obtained	

Table 6 Iterations using IPO3.

	4	5	6	7	8	9
Number of items $n =$	4	5	6	7	8	9
Number of variables $=$	28	41	56	73	92	113
Number of constraints $=$	13	17	21	25	29	33
Table 5A	261	613	807	85	1000*	1000*
Table 5B	31	71	83	105	283	1000*
Table 5C	59	141	891	1000*	1000*	1000*
Table 5D	37	46	55	78	538	545
Table 5E	261	1000*	1000*	1000*	1000*	1000*
Table 5F	62	323	1000*	1000*	1000*	1000*
Number of permutations $n! =$	24	120	720	5,040	40,320	362,880

1000 iterations for solution, we were unable to attain a solution for any larger version of the model; in only one instance were we able to obtain a solution to a nine-item problem. In the three most successful cases, Tables 5A, 5B, and 5D, adding a new item had little or no effect on the previous optimal ordering. For the smaller models—four, five, and six items—the number of iterations often exceeded the total number of possible permutations. We concluded from these tests that this particular programming approach did not seem well suited for solving machine scheduling problems.[3]

Our second group of trial tests was conducted on a Burroughs 220 and mainly explored various techniques for solving the four-item problem in Table 5A. All the techniques considered were variants on Gomory's original notion [1] of starting with an optimal simplex solution and adding constraints until an integer solution is found. In carrying out this approach, a decision must be made on the following questions: What equation for a current basic nonintegral-valued variable should be selected for the purpose of generating a new constraint? How should the new constraint be formed, if we are given the source equation just selected? We considered several possibilities for each of these decisions.

We formulated eight schemes for selecting the basic variable and its corresponding equation on which to form the new constraint:

1. Select a basic variable having the largest fractional part.
2. Select an x_{ij} closest to .5.
3. Select an $x_{ij} < 1$ closest to 1.
4. Select an $x_{ij} > 0$ closest to 0.
5. Select an $x_{ij} < 1$ closest to 1; whenever the objective function has a fractional part, force the value of the objective function to the next integer level.
6. Select an x_{ij} closest to .5; whenever the objective function has a fractional part, force the value of the objective function to the next integer level.
7. Add several constraints simultaneously: one for each basic variable having a fractional part.
8. Select the equation by following a sequential (cyclic) order; whenever the objective function has a fractional part, force the value of the objective function to the next integer level.

Several comments on these rules are warranted. Methods 1 and 3

---

[3] We believe that research of this nature must be approached from an experimental point of view, in that on the basis of accumulated experience one must at some point decide whether a method being tested warrants further research or whether some alternative method appears more promising. There is no guarantee that a discarded approach will not turn out ultimately to be the best available method.

may operate identically for many problems.   It is necessary to specify a tolerance factor α to determine whether a variable has reached an integer value; this tolerance factor is crucial in employing methods 3, 4, and 5.   We used $\alpha = .0001$ and $.00001$.   In applying methods 1 through 6, we often observed that the same basic variable kept being selected; this tendency resulted in no significant change in the objective function value.   Such persistency in selection can be alleviated to some extent by relaxing the tolerance factor, but this expedient has its obvious limitations.   Method 8, and to some extent method 7, are attempts to correct this same problem.   Methods 5, 6, and 8 explicitly recognize that the objective function must have an integer value; consequently, whenever a trial solution produced a fractional part in the value of the objective function, we forced the objective function to the next integer level.   It was hoped that this forcing technique would accelerate convergence.

We also viewed several methods for generating new constraints:

1. Gomory's all-integer method [1].
2. Gomory's mixed-integer method [2],
   a. where only the x_{ij} are declared integer-valued;
   b. where all the variables described in Section 3 are declared integer-valued.

Table 7 Four-item model in Table 5A.

Optimal integer solution obtained

Algorithmic method	Number of iterations at termination	Number of additional constraints at termination
1–1	50	3
1–3	50	3
2a–2	62	6
2a–3	62	8
2b–3	65	10

Optimal integer solution not obtained; optimal value of objective function obtained

Algorithmic method	Number of iterations at termination	Number of additional constraints at termination
1–2	197	36
1–5	84	21
1–8	79	15
2b–6	78	11

Optimal integer solution and optimal value of objective function not obtained

Algorithmic method	Number of iterations at termination	Number of additional constraints at termination
1–4	50	10
1–6	81	21
2a–4	76	10
2a–7	54	21

Whereas one would expect a priori that method 1 would be superior to method 2 on a given problem, since the former method takes full account of all variables being integer, we did have a test case where method 2 proved better, Table 7.

We did not try all possible combinations of each of the eight methods above coupled with each of the generating approaches. The results of 13 cases we did test, utilizing the four-item model in Table 5A, fall into the categories (a) optimal integer solution was obtained; (b) iterations terminated before optimal integer solution was obtained, but the objective function had reached its optimal value; and (c) iterations terminated before optimal integer solution was obtained, and the objective function had not reached its optimal value.[4] In Table 7 we summarize the results from the 13 cases. It can be seen immediately that the evidence is not conclusive for selecting a best approach. On the basis of the limited testing, generating method 1 looks only negligibly better than methods 2a and 2b. (Method 1 was tested further, as will be reported in the analysis of Table 8 below.)

Table 8

4-Item model	Number of iterations at termination	Number of additional constraints at termination
Table 5A	28	1
Table 5B	38	2
Table 5C	85	22
Table 5E	322	118 Solution not obtained at termination
Table 5F	27	1

Selecting the $x_{ij} < 1$ closest to 1 looks better than selecting x_{ij} closest to .5. And selecting $x_{ij} > 0$ closest to 0 does not appear promising. Methods 5,6, and 8 never produced an optimal integer solution in the tests. This latter result was disheartening, for it was hoped that the forcing approach would appreciably accelerate convergence to an optimal integer solution. To obtain additional insight on this latter point another experiment was performed, as we describe in the next paragraph.

The forcing methods 5, 6, and 8 did, in the foregoing tests, bring the value of the objective function to its optimal level rather rapidly, but then the iterative process stalled in trying to find an optimal integer solution. We wished to explore how rapidly we might discover an optimal integer solution if we began the iterative process with a constraint specifying the optimal value of the objective function (which we knew from our previous analyses). We used the four-item models in Tables 5A, 5C, 5E, and 5F, and generated equations according to method 1-8. Our findings are given in Table 8. The results

[4] The iteration count includes the number of iterations to obtain the simplex solution.

are erratic, to say the least.   The problem from Table 5A was rapidly solved under this approach, as was the problem from Table 5F. But in three other problems the method in Table 6, which did not assume as given the optimal objective function value, produced an optimal answer in fewer iterations.

5. CONCLUSIONS AND FUTURE RESEARCH

One conclusion is evident from the tests: we have not yet found an integer programming method that can be relied upon to solve most machine sequencing problems rapidly.   We believe that future study must concentrate on deriving methods which more fully take into account the special structure of machine sequencing problems, which avoid repetitively selecting the same basic variable to generate a new constraint, and which are capable of finding quickly an integer solution when the optimal objective value has indeed been obtained.   A supplementary effort should be the devising of efficient approaches for finding generating equations that force the objective function to change; such methods would reduce the number of iterations necessary to reach the optimal objective function value.[5] Research of this nature is currently underway by the authors.

[5] It is a straightforward matter to devise a rule to determine whether a basic variable exists such that an equation generated from this basic relation will result in a change in the objective function.   The issue is to find, if possible, rapidly performed tests for ascertaining such relations.

REFERENCES

1. Gomory, R. E., "Outline of an Algorithm" for Integer Solutions to Linear Programs," *Bulletin of the American Mathematics Society* **64** (1958), 275-78.

2. Gomory, R. E., "Mixed Integer Programming Algorithm," unpublished RAND memorandum, RM2597, 1960.

3. Sisson, R. L., "Sequencing Theory," Chapter 7 in *Progress in Operations Research*, R. L., Ackoff, ed., New York: John Wiley & Sons, Inc., 1961.

4. Wagner, H. M., "An Integer Programming Model for Machine Scheduling," *Naval Research Logistics Quarterly* **6** (1959), 131-140.

IV

Simulation of Scheduling Procedures and Scheduling Performance

With the exception of the special case considered by Johnson (Chapter 2), the exact approaches (complete enumeration and integer programming) to solving scheduling problems have met with limited success (see Chapters 3 and 14). The most prominent difficulty connected with exact algorithms is the fact that the number of computations tends to rise rapidly (as the cube or exponentially) with the size of the problem. On the other hand, computational difficulty in simulation tends to increase linearly with the size of the problem. For this reason, simulation efforts have already found limited practical application as well as eliciting a great deal of theoretical study.

In Chapter 15, Henry Fischer and Gerald L. Thompson discuss "Probabilistic Learning Combinations of Local Job-Shop Scheduling Rules." A local job-shop scheduling or loading rule is one that can be applied by an operator of a machine to select one of the items in the queue before his machine to work on. The two rules considered here are the SIO rule (put that job on the machine that you can finish first) and LRT rule (work on the job that has the most unfinished work remaining). On the hypothesis that there are some situations in which one rule is likely to be preferable to the other,

Fischer and Thompson developed a computer program that simply tries probabilistic combinations of these rules and modifies its probability of choosing each of these rules according to the relative success or failure it has experienced with their use in the past. Their experiments show that learning is possible in this sense, but that such learning does not do significantly better than an unbiased random conbination of the same local scheduling rules. However, the unbiased random combination is considerably better than any given rule applied singly. The authors have thus made a start on an interesting line of attack on the scheduling problem.

A very similar idea is pursued by Morton Allen in "The Efficient Utilization of Labor under Conditions of Fluctuating Demand," Chapter 16. He considers a job shop that is closing down its operations and must finish its backlog of orders. He simulates the effect of the same two loading rules (SIO and LRT) and evaluates them with regard to their labor utilization effectiveness. He also compares them with random priority rules, and considers the effect of alternate routing. From experience gained with these, he constructs a switching rule that uses one of the local rules for a while and then, at a given a time, starts using the other. The two-class switching rule proved to give the best results. The results of his study demonstrate that such strategies in the use of loading rules can be quite effective.

The shortest operation (SIO) rule is the subject for analysis by R. W. Conway and W. L. Maxwell in "Network Scheduling by the Shortest-Operation Discipline," Chapter 17. They consider first a simple shop with n jobs and one machine and show that all rules that are independent of processing time are equivalent, while the shortest-operation rule is optimal. Essentially the same result is shown to hold for simple queuing systems with exponentially distributed arrival times. They then characterize a job shop as a network of queues and conjecture that the above-mentioned results will continue to hold for a job shop. Results of simulation runs give support to this conjecture, and also show that the results are not strongly dependent on the transition matrix of the job shop. Further simulation runs were made to show that accurate time estimates for job times are not necessary for the shortest-operation rule to be effective. The paper then concludes with a discussion of the drawbacks of the shortest-operation rule and suggestions for circumventing them.

In Chapter 18, John F. Muth uses simulation runs to study "The Effect of Uncertainty in Job Times on Optimal Schedules." In order to study in isolation this one kind of error and its effect on scheduling times, he uses the two-machine model and optimal decision rule of S. M. Johnson discussed in Chapter 2. Schedules drawn at random from the population of active schedules were compared with the schedules generated by Johnson's rule under perfect and imperfect information concerning job times. Job times were selected by independent drawings from the bivariate log normal distribution. In some cases job times on the two machines were either positively or negatively correlated. The means and variance of job times were varied, as was the length of the job list. The results of the simulation runs show that forecast errors in job times have relatively little effect on the total schedule time. In fact, Muth estimates that about 90 percent of the difference between good and bad schedules can be attributed to the scheduling procedure, whereas only 10 percent can be attributed to the improvement of knowledge of processing time. These results agree with similar conclusions drawn by Conway and Maxwell in the preceding chapter.

Simulation studies used to support mathematical conjectures concerning queuing systems subject to "dynamic-priority" rules are the subject of Chapter 19, "Queues with Dynamic Priority Discipline," by James R. Jackson. He assumes that each customer in a queue will have his scheduled start times determined as the sum of his arrival time plus an "urgency number," which is drawn from a fixed probability distribution. Jackson then conjectures that, if $u < v$ are urgency numbers and if the queue is long enough that any arriving customer is sure to have a long wait, new arrivals with urgency number u will have approximately the same wait as customers already in the queue with urgency numbers v who have already waited $v - u$ units of time. This can be given a more precise formulation as properties of asymptotic behavior of the waiting-time distributions. Jackson then presents simulation evidence that supports these conjectures, as well as additional conjectures.

15

Probabilistic Learning Combinations of Local Job=shop Scheduling Rules

H. Fisher, G. L. Thompson
UNIVERSITY OF WASHINGTON
and
CARNEGIE INSTITUTE OF TECHNOLOGY

1. INTRODUCTION

In [2], Giffler, Thompson, and Van Ness report on some computational experience with complete enumeration and Monte Carlo algorithms described by Giffler and Thompson [1]. They found that the complete enumeration method was highly impractical, except for trivially small problems, but that the Monte Carlo version could handle medium-sized problems. However, the latter method did not guarantee an optimum schedule, and was on the average only about as good as using the SIO (FOFO) rule for machine loading.

One of the sample problems that was run is shown in Figure 1. There are six goods and six machines, and each good must be processed by each machine in the order shown. The times for the various operations are indicated in parentheses after the facility number. The number of feasible active schedules for this problem is, by a conserv-

A paper presented at the Factory Scheduling Conference, Carnegie Institute of Technology May 10–12, 1961. The work on this paper was supported by the Office of Naval Research and the Bureau of Ships through grants to the Carnegie Institute of Technology.

ative estimate, well over a million, so their complete enumeration is out of the question.   Monte Carlo sampling of 5000 active schedules

Good number	Facility order matrix					
1	3(1)	1(3)	2(6)	4(7)	6(3)	5(6)
2	2(8)	3(5)	5(10)	6(10)	1(10)	4(4)
3	3(5)	4(4)	6(8)	1(9)	2(1)	5(7)
4	2(5)	1(5)	3(5)	4(3)	5(8)	6(9)
5	3(9)	2(3)	5(5)	6(4)	1(3)	4(1)
6	2(3)	4(3)	6(9)	1(10)	5(4)	3(1)

6 × 6 * 6 Test problem (times in parentheses)

Figure 1

produced a schedule that completed in 58 time units, and such a schedule was observed only once.   When given as a problem to a production class, a schedule that completes in time 55 was devised, and required about two man-hours to complete.   By careful examination of lower bound requirements, this schedule was proved to be optimal.

It should be remarked that square problems (i.e., with $m=n$) have been found the most difficult to schedule, rectangular ones being much easier.   Nevertheless, the experience on this problem indicates that additional refinements were needed to improve the performance of the Monte Carlo rule.   For this reason the probabilistic learning programs described in the present paper were developed.

The reader may wish to work the problem in Figure 1 for himself. If he does so he will find that bottlenecks tend to develop on machines 5 and 6, so that initially the problem is to get them started as soon as possible.   Once they are started, it is desirable to keep them fully occupied.

Let us define *local job-shop scheduling rules* to be ones that can be applied by machine operators and that require only his knowledge of the work that is waiting for his machine to perform.   Two common loading rules for scheduling are the SIO ("shortest imminent operation," also called FOFO for "first off, first on") rule and the LRT (for "longest remaining time") rule.   For the problem of Figure 1 the SIO rule gave a schedule that completed in time 67, and the LRT rule gave a schedule that completed in time 61.   In this case the Monte Carlo sampling produced a better schedule than either of these.

In considering the problem of Figure 1 further, it seems reasonable that initially the SIO rule should be used, since it has the effect of getting machines to work quickly; later the LRT rule seems more desirable, since it will concentrate on working on the longest jobs. Hence, the idea of a combination of the two rules being superior to either one separately was developed.

In this paper we shall describe a method of combining in a "probabilistic learning'' way the SIO and LRT rules. We shall indicate how the method can be extended to combine any number of local decision rules in such a way that the resulting program will do no worse than the best of these local rules. In our experience the combined rule invariably does much better than any of the local rules taken singly.

Our objective throughout will be to select a schedule (i.e., Gantt chart) that has as small a completion time as possible. This may not always be the correct objective, but we shall keep it for our present purposes. It would be easy to modify what we do to take into account other objectives. We also assumed that operation times were known with certainty. That this is a reasonable assumption is supported by the work of J. Muth [3].

2. GENERATING GOOD SCHEDULES BY AN UNBIASED RANDOM PROCESS

To schedule m goods to be processed on n facilities required mn scheduling decisions, the time for the ith good to start being processed by the jth machine. Thus, in Figure 1, 36 scheduling decisions must be made. Ideally, one would like to keep track of the identity of the machine together with the time the decision was made. However, the more information one wants to keep in hand, the greater the demands on the memory system of the computer, and we were limited by the particular computer we had available (IBM 650). Hence, we kept track of only the 36 (in general, mn) decisions as they were made in time, without keeping track of the identity of the machine at which the decision was made. We could thus record a decision by means of a 36-component (in general, mn-component) vector. Our results could be considerably improved by making use of a larger computer to record more information.

Each time a decision is to be made, a machine is involved which has a queue of unfinished work, and one of the jobs must be selected for the machine to actually work on. By an *unbiased random process* we shall mean a rule that selects at random among the set of local decision rules and then applies it to make the actual scheduling decision. In the present paper the set consisted of just two rules, the SIO and the LRT rules. But, in principle, the set could consist of any number of such rules. The only requirement that each such rule must satisfy is that it must be capable of unambiguously specifying the next operation to be scheduled and defining the time at which it is to start, without creating conflicts or unfeasible schedules.

In the case of the SIO and LRT rules, it is possible that in a given queue there may be more than one operation that satisfies the rule.

In that case, our program chose at random among all the operations satisfying the given criterion.

In our experience, to be reported in later sections, we found that the unbiased random process did quite well as a scheduling heuristic, and invariably did better than the worst of the decision rules in the set.

In the unbiased random process, we depended upon chance to find a sequence of decision rules that would produce a good set of scheduling decisions. It was felt that perhaps computational experimentation could produce learning of some systematic way in which to vary the frequency of use of each of these rules. For instance, in the problem of Figure 1 it seemed to us reasonable that initially the SIO rule should be used and then later the LRT rule should be used. If this is the case, it should be possible to write a program that will modify its behavior as the result of its experience and hence learn what kind of scheduling behavior is desirable. We describe such a learning program next.

3. THE LEARNING PROCESS

The reward-punishment psychological learning model in essence says that learning results from experience. When we are confronted with an entirely new situation or problem, an action is taken, and the result recorded in memory. When a similar or identical situation reappears, another action is taken and evaluated relative to previous results. The two actions may be similar or different. If the later action is effective, the probability of repeating this action in the next event is increased. If the action is ineffective or unsatisfactory, the probability of repeating this action is decreased. Thus, humans tend to reinforce actions that are associated with satisfactory results and deviate from actions associated with ineffective and unsatisfactory results.

The random scheduling process can be made to simulate this behavior by varying the probabilities of selecting specific decision rules at any particular point in the scheduling process, depending upon the history of actions and results encountered by previous decisions at the same point. Actions can be defined as the specific sequence of rule choices; results, as the total schedule time, i.e., the time span between the start of the earliest operation and the completion of the latest operation. Identical action constitutes the same sequence of rule choices, and similarity is measured by the number of sequentially identical elements in each sequence of choices. The lowest possible similarity consists of no identical choices and the highest similarity of identical action.

Satisfactory results constitute the generation of a schedule better than the *standard schedule*. For all but one of the learning processes that we shall use, the standard schedule is defined as the best schedule generated to date. This definition was made because a schedule once found remains available for use, and any schedule not better than the best to date is not worth the effort required for its generation. Thus, according to the model, whenever a better schedule is produced, it becomes the performance norm and the associated actions (sequence of decision rules) become the standard action pattern toward which subsequent actions will tend as long as unsatisfactory performance continues.

Before we describe the specific set of local scheduling rules and learning processes employed in the model to be considered, we shall discuss two items that appear to be relevant. The first item is that the limited evidence which exists indicates that the unbiased random process is relatively efficient when compared with other general scheduling techniques.[1] Thus, any learning must be highly effective or must require but little effort to prove more economical than the random process. Second, the learning process described can be effective only if schedules with small total schedule times tend to be producible by similar actions (sequences of decisions). At present, we are not quite certain whether or not a significant relationship exists. In fact, it may exist for some sets of rules and be nonexistent for others.

4. DECISION RULES ACTUALLY TESTED

Because of the limitations of the IBM 650 computer, only a simple case (three rules) was programmed. The rules, as previously stated, consist of modified SIO and LRT rules and a fill-in rule which does not enter the decision process. The modified SIO and LRT rules which we used differ from the standard SIO and LRT rules previously defined in that an operation is not scheduled if a job of higher priority and presently being processed on another facility will arrive prior to the expected completion of the highest-priority operation in the queue. If this situation occurs, the facility is held idle until the new operation arrives. However, an operation is not delayed because of the possible arrival of a higher-priority operation which is now standing idle in some other queue. In contrast, the usual SIO and LRT rules allow a machine to stand idle only if there is no work available.

The modified SIO and LRT rules allow unnecessary idle gaps to occur in the final schedule if used without any additional rule. For

---

[1] All evidence relates to problems of the magnitude of 100 operations and ten facilities or less.

example: facility 1 may be held idle to await a higher-priority operation to be completed on another facility. Before this operation enters the queue of facility 1, another even higher-priority operation may have been started on another facility, thus bringing about an additional delay. This situation may cause an idle delay during which one or more of the operations in the queue could have been completed without delaying the start of the operation whose arrival is being awaited.

The fill-in feature attempts to overcome this problem. It specifies that whenever an idle delay is incurred, the entire queue shall be scanned for any operation that can be scheduled to fill the gap without delaying the start of the operation which is being awaited.

Scanning occurs from the job requiring the most machining downward. As many operations are filled in as possible; a single scan is utilized, and operations are scheduled so that they complete at the latest possible time. Since this rule can only improve a schedule and cannot deter the scheduling of any higher-priority job, it is applied whenever possible.

5. LEARNING PROCESSES USED

Four specific learning processes have been applied with the decision rules just discussed. These processes hereafter will be referred to as type 1 learning, type 2 learning, etc. The four processes differ by one or more of the following characteristics:

1) The initial standard schedule.

2) The determination of a new standard schedule.

3) The adjustment of probabilities when subsequent schedules are generated and evaluated.

4) The maximum degree of certainty with which a specific rule can be selected at any given decision point.

5.1 Type 1 Learning

Type 1 learning is characterized by an unbiased starting position and by a learning process that produces a unique decision sequence. An unbiased starting position implies that, for the first schedule after the initial standard has been determined, the probabilitiy of selecting each decision rule is equal at all decision points. Convergence toward a unique decision vector is accomplished by two classes of probability changes. When a superior schedule is generated[2] the current schedule becomes the new standard, and all previous probabilities are biased toward the new standard. When an equivalent or worse schedule is

---

[2] Total schedule time is less than current standard schedule.

generated, the existing standard remains, and all probabilities are biased toward this standard. Thus, when a standard is achieved such that subsequent schedules generated continue to be no better than the standard, the probabilities converge on this standard. Included in this process is an upper probability limit at which point a decision vector element is set to certainty in a single step rather than following the learning process. Four different changes in probabilities are provided:

1. Better schedule, same rule choice as standard schedule.
2. Better schedule, rule choice different than for standard schedule.
3. Worse or equivalent schedule, same choice as standard schedule.
4. Worse or equivalent schedule, rule choice different from that for standard schedule.

The probability changes as defined above are of fixed absolute magnitude and remain constant throughout the learning process.

Note that, because the decision rule incorporates a secondary random selection rule, a unique decision vector may be associated with more than one schedule (Gantt Chart) and total schedule time. The initial standard is determined by selecting the best of a 100 percent modified SIO and LRT schedule.

5.2 Type 2 Learning

This process differs from process 1 on three counts. First, the initial set of probabilities (after the standard has been determined) may be biased. Second, when a new standard is achieved, the probabilities of all decision points for which the rule choice for the new and previous standard differ are reset to a predetermined bias associated with the new choice rather than being incremented by some fixed amount. Finally, when the probability value reaches a specified upper limit, it remains at this point rather than being set to certainty or further incremented. This process is characterized by the fact that any schedule in the entire possibility set has some probability of being generated at any time, and by designating an appropriate upper limit for the elements of the decision vector, the decision sequences generated will approach an expected degree of similarity. If the upper limit is set at unity, a unique sequence will result.

5.3 Type 3 Learning

This type of learning differs from types 1 and 2 in that it uses an unbiased random schedule as an initial standard and immediately sets the decision vector elements at their maximum bias. When subsequent worse or equal schedules are generated, no learning or probability changes occur. When a satisfactory schedule is generated, it becomes the new standard, and all decision vector elements are given appropriate maximum biases.

This process, after having determined a standard, generates schedules with a given expected similarity to the standard until a better schedule is found. In a sense, this process learns the decision sequence of the best schedule to date and searches the neighborhood of schedules having a specified expected similarity of decision sequences.

5.4 Type 4 Learning

This process is substantially different from processes 1, 2, and 3. The initial standard, like process 3, is an unbiased random schedule, whereas, like process 1, the initial decision vector is unbiased. It differs from all previous processes in that the standard is always the previous schedule generated. When a better schedule is generated, all decision points differing from the previous schedule (standard) are biased toward the new choice. When an equal or worse schedule is generated, all decision points differing from the previous schedule are biased toward the previous choice. The process is also characterized by an upper limit on the probability of selecting a given rule.

This particular type of learning attempts to determine which rule, when applied to a particular decision point, is most often associated with a better schedule,[3] and then biases future rule choices relative to the last experience gained.

6. TYPE 1 VS. TYPE 2 LEARNING

Type 2 learning was motivated by the shortcoming of type 1 learning and the desire to conduct extended search among schedules having specific degrees of similarity. Type 1 learning has one possible advantage over type 2 learning. As the learning process progresses, some of the decision points reach a certainty value, thus hopefully avoiding future "wrong" decisions at these points. As decision points reach certainty, the number of interdependencies in the over-all problem are reduced, and learning at the other points may be more efficient. Because of the vast interdependencies of the scheduling problem, much of what is learned from each schedule is incorrect. It is hoped that the balance between correct and incorrect learning will favor correct learning and lead to better schedules. Reducing the interdependencies within a given problem increases the probability of effective learning.

---

[3] Better than the previous schedule.

The biased starting position of process 2 assumes that something can be learned from the standard itself. This has some rationale when the initial standard is determined by selecting the best of several schedules. In the case of selecting the best of a 100 percent SIO or LRT schedule as a standard, it appears that subsequent schedules should emphasize the choice made by the standard. The amount of bias should depend on the expected closeness of the standard to the best attainable schedule. This feature can be nullified by setting the bias equal to zero.

The reset feature is of definite advantage in that when a new standard is achieved, all decision vector elements which differ from the old standard are given a known value and have equal future learning opportunity. In type 1 learning the residual bias could be either negative or positive relative to a new standard, and the amount of learning opportunity could be correspondingly large or small before reaching an end point.

The final difference was added to allow extended search in a highly biased state. By using fixed absolute probability changes and no initial bias (type 1 learning), a major portion of the total search is conducted in the near unbiased state. Thus, a large number of schedules must be generated to achieve any quantity of search in the highly biased state. Process 2 allows rapid or slow movement though the near unbiased state and unlimited search in any desired biased state defined by the expected similarity of decision vectors between subsequent schedules and the current standard schedule.

Process 2 may be used to test the hypothesis that there is a correspondence between similar decision vectors and their associated total schedule times. By setting the initial bias equal to the upper limit, schedules with different expected degrees of similarity can be generated. It can then be determined whether decision vectors possessing close similarity have, in general, similar total schedule times. If this occurs, one of the principal conditions necessary for the learning process to be successful will be fulfilled.

A test of the learning process itself could consist of reversing the learning process to attempt to produce "bad" schedules to see if the shortest of the "bad" schedules is significantly different from the shortest of the "good" schedules. If, in general, this is not the case, one should be able to assume that either the learning process used is ineffective or that the best of the "bad" schedules was a random mishap, and that, the learning process is no better than an unbiased random process.

7. TYPE 3 VS. TYPES 1 AND 2 LEARNING

Type 1 and type 2 learning begins search by taking a relatively unbiased random sample of schedules and gradually directing the search toward schedules with a given expected similarity to the best schedule found.   Type 3 learning omits the initial random search and conducts its search by beginning with a random schedule and searching the neighborhood of schedules with an expected degree of similarity until a better schedule is found.   This schedule becomes the new standard, and its neighborhood is searched, etc.   In actual practice, it might be better to select the best of several random schedules as an initial standard hoping to get a better start.   For experimental purposes it might be useful to start with all types of schedules to see if the method encounters the expected difficulty when it begins with a relatively bad initial standard.   Also, one would expect in the latter case that there is more opportunity for learning and thus more clear evidence of learning having occurred when a particular sequence of schedules generated is being analyzed.

8. TYPE 4 VS. TYPES 1, 2, AND 3 LEARNING

Types 1, 2, and 3 learning are all similar in that at some point in the search process, major decision sequences found in the standard schedule are repeated in subsequent schedules.   This is particularly true when all the elements of the decision vector reach their maximum certainty values.   Type 4 learning differs in that there is no guarantee that any element of the decision vector will achieve its maximum certainty value.   If this does not occur, there is no reason to expect any stability or repetition of the decision sequences of subsequent schedules.

This type of learning anticipates that at any time in the learning process there are key decision points which determine the quality of a schedule.   Hopefully, there is adequate independence among individual decisions so that the key points can be located and biased toward the correct decision rule.   As the bias approaches the upper limit and these particular decisions are repeated with high probability, it is hoped that a new set of key decision points will arise, etc.   This method of learning requires a greater independence between decision points than the other three methods, and thus may be expected to be the least efficient of all the methods considered.   However, if adequate independence exists, and if, in effect, there is a limited number of key points which govern the quality of a schedule, this method would have some advantages over the others.   Because of the different character of this type of learning and because some a priori expectations exist, it appears to be worth a sample test.

9. THE PROGRAM

The program essentially consists of two parts; an initialization segment and a scheduling and learning segment. The initialization segment processes the input data and sets up the necessary list structures and parameters for the scheduling and learning segment. The scheduling and learning segment generates a complete SIO or LRT schedule, selects the best of these as a standard, and produces additional schedules by combining locally the SIO and LRT rules. The schedules can be generated by a random process, or they can incorporate the learning process previously described. Random schedules can be produced by starting with zero bias and setting the learning parameters equal to zero. Space does not permit further detailed description of the program.

10. DESCRIPTION OF TEST RESULTS

What follows is a summary of an extremely limited amount of data which has been generated to determine whether or not the learning approach offers significant promise for continued work.

Results for each of the learning models mentioned will be described and discussed, as well as the results of a similarity test and pattern analysis which will be defined and described.

Three problems were used in testing the different learning processes. However, as will be seen, not all processes were tested with each problem.

The first problem is a $6 \times 6 \times 6$ (Table 1A) problem, i.e., six jobs, each requiring six operations, with one operation performed on each of six available machines. Operation times were selected from a table of random numbers and vary from one to ten hours in duration. The machine order was also assigned randomly with the added restriction that each job has one operation on each machine.

The second problem is a $10 \times 10 \times 10$ (Table 1B) problem, i.e., ten jobs, each requiring ten different operations, with one operation performed on each of ten machines. Operation times were selected by a random process and range from 1 to 99 hours. Machines were assigned so that the lower-numbered machines *tend* to be used for the earlier operations and the higher-numbered machines for later operations. This is typical of a machine shop situation, where, in general, planers, shapers, lathes, screw machines, etc. are initial operation machines;

Table 1 Job file.

A. 6 × 6 × 6 Test problem

Operation number	Machine number	Operating time (hours)	Machine number	Operating time (hours)	Machine number	Operating time (hours)	Machine number	Operating time (hours)	Machine number	Operating time (hours)	Machine number	Operating time (hours)
	Job 1		Job 2		Job 3		Job 4		Job 5		Job 6	
1	3	1	2	8	3	5	2	5	3	9	2	3
2	1	3	3	5	4	4	1	5	2	3	4	3
3	2	6	5	10	6	8	3	5	5	5	6	9
4	4	7	6	10	1	9	4	3	6	4	1	10
5	6	3	1	10	2	1	5	8	1	3	5	4
6	5	6	4	4	5	7	6	9	4	1	3	1

B. 10 × 10 × 10 Test problem

Operation number	Job									
	I		II		III		IV		V	
	Machine number	Operating time	Machine number	Operating time	Machine number	Operating time	Machine number	Operating time	Machine number	Operating time
1	1	29	1	43	2	91	2	81	3	14
2	2	78	3	90	1	85	3	95	1	6
3	3	9	5	75	4	39	1	71	2	22
4	4	36	10	11	3	74	5	99	6	61
5	5	49	4	69	9	90	7	9	4	26
6	6	11	2	28	6	10	9	52	5	69
7	7	62	7	46	8	12	8	85	9	21
8	8	56	6	46	7	89	4	98	8	49
9	9	44	8	72	10	45	10	22	10	72
10	10	21	9	30	5	33	6	43	7	53

Operation number	VI		VII		VIII		IX		X	
	Machine number	Operating time	Machine number	Operating time	Machine number	Operating time	Machine number	Operating time	Machine number	Operating time
1	3	84	2	46	3	31	1	76	2	85
2	2	2	1	37	1	86	2	69	1	13
3	6	52	4	61	2	46	4	76	3	61
4	4	95	3	13	6	74	6	51	7	7
5	9	48	7	32	5	32	3	85	9	64
6	10	72	6	21	7	88	10	11	10	76
7	1	47	10	32	9	19	7	40	6	47
8	7	65	9	89	10	48	8	89	4	52
9	5	6	8	30	8	36	5	26	5	90
10	8	25	5	55	4	79	9	74	8	45

C. 20 × 5 × 5 Test problem

Operation number	Job									
	I		II		III		IV		V	
	Machine number	Oper-ating time	Machine number	Oper-ating time	Machine number	Oper-ating time	Machine number	Oper-ating time	Machine number	Oper-ating time
1	1	29	1	43	2	91	2	81	3	14
2	2	9	2	75	1	39	1	71	2	22
3	3	49	4	69	3	90	5	9	1	26
4	4	62	3	46	5	12	3	85	4	21
5	5	44	5	72	4	45	4	22	5	72

Operation number	VI		VII		VIII		IX		X	
	Machine number	Oper-ating time	Machine number	Oper-ating time	Machine number	Oper-ating time	Machine number	Oper-ating time	Machine number	Oper-ating time
1	3	84	2	46	3	31	1	76	2	85
2	2	52	1	61	2	46	4	76	3	61
3	5	48	3	32	1	32	3	85	1	64
4	1	47	4	32	4	19	2	40	4	47
5	4	6	5	30	5	36	5	26	5	90

Operation number	XI		XII		XIII		XIV		XV	
	Machine number	Oper-ating time	Machine number	Oper-ating time	Machine number	Oper-ating time	Machine number	Oper-ating time	Machine number	Oper-ating time
1	2	78	3	90	1	85	3	95	1	6
2	4	36	1	11	3	74	1	99	2	61
3	1	11	2	28	2	10	2	52	5	69
4	5	56	4	46	4	89	4	98	3	49
5	3	21	5	30	5	33	5	43	4	53

Operation number	XVI		XVII		XVIII		XIX		XX	
	Machine number	Oper-ating time	Machine number	Oper-ating time	Machine number	Oper-ating time	Machine number	Oper-ating time	Machine number	Oper-ating time
1	2	2	1	37	1	86	2	69	1	13
2	1	95	3	13	2	74	3	51	2	7
3	4	72	2	21	5	88	1	11	3	76
4	5	65	4	89	3	48	4	89	4	52
5	3	25	5	55	4	79	5	74	5	45

mills, drills, and borers are secondary operation machines; and grinding, polishing, painting, etc. are final operations.

The third problem is a 20 × 5 × 5 (Table 1C) problem, i.e., 20 jobs, each requiring five operations, with one operation on each of five available machines. The operation times are identical to the

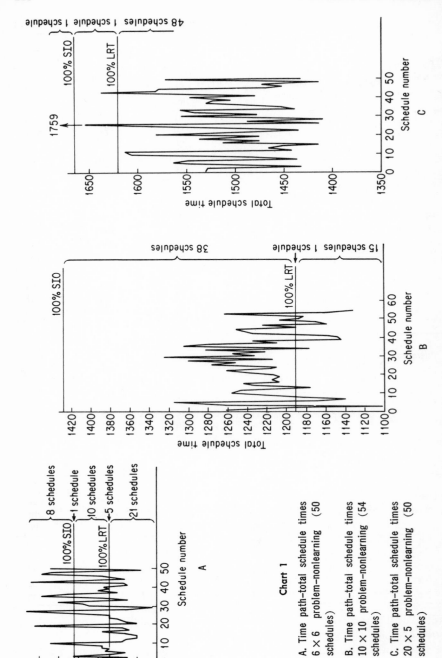

Chart 1

A. Time path–total schedule times 6 × 6 problem–nonlearning (50 schedules)

B. Time path–total schedule times 10 × 10 problem–nonlearning (54 schedules)

C. Time path–total schedule times 20 × 5 problem–nonlearning (50 schedules)

10 × 10 × 10 problem. The machine assignment is similar except that only five machines are available instead of ten. This means that half as many machines must do the same amount of work.

11. THE RANDOM UNBIASED MODEL

The random unbiased process using local schedule rules has already been described (Section 2) and, in general, will be the basis of comparison in evaluating the performance of the learning models. The results of the nonlearning random schedule obtained from each of the test problems are shown in Charts 1A–C.

It is interesting that, in all cases, a random combination of the rules resulted in a number of schedules significantly better than the best schedule resulting from the application of either of the rules individually. In all cases a majority of the schedules produced by the two rules were better than the least good of the 100 percent SIO and LRT schedules.

For the 6 × 6 problem an unbiased random model using no rules generated a single best schedule of 60 hours in 500 schedules. If this is a true sample of the distribution of schedules for the model, the probability of getting no schedule as good as 60 hours in 50 attempts would be .62, or approximately two out of three. The random model using the rules already specified generated five out of 50 schedules with a total schedule time of 60 or better. Again, if this is assumed to be a representative sample, the probability of this model not producing a schedule as good as 60 hours in 50 trials is less than .00001, or one chance out of 100,000.

12. TYPE 1 LEARNING MODEL

Because the disadvantages of the type 1 learning model, which have been previously described, were discovered early, only tests on the 6 × 6 × 6 problem were conducted. The results appear in Charts 2 A–D. Compared with the nonlearning or random run of 50 schedules (Chart 1A), a significant difference is observable. With the exception of run 3 (Chart 2C), the learning processes produced sets of schedules with a smaller proportion of bad schedules, and, with the exception of the 56 hour schedule found by the random process, more good schedules than the random process.

Run 3 (Chart 2C) is interesting in that a good schedule was found in a region of generally poor schedules, and search was directed into an area where good schedules were scarce. With the exception of schedule 69, all schedules after schedule 63 were generated by the

Chart 2

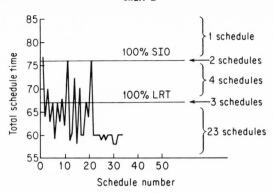

A. Time path–total schedule times
6 × 6 problem–type 1 learning
(33 schedules)

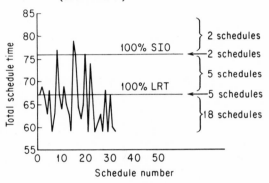

B. Time path–total schedule times
6 × 6 problem–type 1 learning (32
schedules)

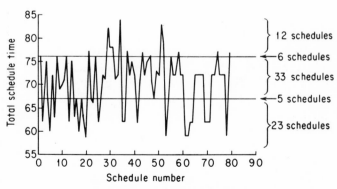

C. Time path–total schedule times
6 × 6 problem–type 1 learning (79
schedules)

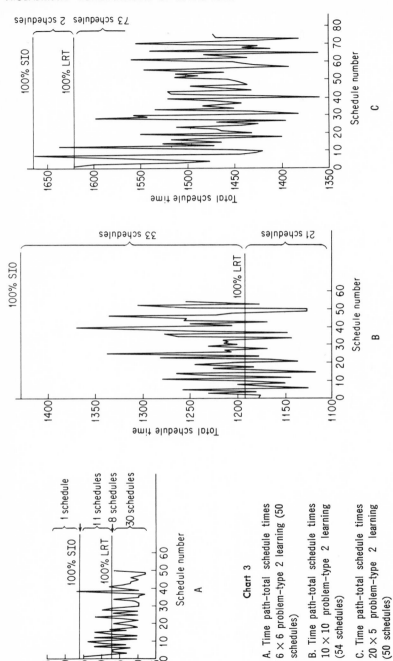

Chart 3

A. Time path–total schedule times 6 × 6 problem–type 2 learning (50 schedules)

B. Time path–total schedule times 10 × 10 problem–type 2 learning (54 schedules)

C. Time path–total schedule times 20 × 5 problem–type 2 learning (50 schedules)

same decision sequence. A unique decision sequence can generate more than one schedule if, when a rule is applied, two or more operations have the same priority and complete at the same time. A random process then breaks the tie, making it possible for several schedules to be generated by repeated applications of a single decision sequence.

A note of interest is that an over-all optimum for the $6 \times 6 \times 6$ problem is 55 hours. (This can be shown by various arguments involving lower bounds on times.) This does not imply, however, that any combination of the two rules we used is capable of generating the optimum schedule.

13. TYPE 2 LEARNING

Type 2 learning was applied to each of the three problems used for testing. Results for the $6 \times 6 \times 6$ problem were comparable to those of type 1 learning. Because type 2 learning starts from a biased state, it was anticipated that the set of schedules generated would display less variability in total schedule times than those generated by type 1 learning. Comparison of Chart 3A will Charts 2 A–C supports this expectation. However, a single example is far from conclusive evidence that the relationship in fact exists.

In the $10 \times 10 \times 10$ (Chart 3B) problem, evidence of progressive learning is again not evident. Also, with the exception of one occurrence, the learning process produced a greater number of good schedules. However, it produced roughly an equivalent number of bad schedules which were not predominantly among the early schedules where they could be attributed to the relatively unbiased state of the process. Again, it appears that a good schedule was found in a region of high variability, and search was continuously directed toward this area. Chart 4A shows the cumulative number of schedules found with total schedule times less than X hours both for the type 2 learning and nonlearning processes for the $10 \times 10 \times 10$ problem.

The $20 \times 5 \times 5$ problem gives the first evidence of progressive learning and also is the first instance when the learning process generated a schedule superior to the unbiased random process. Again, the best schedule appears to have been found in an area of relatively high variability. Since progressive learning appeared to be occurring, this test was allowed to exceed the approximately 50 schedule limit used in other tests. No better schedule appeared within the next 25 schedules, and the test was terminated. A cumulative frequency chart similar to that for the $10 \times 10 \times 10$ problem is shown in Chart 4B.

The results displayed are again inconclusive because of the sample size. However, it appears that for the larger-size problems the learning

Chart 4

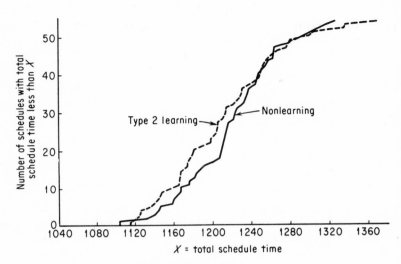

A. Cummulative distribution diagram—10 × 10 problem type 2 learning and nonlearning (54 schedules)

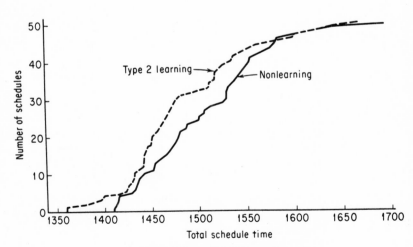

B. Cummulative distribution diagram—20 × 5 problem type 2 learning and nonlearning (50 schedules)

process is likely to pay off. For the $20 \times 5 \times 5$ problem a known optimum of 1165 hours is possible. This is achieved by getting jobs 5 and 17 to machine 4 as quickly as possible and then keeping machine 4 busy. This optimum cannot be obtained by any combination of the two rules used, as the first operation of job 5 is neither an SIO or an LRT operation relative to machine 4 and cannot be started at hour 0, which is required to obtain the optimum. The best schedule possible by application of the rules is unknown, but 1359 hours was the best total schedule time found.

14. TYPE 3 LEARNING

Only the $6 \times 6 \times 6$ problem and the $20 \times 5 \times 5$ problem were used to test the type 3 learning process. The run for the latter problem is shown in Chart 5. Each of these tests was marked by the appearance of a relatively good schedule early in the test and the inability of the process to find a subsequent better schedule. Good schedules appear so early that they could hardly be attributed to the efficiency of the learning process but rather to random circumstance. Evidence again indicates that a good schedule was found in a neighborhood of high variability and that the proportion of good schedules is not overwhelming.

This type of learning might be more practical if it were applied to the neighborhood of the best of a reasonably small number of randomly produced schedules and allowed to expand the area of search over a larger neighborhood if success was not achieved. Such variations were not tested.

15. TYPE 4 LEARNING

Type 4 learning was applied to the $6 \times 6 \times 6$ and $20 \times 5 \times 5$ problem. It was applied in two ways, first, to find a good schedule (Charts 6A and B), and second, to find the poorest possible schedule (Charts 6C and D). Although the characteristics of this type of learning have already been stated, it is worth repeating that this is the only process used which did not guarantee long-run convergence. In fact, unless the probability change parameters were large, convergence did not occur for any decision points for the tests made. With probability changes of .05 per change, only half of the elements of the decision vector reached a value of more than .78 or less than .25 after 50 schedules. With a probability change of .015, no element achieved a value greater than .68 or less than .41 in 50 schedules.

Results from the $6 \times 6 \times 6$ problem indicate some degree of pro-

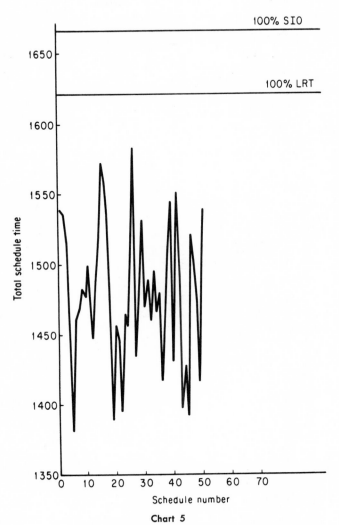

Chart 5

Time path—total schedule times
20 × 5 problem—type 3 learning
(50 schedules)

Chart 6

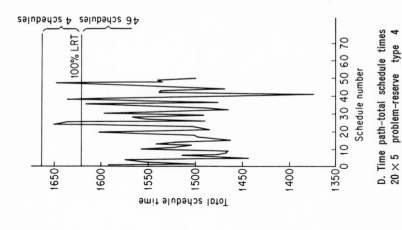

D. Time path–total schedule times
20 × 5 problem–reserve type 4
learning (50 schedules)

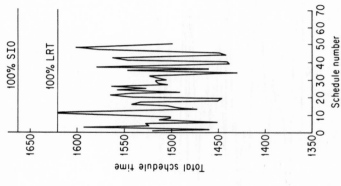

C. Time path–total schedule times
6 × 6 problem–type 4 learning
(63 schedules)

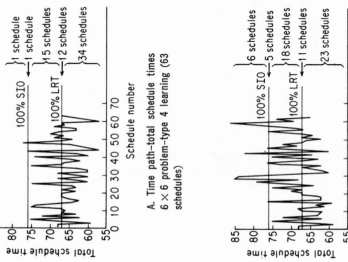

A. Time path–total schedule times
6 × 6 problem–type 4 learning (63
schedules)

B. Time path–total schedule times
20 × 5 problem–type 4 learning
(50 schedules)

gressive learning. The proportion of good schedules is significantly less than for type 2 learning, indicating that the learning process is slower and in a more random state. That is what was anticipated, since no guaranteed stability is built into the model. Progressive learning may be explained by the fact that a single good schedule does not continually influence search but yields an amount of information and is forgotten. Hence, direction and stability are achieved only after much experience,

The 20 × 5 × 5 problem indicates mediocre results in finding a good schedule. However, it strengthens the assumption that a slower learning process is occurring, possibly so slow that 50 schedules are completely insufficient for effective learning to occur.

Comparison of the respective forward and reverse processes indicates again that learning may be occurring. Although this process does not seem to be an effective process in light of the results obtained, it appears to yield some information about the over-all learning problem.

16. SIMILARITY TEST

To evaluate the applicability of the learning processes, a test, which we named a *similarity test*, was designed. This test attempts to determine if there is a significant relationship between the total schedules generated by similar decision sequences. If not, the types of learning applied would likely be completely ineffective.

The tests consist of selecting a particular schedule and its total schedule time as a permanent standard and generating a large set of additional schedules with varying degrees of similarity from zero to complete similarity. These schedules are observed to determine if similar decision sequences, in general, produce schedules with total schedule times closer to the standard than less similar sequences.

Tests were made only on the 6 × 6 × 6 problem and for three different decision sequences. One standard which was selected was the sequence which produced the best schedule found in all previous tests. This was a 56 hour schedule. It was found that the same sequence could produce a schedule of 60 hours. A second standard representing the sequence which generated the greatest total schedule time (93 hours) was tested. This sequence also produced schedules with total schedule time of 74 and 85 hours. Finally, a sequence which had a total schedule time of 64 hours was chosen. This sequence also generated schedules with total schedule times of 57, 58, and 67 hours. Thus, tests were made on two sequences which represented good schedules and one which represented a relatively bad schedule.

Graphic results of these tests are shown in Charts 7A–C. It is clearly evident that there is a general similarity between similar schedules and their respective total schedule times.

The data indicate that the mean total schedule time of schedules increasingly dissimilar to a good standard increases with the amount of dissimilarity. The opposite is true in the case of a poor standard.

The over-all result appears to indicate that the set of all relatively good or bad schedules includes highly dissimilar schedules. It appears that this set is distributed by communities or areas of concentration rather than uniformly throughout the decision sequence space. Also, it appears that these communities contain only a small proportion of the desired schedules and are accompanied by a large number of schedules of intermediate total schedule times. If this is a correct statement about the decision sequence space, an appropriate learning technique would be to locate prospectively good areas of search and to search these areas rather thoroughly.

17. PATTERN ANALYSIS

A final analysis of the data generated was made to determine whether our a priori expectation that good schedules will use a high proportion of SIO choices in the early stages of scheduling and a high proportion of LRT choices in the latter stages is, in fact, true. The analysis consisted of ordering a large set of random (nonlearning) schedules for each of the problems by their respective total schedule times and determining the percentage of SIO choices made during the early and late stages of the scheduling process. Tables 2A–C give the quantitative results of this analysis. Comparison of the percentage of SIO choices for the best fifth and the worst fifth of the schedules are given in the second section of each table.

Only the $6 \times 6 \times 6$ problem (Table 2A) significantly supports the first part of the above proposition; i.e., good schedules are generated by a high proportion of SIO choices in the early stages of a schedule. Only the $20 \times 5 \times 5$ problem supports the second part of the proposition. Thus, for these examples the complete hypothesis is not confirmed. The milder hypothesis that good schedules will have a higher percentage of early SIO choices and late LRT choices than bad schedules is only slightly confirmed. The whole issue, however, is obscured by the fact that the SIO and LRT rules frequently give the same decision, and there is no way of separating out this factor. The one positive conclusion that can be drawn is that a probabilistic combination of scheduling rules is better than any one of them separately.

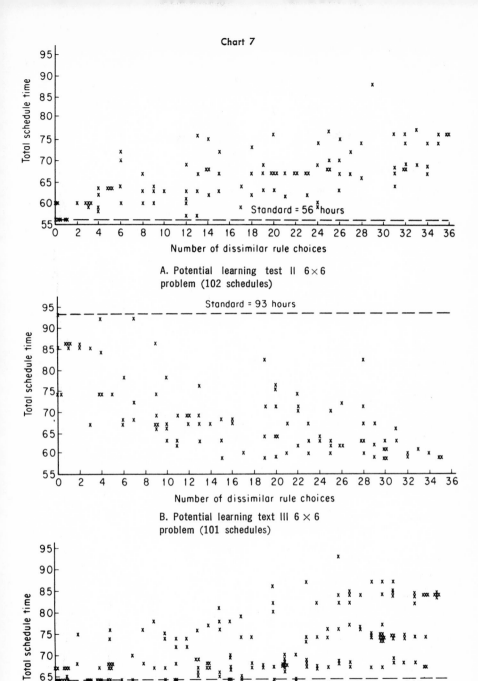

Chart 7

A. Potential learning test II 6×6
problem (102 schedules)

B. Potential learning text III 6 × 6
problem (101 schedules)

C. Potential learning test I 6 × 6
problem (200 schedules)

Table 2 Percentage of SIO choices.

A. (6 × 6 × 6 problem)

Schedule	Hour range	% SIO choices by quarters				% SIO choices by halves		% SIO choices total
Best 20%	57–62	62.5	61.2	53.8	52.6	61.9	53.2	56.7
2nd 20%	63–66	56.8	60.4	51.0	53.4	58.6	52.2	55.4
3rd 20%	67–68	52.7	51.4	50.0	53.6	52.1	51.8	51.9
4th 20%	69–75	41.6	47.5	46.3	47.5	44.6	46.9	45.6
5th 20%	76–93	42.9	41.6	50.3	48.4	42.3	49.4	45.8
Total		53.4	54.5	52.3	53.3	54.0	52.8	53.4

Comparison							
Best 20%	63	61	54	53	62	53	57
Worst 20%	43	42	50	48	42	49	46
Difference	+20	+19	+ 4	+ 5	+20	+ 4	+11

B. (10 × 10 × 10 problem)

Schedule	Hour range	% SIO choices by quarters				% SIO choices by halves		% SIO choices total
Best 20%	1103–1167	51.4	47.6	47.5	53.6	49.5	50.6	50.0
2nd 20%	1168–1205	55.3	50.0	54.9	52.7	52.7	53.8	53.2
3rd 20%	1207–1225	53.4	48.4	49.0	50.6	50.9	49.8	50.4
4th 20%	1229–1255	53.0	48.6	47.6	48.0	50.8	47.8	49.3
5th 20%	1258–1370	49.1	46.8	50.8	50.9	48.0	50.9	49.4
Total		51.9	47.8	49.3	50.7	49.9	50.0	50.0

Comparison							
Best 20%	51	48	48	54	50	51	50
Worst 20%	49	47	51	51	48	51	49
Difference	+ 2	− 1	− 3	+ 3	+ 2	0	+ 1

C. (20 × 5 × 5 problem)

Schedule	Hour range	% SIO choices by quarters				% SIO choices by halves		% SIO choices total
Best 20%	1359–1438	51	53	37	40	52	39	45
2nd 20%	1442–1463	54	54	43	37	54	40	47
3rd 20%	1465–1511	51	53	43	45	52	44	48
4th 20%	1511–1543	48	51	48	45	50	46	48
5th 20%	1550–1759	45	49	45	47	47	46	47
Total	1359–1759	50	52	43	43	51	43	47

Comparison							
Best 20%	51	53	37	40	52	39	45
Worst 20%	45	49	45	47	47	46	47
Difference	+ 6	+ 4	− 8	− 7	+ 5	− 7	− 2

18. CONCLUSIONS

The two most important conclusions that can be drawn from the above results are the following: (1) an unbiased random combination of scheduling rules is better than any of them taken separately; (2) learning is possible. There is still a question as to whether learning is desirable, in view of the fact that the unbiased random combination of rules was so effective. It is also not clear what is to be learned, since our original conjecture was not supported very strongly. Although humans seem to do very well with the relatively simple problems we tried here, it is quite likely that an unbiased random combination of five to ten local rules would be considerably superior to human efforts on somewhat larger problems. At least, it would be desirable to test this hypothesis. Since the learning program requires an effort that increases linearly with the size of the problem, relatively large problems should be feasible with present computers.

Finally, we do not feel that we have fully tried out all possible ideas connected with probabilistic learning programs for the scheduling problem, and we hope that our work will stimulate others to make further investigations in this direction.

REFERENCES

1. Giffler, B. and G. L. Thompson, "Algorithms for Solving Production Scheduling Problems," *Operations Research*, 8 (1960), 487-503.

2. Giffler, B., G. L. Thompson, and V. Van Ness, "Numerical Experience with the Linear and Monte Carlo Algorithms for Solving Production Scheduling Problems," Chapter 3 of this volume.

3. Muth, J., "The Effect of Uncertainty in Job Times on Optimal Schedules," Chapter 18 of this volume.

16

The Efficient Utilization of Labor under Conditions of Fluctuating Demand

Morton Allen

GENERAL ELECTRIC COMPANY

1. INTRODUCTION

Production leveling is one of the classic problems of production and inventory control. The problem, quite simply, is to determine how best to respond to widely fluctuating customer demand. For example, if incoming orders are declining, the following alternatives are available to the business:

1. Where manufacture for stock is possible, management may elect to maintain the same rate of production and make no adjustments in the labor force. In this case, inventory will, of course, increase, which may result in excessive carrying costs.

2. If the business in question cannot manufacture for stock, or elects not to, another alternative is to respond directly to customer demand by reducing the production rate. If corresponding reductions

A paper presented at the Factory Scheduling Conference, Carnegie Institute of Technology, May 10–12, 1961. The research reported in this paper was originally a part of the author's S. M. thesis, "A Detailed Simulation of a Non-Stock Production Leveling Problem," submitted to the Massachusetts Institute of Technology, 1962.

252

are not made in the labor supply, the result will be an increase in idle labor hours. With present high wage rate levels, idle time can be quite costly.

3. In order to keep idle labor hours within reasonable limits, management may decide that a certain number of layoffs are unavoidable. Responding to customer demand in this manner can result in excessive administrative costs.

Generally, lower costs result if management elects to meet fluctuating demand through a combination of these alternatives. In fact, it is possible to develop a set of rules from which the optimal combination can be computed [2].

1.1 Nonrepetitive Manufacture

It is very often true, however, that the business in question produces a product with a high rate of obsolescence so that manufacture for either finished or intermediate stock is impossible. With no inventory buffer to smooth out production, the size of the work force and/or the amount of idle time must fluctuate even more widely than when manufacture for stock is possible.

1.2 Defense-Oriented Industries

This problem is particularly acute in the defense-oriented industries, where the high rate of technological obsolescence often prohibits manufacture for stock. Unfortunately, it is just this class of businesses which must contend with the most widely fluctuating customer demand.

In these cases, the application of such a set of rules may still determine the "optimal" combination of these alternatives. However, this course of action will most likely not be very desirable. Fluctuating demand and a nonrepetitive product can lead to quite chaotic conditions. A closer, more detailed analysis of the business seems to be needed, in order to determine additional alternatives for responding to such situations.

1.3 Detailed Analysis

The purpose of this research paper is to study, through detailed computer simulation, the problems of shop operation under conditions of fluctuating customer demand. In particular, two different but related sets of questions are considered:

1. With a given labor force, can appropriate dispatching significantly reduce idle time when incoming customer orders are falling?

Can dispatching also reduce the need for overtime at the other extreme, when the shop is heavily loaded?

2. How can the configuration of the shop be altered so that wide swings in customer demand can be absorbed more efficiently? In particular, what is the effect of greater labor flexibility? How can this flexibility be achieved?

1.4 A Product Department Study

This research was conducted on behalf of manufacturing management for a large job shop in a product Department of the General Electric Company. The shop consists of 78 machines classified into 18 machine groups. Orders are routed through a series of machine groups, and it was assumed any machine in the group could perform the required operation with the same set-up and processing time. There is the usual complement of job-shop equipment, ranging in size from small sensitive drills, where the average operation time per order is substantially less than two hours, to large boring mills, where the average operation time per order is over fifty hours. Routing through the shop is quite random, although certain traditional metal-cutting patterns of job flow do exist.

The work force consists of 40 men, who are presently classified into 13 labor classes. All men in a given labor class are regarded as interchangeable. The man-machine relationship is specified in terms of which labor class (or classes) can operate which machine group (or groups). There is some overlapping of capability among the labor classes, but many of the machine groups can be operated by only one labor class, so that opportunities for increased labor flexibility do exist.

Since the shop consists of 78 machines and only 40 men, the facility is, as a whole, labor limited. On the other hand, there are certain machine groups, particularly among some of the larger pieces of equipment, such as the boring mills, where machine capacity is quite limited relative to normal requirements.

1.5 The Computer Program

This manufacturing system was simulated by using the General Electric Manufacturing Simulator (GEMS) program, which was developed by the company's Production Control Service in cooperation with the product Department. The GEMS model is a flexible, general-purpose simulation program, written in the FORTRAN II language, for the 704 computer.

2. DISPATCHING RULES

The first set of simulation experiments was concerned with an evaluation of alternative dispatching rules under conditions of decreasing shop load. A dispatch rule, very simply, is a method for determining which job to process next. For example, the first come, first served rule says to select that job which was first to arrive in queue. Countless numbers of such rules can be formulated, depending upon the objectives of the business. Under the conditions in these experiments, the primary objective is to maintain labor utilization at as high a level as possible until additional orders are received. Problems associated with due dates are typically not important, since the reduced load generally results in shorter waiting times. If anything, jobs should tend to be completed early relative to their final due dates. For the same reason, the size of the in-process inventory is not an important consideration in this case.

2.1 Shortest-Processing-Time Rule

Conway [1] has shown that under certain "steady-state" conditions, utilization can be influenced by dispatching rules which, in some way, consider job processing times in assigning priorities. In particular, of those rules tested under conditions of steady state, the shortest-processing-time rule has consistently yielded the highest utilization (see [1], pp. 221–229). This rule, very simply, gives highest priority to that job which requires the least amount of processing for this operation. The problem under consideration here, however, is the antithesis of steady state. The intent of this research is to consider ways in which the shop can better adjust to, more or less, unstable conditions. Therefore, as a starting point, it seemed most appropriate to *re-examine* the shortest-processing-time rule under these new conditions.

2.2 Alternate Routing

Another factor to be considered in improving utilization is the possibility of alternate routing. For the particular order mix studied, approximately one-third of the required operations could be performed at more than one machine group. However, there were some machine groups from which no alternate routing was possible. In particular, large machines might substitute for small, but the reverse is seldom true. Unfortunately, as has already been indicated, some of these larger machines were sometimes overloaded and became bottlenecks. Nevertheless, the use of alternate routing seemed to be a good way in which at least some of the imbalances in the labor load could be relieved. The question, therefore, was not whether this alternate routing capability could improve performance, but rather how much of an improvement was possible, with this set of orders in this shop.

The alternate routing decision for a particular operation can be made, conceptually, at any point between the time at which the job is released to the shop and the time at which the operation in question is to be performed. To the extent that this decision is deferred until processing can actually begin on the operation, alternate routing becomes part of the dispatching decision. In this case, the dispatching rule not only assigns job priorities but also selects the machine groups at which processing is to take place.

In these simulations, the alternate routing decision was deferred until the job become available for the operation in question, and for this reason alternate routing will be considered as part of dispatching. The specific method of alternate routing was to re-examine each queue once each shift. If the backlog was such that there were jobs in a queue which could not possibly be processed in the forthcoming shift, an attempt was made to alternate route work out of this queue into other queues which did not have a shift's worth of work.

2.3 Simulation Experiments—Set 1

The first set of simulation experiments, therefore, consisted of an evaluation of four methods of dispatching:
1. The shortest-processing-time rule with alternate routing.
2. The longest-processing-time rule with alternate routing.
3. A random rule with alternate routing.
4. A random rule *without* alternate routing.

The longest-processing-time rule was used simply as a contrast to shortest processing time. The random rule based priority upon the value of a random number. The purpose of the rule was to provide a method of dispatching which was not intentionally correlated with processing time, thus providing a standard for comparison.

The initial load in the shop, taken from actual product department data, was more than enough to fully utilize the labor resources. However, because of contract cancellation or contract completion, it was postulated, for experimental purposes, that no additional work was available to be released to the shop. Therefore, as jobs in the initial load were completed, a run-out condition began to take place. The results are summarized in Table 1.

2.4 Results

The most significant points to be observed from this data are

Table 1 simulation experiments—set 1 13-labor-class group.

	RULE 1			RULE 2			RULE 3			RULE 4		
Week	% labor util.	Cum. labor util.	Avg. no. jobs shop	% labor util.	Cum. labor util.	Avg. no. jobs shop	% labor util.	Cum. labor util.	Avg. no. jobs shop	% labor util.	Cum. labor util.	Avg. no. jobs shop
1	100	100	771	100	100	953	100	100	912	100	100	912
2	100	200	583	100	200	917	100	200	828	100	200	827
3	100	300	470	100	300	859	100	300	745	100	300	734
4	100	400	382	100	400	796	100	400	655	99	399	634
5	100	500	313	100	500	710	100	500	543	99	498	547
6	100	600	255	100	600	618	100	600	431	99	597	438
7	94	694	198	86	686	480	91	691	336	85	682	340
8	71	765	154	65	751	379	66	757	268	51	733	281
9	50	815	122	44	795	299	48	805	223	36	769	239
10	36	851	96	23	818	255	29	834	187	26	795	206
11	31	882	72	43	861	215	31	865	147	30	825	185
12	29	911	53	38	899	177	29	894	110	22	847	163
13	26	937	38	14	913	119	30	924	82	18	865	144
14	15	952	24	19	932	84	21	945	52	23	888	127
.	.		.		.		.		.		.	
.	.		.		.		.		.		.	
.	.		.		.		.		.		.	
Total weeks to empty shop	27			27			27			27		

Rule 1: Shortest processing time with alternate routing.
Rule 2: Longest processing time with alternate routing.
Rule 3: Random rule with alternate routing.
Rule 4: Random rule without alternate routing.

1. The superiority of the shortest-processing-time rule in maintaining higher utilization.

2. The important benefits to be derived from even a limited alternate routing capability.

Relative to point 1, the superiority of the shortest-processing-time rule was greatest during the initial ten weeks of the contract run-out. During this time, the shortest-processing-time rule increased utilization by an average of 3.3 percent, compared to the longest-processing-time rule. Compared to the particular random rule used, the shortest-processing-time rule increased utilization by 1.7 percent during this ten-week period.

After week ten, the rules seem to converge so that all rules required 27 weeks to completely empty the shop. Apparently, with this set of orders and the given shop configuration, the choice of a dispatch rule could affect only short-run performance. Most usually, however, a complete run-out is not anticipated, so that short-run differences are important. For those cases where a total run-out does occur, there may be a more meaningful criterion than the number of weeks required to empty the shop. This topic will be discussed shortly.

The second observation from this first set of runs concerns the effectiveness of the alternate routing feature. With even limited alternate routing opportunities, and with the relatively unsophisticated alternate routing rule used, this feature led to a significant performance improvement. In fact, as of any point in time, the difference in utilizations between the random rule *with* alternate routing and the random rule *without* alternate routing exceeded the difference in utilizations between the shortest- and longest-processing-time rules. The use of alternate routing has been analyzed mathematically for some very simple cases (see [3]), and has been found very advantageous. It would appear, based upon the results just discussed, that the advantages of alternate routing can be extrapolated to more complex situations, such as those considered here.

2.5 Complete Run-out

In the preceding paragraphs, emphasis has been placed upon improving short-run utilization. There are times, however, in which complete shop run-outs do occur, although it is to be hoped that this is not a frequent occurrence. When this is the case, however, one objective is to expedite the reallocation of labor to other areas, or, if necessary, to lay off as expeditiously as possible.

In this respect it should be noted that at least one man must be retained in each labor class for which some work still remains in the shop. One objective in the event of a complete run-out, therefore,

Table 2 Simulation experiments—set 1 13-labor-class shop. Number of labor classes having no remaining work beyond this point.

Week	Rule 1	Rule 3
13	0	0
14	2	0
15	3	0
16	3	0
17	3	1
18	3	1
19	3	1
20	3	1
21	7	1
22	9	4
23	10	5
24	11	5
25	11	8
26	11	10
27	13	13

might be to reduce, as rapidly as possible, the number of labor classes with outstanding work.

Table 2 indicates that the shortest-processing-time rule is once again quite effective. For example, as of week 21, seven of the 13 labor classes had completed all of their work, using the shortest-processing-time rule, compared to only one labor class using random dispatching. In order to empty the shop, it can be easily computed that a minimum of 90 man-weeks beyond week 14 would be required when shortest processing time is used, compared to a minimum of 132 man-weeks with the random rule. These are minimum figures and may or may not reflect what can be actually achieved.

The apparent explanation for this result is twofold. First, the shortest-processing-time rule, for a given number of utilized hours, completes more operations than any other rule. For example, both rule 1 and rule 3 achieved 100 percent utilization during the first six weeks. However, as can be seen from Table 1, there are only 255 jobs left as of the end of this six-week period with rule 1, compared to 431 jobs with rule 3. If it is assumed that there is no correlation between operation times and the number of operations per job, rule 1 had a smaller number of remaining operations as of the end of week six. With fewer remaining operations to be performed, more labor classes should have completed all of their outstanding operations, all else being equal.

The second apparent reason for this result is, of course, the increased utilization with the shortest-processing-time rule. Thus, not only does rule 1 complete more operations for a given utilization, but this rule also achieves greater utilization. Accordingly, the effectiveness of rule 1 in releasing labor for other uses is not surprising.

2.6 Summary

To summarize this first set of runs, it appears that the choice of a dispatch rule *can* effect short-run utilization even if the long-run utilization is quite insensitive to this choice. Thus, all rules required the same amount of time, 27 weeks, to empty the shop. Over any time interval less than 27 weeks, however, the shortest-processing-time rule with alternate routing yielded higher utilization than any of the other rules tested. The advantage of this rule was greatest during the first ten weeks, when an average utilization of 85.1 percent was achieved. The longest-processing-time rule with alternate routing led to an average utilization of only 81.8 percent over this same ten-week period. Although these differences are not great, they are by no means negligible. There also appears to be a significant difference among dispatch rules when the objective is to make labor available for other uses as quickly as possible. Here, once again, the shortest-processing-time rule was superior to any of the other rules tested, partly because it tended to maximize utilization over the short run, but more because of its other inherent properties.

2.7 An Attempt at Explanation

At first glance, an explanation for the apparent superiority of the shortest-processing-time rule seems rather obvious. By working on the shortest jobs available, the rate of job flow in the shop is increased. Accordingly, any load imbalances which should develop tend to be dissipated more quickly, thus reducing idle time at the downstream machines.

It is equally apparent, however, that the shortest-processing-time rule cannot maintain this advantage indefinitely, since there is no additional work available to be released to the shop. Each week, therefore, the average operation time of the jobs processed is greater than the average of the previous week. For example, with 100 percent labor utilization, 188 jobs were completed, when the shortest-processing-time rule was used, between weeks one and two. On the other hand, only 58 jobs were completed between weeks five and six, even though the utilization during this period was also 100 percent.

While the average operation time when the shortest-processing-time rule is used is increasing, the average operation time when the longest-processing-time rule is used is, of course, decreasing. At some point in time, the rate of job flow with rule 2 should begin to exceed the rate of job flow with rule 1. At this point, it would be quite reasonable to expect higher utilization with the longest-processing-time rule. This is not the case, however. Between weeks six and seven, 57 jobs were completed, with a 94 percent labor utilization, when rule 1 was used. In this same interval, 138 jobs were completed when rule 2 was used, even though utilization was only 86 percent. A similar conclusion can be reached concerning the relative performance of these two rules during weeks eight, nine, and ten.

A closer examination of the simulation output reports suggested one possible explanation. There was a very large variance in the processing times of the operations performed during this four-week interval, when rule 2 was used. Thus, although the average operation time was quite low and was becoming lower, there were some machine groups at which very lengthy operations were still being performed. This was particularly true among the larger pieces of equipment, such as

the boring mills.   As a result, sizable backlogs began to develop behind
these machines so that the amount of work available elsewhere in the
shop began to dwindle rapidly.   The result, of course, was idle time.

2.8 A Hypothesis

Although the preceding analysis was more speculative than factual,
it did, however, suggest some additional dispatching strategies to be
evaluated through simulation.   One possibility was to use the longest-
processing-time rule for as long as possible without hurting utilization.
When utilization began to fall, the longest-processing-time rule would
be abandoned in favor of the shortest-processing-time rule.   In this
way, the reasoning went, as many of the long jobs as possible would
be completed without creating idle time, and the shorter jobs would be
saved until a high rate of job flow became necessary to maintain
utilization.   The results with this strategy, rule 5, are shown in
Table 3, together with the results obtained through the exclusive use
of either rule 1 or rule 2.

Table 3 Multirule dispatching evaluation—set 1.

	RULE 1		RULE 2		RULE 5		RULE 6	
Week	% labor util.	Cum. labor util.	% labor util.	Cum. labor util.	% labor util.	Cum. labor util.	% labor util.	Cum. labor util.
1	100	100	100	100	100	100	100	100
2	100	200	100	200	100	200	100	200
3	100	300	100	300	100	300	100	300
4	100	400	100	400	100	400	100	400
5	100	500	100	500	100	500	100	500
6	100	600	100	600	100	600	100	600
7	94	694	86	686	90	690	94	694
8	71	765	65	751	79	769	79	773
9	50	815	44	795	59	828	56	829
10	36	851	23	818	39	867	36	865
Avg. Util.								
Wks. 1–10	85.1 %		81.8 %		86.7 %		86.5 %	
Wks. 7–10	62.8 %		54.5 %		66.8 %		66.3 %	

Rule 1 :   Shortest processing time.
Rule 2 :   Longest processing time.
Rule 5 :   Longest processing time until week 6, then shortest processing time.
Rule 6 :   Shortest processing time on bottleneck machines, longest processing time else-
where.

The switch from longest to shortest processing occurred in week
six.   Utilization for week six was maintained at 100 percent.   Utilization for week seven was increased from 86 percent to 90 percent,
which still was less than the 94 percent achieved through exclusive

use of rule 1. However, in weeks eight through ten, rule 5 achieved substantially higher utilization than rule 1. As a result, the ten-week average utilization for rule 5 was 1.6 percent greater than for rule 1, and 4.9 percent greater than for rule 2. Although these figures are hardly conclusive, further experimentation with this kind of a switching rule does seem worthwhile. In particular, the relationship between the time distribution of utilization and the point at which the rule is switched could be studied to ascertain sensitivity.

2.9 A Second Hypothesis

Another dispatching strategy was formulated by a somewhat different combination of the longest and shortest-processing-time rules. The shortest-processing-time rule was used through the entire simulation at those machine groups which were particularly bad bottlenecks, as determined by a more detailed examination of the preceding experiments. The longest-processing-time rule was used through the entire simulation at all other machine groups. The reasoning here was the same as with rule 5, namely, to complete as many of the long jobs as possible while the shop was heavily loaded and thus to compensate for a slow rate of job flow. The results with this strategy, rule 6, are shown in Table 3.

Once again, through a combination of the longest- and shortest-processing-time rules, utilization was improved relative to that obtained through use of the shortest-processing-time rule alone. During the first seven weeks, the utilization with rule 6 equalled the utilization with rule 1. However, in week eight, rule 6 achieved 79 percent utilization, compared to only 71 percent for rule 1. In week nine, rule 6 achieved 56 percent utilization, whereas rule 1 achieved only 50 percent. These differences are not large, but it is still noteworthy that through appropriate use of the longest-processing-time rule, which, by itself, is quite poor, utilization can be improved.

2.10 A Third Hypothesis

Further reflection upon the properties of the shortest-processing-time rule suggested still another approach to dispatching when the criterion to be maximized is utilization. If utilization can be improved through accelerating the rate of job flow, then it would seem desirable for a dispatching rule to consider the number of remaining operations, as well as the operation time, of those jobs waiting in queue. To investigate this approach, a new dispatching strategy, rule 7, was formulated. All jobs waiting in queue were divided into two classes—

those which required additional processing beyond the operation in question and those for which this was the final operation.   Higher priority was always given to the class of jobs that required additional processing, irrespective of operation time.   Within each class, however, the jobs were ordered by the shortest-processing-time rule.   Results with rule 7 are shown in Table 4.

Table 4 Multirule dispatching evaluation—set 1.

Week	RULE 1		RULE 7		RULE 5		RULE 8	
	% labor util.	Cum. labor util.	% labor util.	Cum. labor util.	% labor util.	Cum. labor util.	% labor util.	Cum. labor util.
1	100	100	100	100	100	100	100	100
2	100	200	100	200	100	200	100	200
3	100	300	100	300	100	300	100	300
4	100	400	100	400	100	400	100	400
5	100	500	100	500	100	500	100	500
6	100	600	100	600	100	600	100	600
7	94	694	95	695	90	690	93	693
8	71	765	80	775	79	769	79	772
9	50	815	61	836	59	828	63	835
10	36	851	43	879	39	867	48	883
Avg. Util.								
Wks. 1–10	85.1 %		87.9 %		86.7 %		88.3 %	
Wks. 7–10	62.8 %		69.8 %		66.8 %		70.8 %	

Rule 7 : Two-class shortest-processing-time rule.
Rule 8 : Two-class switching rule.

The superiority of this two-class shortest-processing-time rule, rule 7, seems fairly apparent compared to the original one-class shortest-processing-time rule, rule 1.   During the entire ten-week period, rule 7 improved utilization by an average of 2.8 percent per week.   During weeks seven through ten, the improvement averaged 7 percent per week.   Upon examination of these favorable results, the question arose as to whether classification of jobs according to the number of remaining operations might also improve utilization when superimposed upon one of the more complex dispatching strategies, in particular, one which of itself had yielded higher utilization during the initial ten weeks than the shortest processing time.   Accordingly, an additional simulation was conducted in which, once again, higher priority was given to the class of jobs that required additional processing.   In this experiment, however, the two classes of jobs were ordered by the longest-processing-time rule until week six, at which point each class of jobs was reordered according to the shortest-processing-time rule.   The results with this two-class switching rule, rule 8, compared with the original one-class version, rule 5, are shown in Table 4.

Once again, consideration of the number of remaining operations led to an improvement in utilization, although the difference between rule 8 and rule 5 is not as great as the difference previously noted between rule 7 and rule 1. Still, utilization did increase by 1.6 percent per week during the first ten weeks, and by 4 percent per week during weeks seven through ten.

2.11 Summary—There is a Difference

When we summarize the results discussed thus far, it does appear that appropriate dispatching can *appreciably* alter short-run utilization, even if long-run utilization is more or less fixed. Table 5 shows a

Table 5 Maximum difference between dispatch rules—set 1.

Week	RULE 2		RULE 8	
	% labor util.	Cum. labor util.	% labor util.	Cum. labor util.
1	100	100	100	100
2	100	200	100	200
3	100	300	100	300
4	100	400	100	400
5	100	500	100	500
6	100	600	100	600
7	86	686	93	693
8	65	751	79	772
9	44	795	63	835
10	23	818	48	883

Avg. Util.
Wks. 1–10   81.8 %   88.3 %
Wks. 7–10   54.5 %   70.8 %

Rule 2 : Longest processing time.
Rule 8 : Two-class switching rule.

comparison of shop performance when rule 2, the worst of the simple rules tested, is used and when rule 8, the best of the complex rules tested, is used. With rule 8, labor utilization during the initial ten weeks of the contract run-out was 6.5 percent per week higher than with rule 2. During weeks seven through ten, rule 8 achieved 16.3 percent per week higher utilization than did rule 2. Of equal note is the apparent superiority of a combination longest-shortest-processing-time rule relative to use of the shortest-processing-time rule alone. This is particularly intriguing because of the poor performance obtained with exclusive use of the longest-processing-time rule.

2.12. A Second Set of Orders

All of the results discussed thus far have been examined for only the *one* sample of orders. An appropriate question at this point, therefore, is whether or not these results can be extrapolated to *other* samples of orders from this same population. A complete replication of all the rules tested with the first sample of orders did not seem worthwhile. It did seem appropriate, however, to investigate further the relative effectiveness of:

1. The shortest-processing-time rule—rule 1.
2. The longest-processing-time rule—rule 2.
3. The switching rule—rule 5.
4. The two-class switching rule—rule 8.

Table 6 Evaluation of dispatching rules—set 2.

	RULE 1		RULE 2		RULE 5		RULE 8	
Week	% labor util.	Cum. labor util.	% labor util.	Cum. labor util.	% labor util.	Cum. labor util.	% labor util.	Cum. labor util.
1	100	100	100	100	100	100	100	100
2	100	200	100	200	100	200	100	200
3	100	300	100	300	100	300	100	300
4	100	400	100	400	100	400	100	400
5	100	500	100	500	100	500	100	500
6	94	594	92	592	100	600	100	600
7	88	682	85	677	93	693	93	693
8	79	761	82	759	82	775	83	776
9	58	819	54	813	59	834	64	840
10	41	860	33	846	32	866	35	875
Avg. Util.								
Wks. 1–10	86.0 %		84.6 %		86.6 %		87.5 %	
Wks. 6–10	72.0 %		69.2 %		73.2 %		75.0 %	
Wks. 6–9	79.8 %		78.2 %		83.5 %		85.0 %	

Rule 1 : Shortest processing time. Rule 5 : Switching Rule.
Rule 2 : Longest processing time. Rule 8 : Two-class switching rule.

Table 6 shows the results with these rules for a second sample of orders. To conserve computer time, these experiments were terminated after ten simulated weeks. The objective, therefore, was to maximize utilization during these initial ten weeks of the contract run-out.

In general, the differences between the rules were substantially less than for the first-order sample. However, the *ranking* of the rules was exactly the same. The longest-processing-time rule, rule 2, yielded the poorest utilization over the initial ten-week interval. The shortest-processing-time rule, rule 1, improved utilization, relative to rule 2, by 1.4 percent per week. However, the switching rule, rule 5, raised utilization still further, although improvement was not large when averaged over the ten-week interval. The difference between rule 1 and rule 5 is more apparent during the initial nine weeks of the contract run-out. In week six, for example, rule 5 achieved 100 percent labor utilization compared to only 94 percent for rule 1. In week seven, utilization with rule 5 was 5 percent higher than with rule 1. In week eight, the difference was 3 percent and in week nine 1 percent. Finally, once again, rule 8, the two-class switching rule, achieved highest utilization.

2.13 A Third Set of Orders

Table 7 shows the results with these same four rules for a third sample of orders from this same population. Once more, the differences between the rules were not substantial. Over the initial ten

Table 7 Evaluation of dispatching rules—set 3.

	RULE 1		RULE 2		RULE 5		RULE 8	
Week	% labor util.	Cum. labor util.	% labor util.	Cum. labor util.	% labor util.	Cum. labor util.	% labor util.	Cum. labor util.
1	100	100	100	100	100	100	100	100
2	100	200	100	200	100	200	100	200
3	100	300	100	300	100	300	100	300
4	100	400	100	400	100	400	100	400
5	100	500	100	500	100	500	100	500
6	98	598	100	600	100	600	99	599
7	93	691	86	686	98	698	100	699
8	69	760	62	748	75	773	74	773
9	47	807	31	779	39	812	50	823
10	30	837	30	809	25	837	32	855
Avg. Util.								
Wks. 1–10	83.7 %		80.9 %		83.7 %		85.5 %	
Wks. 6–10	67.4 %		61.8 %		67.4 %		71.0 %	
Wks. 6–9	76.8 %		69.8 %		78.0 %		80.8 %	
Wks. 6–8	86.7 %		82.7 %		91.0 %		91.0 %	

Rule 1: Shortest processing time.
Rule 2: Longest processing time.
Rule 5: Switching rule.
Rule 8: Two-class switching rule.

weeks, however, the longest-processing-time rule, rule 2, yielded lowest utilization, and the two-class switching rule, rule 8, yielded highest utilization, which is consistent with the two previous results. With this sample, however, rules 1 and 5 achieved equal utilization during the initial ten weeks. Nevertheless, rule 5 was superior to rule 1 in maintaining utilization during the early part of the contract run-out, specifically in weeks six, seven, and eight. Furthermore, no attempt was made to find the optimal point at which rule 5 should switch from longest to shortest processing time. Therefore, these results give no reason to doubt that a *combination* of longest and shortest processing could once again yield higher ten-week utilization than the shortest-processing-time rule alone.

2.14 Some Conclusions

In concluding this portion of paper, it would seem fair to make the following statements:

1. The longest-processing-time rule is an undesirable method of dispatching under conditions of decreasing shop load. Not only does this rule lead to relatively poor short-run utilization, but it also seems reasonable to infer that this rule would also be unsatisfactory when the objective is to make the working force available for other uses as quickly as possible.

2. The shortest-processing-time rule is a good but certainly not the best method of dispatching when the objective is to maximize short-run utilization under conditions of decreasing shop load. On the other hand, this rule appears quite good for facilitating the rapid reallocation of labor to other projects.

3. Various combinations of the longest- and shortest-processing-time rules can be found which will yield higher short-run utilization than the shortest-processing-time rule alone.

4. Giving higher priority to the class of jobs which have more than one remaining operation is an effective method fo improving short-run utilization. Furthermore, it seems reasonable to infer that the two-class shortest-processing-time rule would be more effective than the one-class shortest-processing-time rule, when the objective is to reallocate the working force to some other activity as quickly as possible.

5. Although in some cases improvements in short-run utilization can be achieved by appropriate dispatching, it appears that the composition of the shop load and the configuration of the shop itself place very definite limits upon what can be accomplished with a dispatch rule. For example, even a limited capability for alternate routing can lead to a very large improvement in shop performance compared to the difference in the utilizations achieved by some of the dispatch rules.

3. LABOR FLEXIBILITY

Based upon these conclusions, the direction of the research was changed to place greater emphasis upon questions relating to shop configuration, since neither the level nor the mix of the job load could be controlled within desirable limits. An exploration of the potential for increased *labor flexibility* seemed particularly worthwhile for the following reasons:

1. With the exception of two or three machine groups, there was more than enough machine capacity in the shop to handle a wide range of possible order mixes. Bottlenecks could generally be attributed to the limited labor resource.

2. Although the alternate routing capability might be increased through appropriate manufacturing engineering, the opportunities here seemed quite limited.

3. Increased labor flexibility seemed an effective way by which to reduce the number of men required when the shop load is decreasing. As an extreme, it was observed in the preceding section that at least one man must be retained in each labor class for which some work still remains. To the extent that the various labor classes are interchangeable, this requirement becomes less severe.

4. There are many ancillary benefits from increased labor flexibility, such as simplified personnel management, lower bumping costs, etc.

The decision to increase labor flexibility involves a substantial commitment involving several costs, such as: (1) training, (2) transfer of personnel, (3) higher wage rates, (4) less specialized labor. Although changing dispatch rules is easy and to be expected when required by changes in the order mix, it is obviously impractical to make frequent adjustments in the configuration of flexibility. For one thing, increasing labor flexibility is largely an irreversible process; upgrading is much easier than downgrading. Therefore, the decision concerning labor flexibility should be based upon the consideration of whatever range of order mixes seems reasonably likely to occur.

3.1 A Hypothetical One-Labor-Class Shop

As a starting point in the evaluation of labor flexibility, simulations were conducted in which it was assumed that all 40 men were pooled into one extremely versatile labor class that could operate all machines in the shop. Although one-labor-class shops do indeed exist, this proposal is not practical for the shop in question. The intent was merely to determine the maximum benefits which could be attained through increased labor flexibility. Accordingly, no attempt was made to consider any of the costs of flexibility to which reference was previously made. For purposes of comparison, the initial experiments with labor flexibility were conducted on one of the same samples of orders which was used for the thirteen-labor class shop.

Table 8 Comparsion of a 13-labor-class shop with a one-labor-class shop—set 1, both shops using rule 3—the random rule.

Week	13 Labor Classes			1 Labor Class		
	% labor util.	Cum. labor util.	no. jobs	% labor util.	Cum. labor util.	no. jobs
1	100	100	912	100	100	911
2	100	200	828	100	200	814
3	100	300	745	100	300	725
4	100	400	655	100	400	632
5	100	500	543	100	500	527
6	100	600	431	100	600	416
7	91	691	336	100	700	314
8	66	757	263	100	800	220
9	48	805	223	80	880	126
10	29	834	187	56	936	72
11	31	865	147	26	962	45
12	29	894	110	13	975	32
Total weeks to empty shop	27			19		

Table 8 shows a comparison of shop performance with rule 3, the random rule with alternate routing, in both the present thirteen-labor-class shop and in the assumed one-labor-class shop. The advantages of greater labor flexibility seem quite apparent. The one-labor-class shop achieved significantly higher utilization throughout the entire run-out period. As a result, the total number of weeks required to complete all jobs was substantially reduced from 27 to 19. Accordingly, if no additional work were to be received, no one need be retained beyond week 19.

The number of men required beyond week 19 in the *thirteen*-labor-class shop is a function of the number of labor classes which, as of that time, have not completed all outstanding work. This number was considerably reduced, it was found, through use of the shortest-processing-time rule. Even so, a *minimum* of 39 man-weeks would be required beyond week 19 as can easily be verified by reference to Table 2. Random dispatching would require a minimum of 69 man-weeks beyond week 19, for this case. In addition, increased flexibility would, of course, facilitate transfers or layoffs *prior* to week 19. Thus, in the event of a complete contract run-out, increased labor flexibility would facilitate a more rapid reallocation of the working force.

3.2 A Smaller Change in Flexibility

Qualitatively, this result is not surprising. On the other hand, the *magnitude* of the improvement is certainly noteworthy. Upon examination of these results, the question arose as to whether most of this improvement could be obtained with a less drastic and more realistic increase in labor flexibility. A particularly intriguing possibility was to retain the current thirteen-labor-class structure, but to superimpose upon it a small, extremely versatile class of men, capable of performing any required operation. The members of this very flexible class could be selected from among the more skilled of the current operators, and given whatever additional training might be required.

In order to explore this possibility further, a simulation was conducted in which it was assumed that five members of the 40-man working force could operate all machines in the shop. With this configuration, the entire contract run-out once more required only 19 weeks, the *same* amount of time required by the one-labor-class shop. Admittedly, these five men were not selected at random. On the other hand, it should be noted that so long as any *one* man is capable of operating all machines in the shop, it becomes unnecessary to retain someone in each of the thirteen labor classes for which work still remains. This approach to flexibility would seem to be quite attractive not only for a complete run-out, but also for sustained shop operation, in which case the very flexible class could relieve labor bottlenecks wherever they occurred.

3.3 Flexibility—An Alternative to Inventory

Before leaving Table 8, one final observation should be made. With 263 jobs in the shop during week eight, the thirteen-labor-class shop achieved only 66 percent utilization. On the other hand, with only 126 jobs available in week nine, the one-labor-class shop achieved 80 percent utilization. Further experimentation would be required to determine the utilization-load relationships under steady-state conditions. However, the suggestion is that quite a substantial reduction in in-process inventory can be achieved through an increase in labor flexibility. It would appear, therefore, that labor flexibility is an alternative investment not only to finished inventory, but to in-process inventory as well. In other words, an investment in flexibility may reduce the required investment in inventories.

3.4 Labor vs. Machine Flexibility

Another interesting question concerns the relationship between labor flexibility and alternate routing. In analyzing results of shop performance with thirteen labor classes, the advantages of even a limited alternate routing capability were quite apparent. The extent to which alternate routing is possible can be considered as a measure of machine flexibility. Therefore, it seemed worthwhile to explore the relationship between the flexibility of labor and the flexibility of machines. Accordingly, a simulation of the one-labor-class shop was conducted; rule 4, the random rule *without* alternate routing, was used. Table 9 shows a comparison of shop performance with and

Table 9 Alternate routing and labor flexibility—set 1.

| | 13 Labor Classes | | | | 1 Labor Class | | | |
| | RULE 3 | | RULE 4 | | RULE 3 | | RULE 4 | |
Week	% labor util.	Cum. labor util.	% labor util.	Cum. labor util.	% labor util.	Cum. labor util.	% labor util.	Cum. labor util.
1	100	100	100	100	100	100	100	100
2	100	200	100	200	100	200	100	200
3	100	300	100	300	100	300	100	300
4	100	400	99	399	100	400	100	400
5	100	500	99	498	100	500	100	500
6	100	600	99	597	100	600	100	600
7	91	691	85	682	100	700	100	700
8	66	757	51	733	100	800	100	800
9	48	805	36	769	80	880	61	861
10	29	834	26	795	56	936	34	895
11	31	865	30	825	26	962	24	919
12	29	894	22	847				
13	30	924	18	865				

Rule 3 : Random rule with alternate routing.
Rule 4 : Random rule without alternate routing.

without alternate routing in both the one- and thirteen-labor-class shops.

With one labor class, the maximum improvement in performance due to machine flexibility occurs during the initial eleven weeks of the contract run-out. By week eleven, machine flexibility has improved utilization by an average of 4 percent per week. During the same eleven-week period with thirteen labor classes, the improvement due to machine flexibility averaged 3.6 percent per week. By week thirteen, however, the alternate routing improved utilization by 4.5 percent per week.

The marginal value of alternate routing seems to be fairly independent of the level of labor flexibility, for the conditions tested. This result might be explained in terms of a two-fold relationship between labor flexibility and machine flexibility. Thus, the need for alternate routing is no doubt greater when a low level of labor flexibility exists, because bottlenecks are more likely to develop. However, it seems reasonable that the *opportunities* for alternate routing would be greater, once the need arose, when a high level of labor flexibility exists, since labor capacity as well as machine capacity must be available at the alternate machine group before alternate routing can take place. The exact nature of this relationship will, of course, vary according to shop conditions. However, to the extent that the marginal value of machine flexibility is independent of the degree of labor flexibility, and vice versa, the total cost of achieving any given level of shop performance should be greatly reduced. The point is that the cost functions for increasing shop flexibility are no doubt of a nonlinear nature. For example, whereas some of the more skilled workers (toolmakers) might be economically trained to operate every machine in the shop, the cost of providing this training in the case of less skilled workers (sensitive drill operators, for example) would probably be prohibitive. Consequently, it would seem much more economical to consider a *combination* of machine flexibility, labor flexibility, and also order flexibility (alternate sequencing), rather than to focus exclusively upon any one of these approaches.

4. FLEXIBILITY AND DISPATCHING

The final topic to be considered concerns the *relationship* between the two principle subjects of this paper, namely, flexibility and dispatching rules. The desirability of any dispatch rule is a function of the order mix and the shop configuration. Since increased labor flexibility substantially alters the shop configuration, it seemed appropriate to re-evaluate some of the dispatch rules previously examined for the thirteen-labor-class shop. Table 10 shows the results obtained with rule 1, the shortest-processing-time rule, and with rule 2, the longest-processing-time rule, for the one-labor-class shop. Results with rules 3 and 4 are also shown.

4.1 Longest vs. Shortest Processing Time

During the initial seven weeks, all rules achieved 100 percent labor utilization. A difference between the rules did not occur until week eight, at which point the the shortest-processing-time rule began to get into difficulty. In week nine, utilization with this rule fell still further, so that during the initial nine weeks, rule 1 achieved only a 96.3 percent average weekly utilization, compared with a 98.7 percent average for rule 2. During the initial nine weeks in the thirteen-labor-class shop, it will be recalled, rule 1 achieved average weekly utilization of 90.6 percent compared with only 88.3 percent for rule 2. Therefore, as a result of increased labor flexibility, the relative desirability of rules 1 and 2 has been substantially reversed.

Table 10 Simulation experiments—set 1, one labor-class shop.

Week	RULE 1			RULE 2			RULE 3			RULE 4		
	% labor util.	Cum. labor util.	Avg. no. jobs shop	% labor util.	Cum. labor util.	Avg. no. jobs shop	% labor util.	Cum. labor util.	Avg. no. jobs shop	% labor util.	Cum. labor util.	Avg. no. jobs shop
1	100	100	748	100	100	953	100	100	911	100	100	911
2	100	200	554	100	200	921	100	200	814	100	200	814
3	100	300	433	100	300	872	100	300	725	100	300	725
4	100	400	340	100	400	810	100	400	632	100	400	632
5	100	500	268	100	500	749	100	500	527	100	500	520
6	100	600	198	100	600	645	100	600	416	100	600	403
7	100	700	144	100	700	547	100	700	314	100	700	305
8	95	795	102	100	800	422	100	800	220	100	800	214
9	72	867	74	88	888	202	80	880	126	61	861	132
10	52	919	50	50	938	103	56	936	72	34	895	86
11	29	948	31	18	956	60	26	962	45	24	919	60
12	22	970	21	10	966	51	13	975	32	20	939	50
.	.			.			.			.		
.	.			.			.			.		
.	.			.			.			.		
Total weeks to empty shop	20			19			19			19		

Rule 1: Shortest processing time with alternate routing.
Rule 2: Longest processing time with alternate routing.
Rule 3: Random rule with alternate routing.
Rule 4: Random rule without alternate routing.

4.2 Discussion

This result is not inconsistent with the hypothesis developed previously concerning the advantages of the longest-processing-time rule when used appropriately. In the thirteen-labor-class shop, it seemed appropriate to use the longest-processing-time rule at all machine groups during the initial stages of the run-out when the shop was overloaded. Favorable results were also obtained when the longest-processing-time rule was used for the entire run-out at those machine groups which typically were not bottlenecks. The point is that the longest-processing-time rule seems to be helpful, in a period of decreasing shop load, if it is used where a high rate of job flow is not required in order to maintain utilization. An increase in labor flexibility *reduces* the requirement for a high rate of job flow by *increasing* the mobility of the working force. In other words, increased labor flow is compensating for decreased job flow.

The obvious question at this point is why rule 2 does not maintain its advantage relative to rule 1 beyond week nine. The answer appears to involve the bottlenecks caused by the large machines. For example, in week ten, there was an average of 102 jobs in the shop using rule 2. Of this number, however, 47 jobs were in queue at machine group 7, and 16 jobs were in queue at machine group 12. Each of these groups consists of only one machine, so that increased labor flexibility was of no value in relieving these overloaded queues.

Once again, the explanation is more speculative than factual. However, one additional simulation was conducted in order to probe this matter a little more deeply. Rule 5, the switching rule, was used, with the change from longest to shortest processing time taking place in week nine. Utilization in week ten was increased from 50 to 53 percent, compared to the 52 percent achieved by rule 1. Although not a substantial improvement, this result is certainly consistent with the results previously discussed.

4.3 Hazards of Extrapolation

In any event, it would appear that the shortest-processing-time rule is a less desirable method of dispatching for the one-labor-class shop if the objective is to maintain utilization during the initial ten weeks. Moreover, there is no reason to use the shortest-processing-time rule to faciliate a more rapid transfer or layoff of personnel as was the case with the thirteen-labor-class shop. Here, then, is a very strong relationship between the configuration of a shop and the relative desirability of various dispatch rules for this shop. This conclusion suggests that a great deal of caution should be used in attempting to extrapolate results with various scheduling and dispatch rules. We need to know a lot more before generalizations can be made.

4.4 An Overloaded Shop

There is another aspect of the relationship between shop flexibility and dispatching which can be particularly useful when the shop is heavily loaded. Under these conditions, some form of due date dispatching would no doubt be used.   In this case, increased labor flexibility might still be advantageous even though utilization would no longer be a problem.   The point is that an increase in labor flexibility permits consideration of a larger set of jobs when one is selecting the next job to be processed.   Thus, for example, in the one-labor-class shop discussed previously, a worker can select his next job from all jobs in the shop, subject only to the availability of a machine at the required machine group.   In this way, increased labor flexibility would permit a closer adherence to the required job-due dates. Similar remarks can be made concerning the use of alternate routing under these conditions.

A very limited amount of experimentation has been done to evaluate the effectiveness of increased labor flexibility under such conditions of heavy shop load.   Simulations were conducted for both the thirteen- and the one-labor-class shops: an operation due date rule without alternate routing was used.   Although both shops achieved essentially 100 percent labor utilization, the more flexible shop reduced the standard deviation in job lateness from 16 days to 12 days.   Therefore, it appears that increased shop flexibility might reduce the need for overtime when the shop is overloaded, by reducing the standard deviation in job lateness.

5. CONCLUSION

The customary approach to problems of production leveling is to determine aggregate production rates and the required labor force to produce at these rates in such a way as to balance, most economically, the various costs involved [2].   In other words, this type of approach looks at the business from a more or less aggregate point of view and considers the pertinent cost functions as given.

The purpose of this paper has been to explore the use of a more *detailed* computer simulation in order to examine and then modify the existing cost functions.   In particular, two approaches to this problem were found useful:

1. The use of a more sophisticated dispatching strategy consisting of a *combination* of several simple rules.

2. An increase in labor flexibility to improve performance and to facilitate changes to the labor supply when required.

From a theoretical point of view, an increase in labor flexibility, or, indeed, any change in shop configuration, is perhaps uninteresting, since this approach solves the scheduling problem by, in effect, removing it.   On the other hand, it must be recognized that even the "optimal" method of scheduling and dispatching must be limited in effectiveness by the configuration of the shop in question. From a practical point of view, then, the question of improved shop performance should be approached from the standpoint of possible modifications to the shop, as well as from the standpoint of better scheduling and dispatching for the given shop. Indeed, the results of this paper suggest that the former approach is considerably more effective than the latter for the particular problem studied.

6. FUTURE RESEARCH

The objective of our research in Production Control Service is to design and develop rules and principles for efficient shop operation. It is our thesis that a "theory" of production control can be developed, whereby for a given set of shop conditions, a set of operating rules can be formulated which will help meet the objectives of the business.

The development of such a theory is not an easy task. Even for the very simple and specialized conditions and objectives considered in this paper, much more experimentation is required. More complex decision rules must be considered, and additional samples of orders must be tested. There is no shortage of ideas; to the contrary, this problem is difficult because of the many alternatives which present themselves.

The cost of experimentation has been considerably reduced by the development of simulation programs such as GEMS. Still, one of our premises in undertaking such a vast research project is that simulation costs can be still further reduced. This is particularly important when it becomes necessary to consider other aspects of the factory scheduling problems, such as shop loading, master scheduling, and inventory policies. Accordingly, the design and development of more efficient simulators, is a very important part of our future research plans.

REFERENCES

1. Conway, R. W., B. M. Johnson, and W. L. Maxwell, "An Experimental Investigation of Priority Dispatching," *Journal of Industrial Engineering*, May, 1960.

2. Holt, C., F. Modigliani, J. F. Muth, and H. A. Simon, *Planning Production, Inventories and Work Force*, Englewood Cliffs, N. J.: Prentice-Hall, Inc., 1960.

3. Morse, P. M., *Queues, Inventories, and Maintenance*, New York: John Wiley & Sons, Inc., 1958.

17

Network Scheduling by the Shortest-operation Discipline

R. W. Conway, W. L. Maxwell
CORNELL UNIVERSITY

Dispatching is the final step of the production-scheduling process. It is the final decision that is made at the moment that action is imminent. It provides an answer to the question "What should be done next?" that is asked each time a machine or a man completes a task. The sequence of answers to this question represents the actual machine schedule. Dispatching can be considered to operate according to a priority system: the task selected for immediate assignment from among those available is the one with the smallest value of an index called a priority.[1] The study of the dispatching function then becomes a

[1] The assignment of a low numerical index to "high" priority items is perhaps contrary to the usual usage of the word priority, but it is convenient for the following discussion and is rather standard practice in the literature of the field.

This paper was presented at the Factory Scheduling Conference, Carnegie Institute of Technology, May 10–12, 1961. Reprinted from Operations Research 10 (1962), 51–73. A research report of the Cornell Production Control Research Committee, a co-operative research project of Cornell University; The General Electric Company; Touche, Ross, Bailey and Smart; and the Western Electric Company. The authors are indebted to referee J. R. Jackson for many helpful criticisms and suggestions.

study of the different mechanisms which may be used to assign these priority values to the tasks.

The dispatching function is not the complete scheduling process, and probably is not even the most important part of the process. It is likely that the preceding decisions in planning and loading are of greater consequence than the questions of detailed order that are decided by dispatching. But dispatching is nevertheless deserving of systematic study. There are almost an unlimited number of ways to assign priority, and there is evidence that there are interesting differences in the performance of these various methods. It is intuitively obvious and hardly deserving of demonstration that different methods of assigning priority will affect the relative progress of individual jobs. It has also been demonstrated that the choice of priority assignment method can affect aggregate measures of shop performance [2, 6]. Although the dispatching function is not in itself the complete scheduling procedure, it is an essential phase of any scheduling procedure. It is a function that must be performed, by intent or by default, and it might as well be performed properly. There is no real question of practicality. Many different means for assigning priority are essentially equally easy to implement, so that one can readily take advantage of any benefit that may be obtained by appropriate selection of a procedure, regardless of how small that benefit may be.

Perhaps more important that any benefits obtained directly from the selection of an appropriate dispatching procedure is the effect of the dispatching procedure on the over-all scheduling process. The rate at which individual jobs progress through the shop is important in any scheduling procedure, and vital assumptions about this rate must be made. This rate and the validity of the assumptions depend importantly on the dispatching procedure which is employed. It would seem that an understanding of the performance of the dispatching function under different methods of priority assignment could contribute appreciably to the design of a complete scheduling procedure.

It seems clear that any good scheduling procedure, including those that would periodically plan activities for an appreciable interval of time, must include some provision for "last-minute review." A manufacturing shop is an excellent example of an "increasing information" process. Perhaps the only point about which an advance scheduling procedure can be certain is that by the time that a particular decision is to be implemented at least part of the information upon which that decision was based will be incorrect. Tool failure, machine breakdown, employee absenteeism, variability in processing times, material shortage, necessity of rework, design changes, and several score other phenomena contribute to the assurance that the situation will be changed by the time that implementation is imminent, and will demand some form of last-minute review. This review can take the form of a substantial replanning of a long period of time and still be included under the definition of a dispatching procedure given here. Only the cost and mechanics of executing the procedure in "real-time" limit what can be done with a dispatching procedure. The familiar priority rules—first come first served; earliest due-date—are examples of the simplest type of dispatching procedure for which the information requirements are minimal and the mechanics of computation and implementation are trivial. More complicated rules can certainly be used if it can be demonstrated that their superior performance justifies the increased difficulty of implementation.

There are several interesting ways of classifying priority assignment procedures. Jackson has usefully distinguished between static and dynamic procedures [8, 9]. Alternatively, one can categorize procedures according to their information horizons. One can segregate strictly *local* procedures in which the priorities are entirely a function of characteristics of the particular job in question. They do not depend in any way upon the status of the shop, or the presence or absence of characteristics of other jobs.

A local priority rule of considerable interest is the *shortest-operation rule*. Priorities assigned to the job at each operation are proportional to the processing time for that operation. This rule appears to have some significant virtues, but at the same time some unfortunately serious drawbacks. The purpose of the present paper is to summarize the literature which applies to this rule, and to describe some experimental results we have obtained.

1. SINGLE-STAGE SEQUENCING PROBLEMS

Some insight into the performance of different local priority procedures and, in particular, the performance of the shortest-operation rule, may be obtained by examining simple sequencing problems. Isolate a single machine, a set of tasks, and an interval of time. Consider only the problems of sequencing these n jobs on one machine [12, 14]. Each of these n jobs has many different properties—value, urgency, weight, customer importance, etc.

Let
v_{ij} be the value for the ith job of the jth property.
Also let
s_i = the processing time for the ith job (including set-up time, if any). Assume that set-up is independent of preceding job.
C_i = the time at which the ith job is completed. Since all jobs

are presumed starting at the same time $= 0$, C_i is also the manufacturing interval for the ith job.

Applying the shortest-operation rule, the jobs are sequenced so that

$$s_1 \leq s_2 \leq s_3 \leq \cdots \leq s_n$$

(the jobs are renumbered, if necessary).

The following are true :[2]

1. The total completion time ($\sum C_i$) is minimized.
2. The average completion time ($\sum C_i/n$) is minimized.
3. The average number of jobs in process ($\sum C_i/\max_i(C_i)$) is minimized.
4. The average waiting time [$\sum(C_i - s_i)/n$] is minimized.
5. If due-date of the ith job is d_i and "lateness" is defined as $(C_i - d_i)$, then the average lateness [$\sum(C_i - d_i)/n$] is minimized.

For this simple case the shortest-operation rule is an optimum rule *with respect to these particular measures* of performance. Rules based on any other characteristic of the job will in general produce a greater value of each of these measures. These measures are entirely dependent on processing time—assigning priority by any rule or criterion that is independent of the processing time is equivalent to choosing a random permutation, and the expected value of these measures is the same for all other rules.

Even when the measure of performance in the same n job-one machine situation is weighted by one of the other job properties, the processing times are still important. The total weighted completion time

$$\sum v_{ij}C_i$$

is minimized by sequencing the jobs so that

$$\frac{s_1}{v_{ij}} \leq \frac{s_2}{v_{2j}} \leq \cdots \leq \frac{s_n}{v_{nj}}.$$

Measures analogous to 2 through 5 above are also minimized by this sequence. If the completion times are weighted by a linear combination of the properties, then

$$\sum_i \sum_j a_j v_{ij}C_i \qquad (a_j \geq 0, \text{ all } j)$$

is minimized by sequencing the jobs so that

$$\frac{s_1}{\sum_j a_j v_{1j}} \leq \frac{s_2}{\sum_j a_j v_{2j}} \leq \cdots \leq \frac{s_n}{\sum_j a_j v_{nj}}.$$

This example serves well to illustrate both the advantage of the

---

[2] These are all transitive criteria, and proof is easily accomplished by showing the effect of pairwise exchanges. A proof is given in [14].

shortest-operation rule and the equivalence of rules that do not consider processing time. It does not effectively illustrate the unfortunate
aspects of the performance of the shortest-operation rule. It does
point up the fact that, for better or worse, the rule can only be applied if there is some a priori knowledge of the processing time of
individual jobs.

The generalization of these results to situations involving more than
one machine has not yet been accomplished.

2. SIMPLE QUEUING SYSTEMS

The performance of different priority rules can be examined in the
context of a queuing system. The question of discipline in a queuing system has received surprisingly little attention in the literature,
considering the fact that the discipline is usually the easiest and sometimes the only degree of freedom available to one who would improve a queuing operation. The majority of the queuing literature
assumes a first come, first served discipline, either explicitly or implicitly, but in a great many cases the assumption is gratuitous and
the results are applicable to a much larger class of disciplines.

There are a number of notable exceptions [1, 3, 4, 8, 10, 13].
Cobham [4] was apparently the first to publish results for nonpre-
emptive priority queuing systems. He obtained expressions for the
expected number in the system and for the expected waiting time
for each of a finite number of priority classes. Kesten and Runnen-
berg [10] generalized these results and derived the distributions of
both of these quantities. Phipps [13] has examined the shortest-
operation discipline—the special case of a continuum of priority classes in which the priority class is the actual servicing time of the
arriving unit—for a single-channel, unsaturated ($\rho < 1$) queuing system
with exponentially distributed interarrival intervals and arbitrary service distribution and with any priority discipline of the following type:

> A procedure that assigns arriving units to priority classes according to
> some *time independent probability distribution*. The server is to select
> from queue the unit of the priority class with the lowest number. Ties
> are resolved in the order of the units' arrivals.

These results permit the following statements to be made:

1. If the expected service time is the same for each priority class,
then the over-all mean waiting time and the mean system state is
the same for all priority rules.

2. If a priority class can be divided into two subclasses such that
the expected processing time of one subclass is smaller than the ex-

pected processing time of the other, and if a lower priority value is assigned to the subclass with the smaller expected processing time, both the over-all mean waiting time and the mean system state will be decreased. (Note that system state refers to the number of *units* in the system. The mean amount of "work" waiting will not be changed.)

3. If the expected service times of arriving units differ, then the over-all mean waiting time and the mean system state are *minimized* by numbering the priority classes in the order of expected service time.

4. If the expected service times of arriving units differ, then the over-all mean waiting time and the mean system state are *maximized* by numbering the priority classes in the opposite order as the expected service time.

5. If the waiting times of units of priority class p are weighted by a value v, the over-all mean weighted waiting time is minimized by assigning priority class in the order of the ratio $s/v : s_1/v_1 \leq s_2/v_2 \leq \ldots$ where s_p is the expected service time of the pth class.

Thus in the simple queuing system the shortest-operation rule is optimum for certain mean values of system performance with respect to a limited class of priority rules. However, one can begin to appreciate one of the difficulties associated with the use of this rule by considering the plight of the members of the priority class with the greatest processing time—these jobs will be processed only when no job from any other priority class remains in the queue. This can lead to extraordinarily long waiting times for individual jobs even though the mean waiting time has been minimized. There is also the problem that some a priori knowledge of the expected processing time of arriving units is necessary to apply this rule.

3. NETWORKS OF QUEUES

A job shop can be characterized as a network of queues. Some understanding of the performance of priority rules in such a shop would be provided by the generalization of the results for the simple queuing system. Unfortunately, this has not yet been accomplished. The most powerful analytical result available to date is certainly Jackson's decomposition principle [7]:

Given a network of queues such that

1. The interarrival times for arrivals to each center from outside the system are exponentially distributed.

2. The service times at each center are exponentially distributed.

3. The transition matrix giving the probabilities of passing between pairs of centers is fixed in time.

4. The priority rule at each center is first come, first served. Then the individual centers of the network can be treated independently as simple queues.

Essentially this result depends upon the fact that the output of a queuing system with both interarrival times and service times exponentially distributed is also exponential. This is a well-known result when the discipline is first come, first served. We would conjecture that it is true for any priority discipline such that the distribution of processing times is the same for each priority class. If this is the case, then the following statement should also be true:

Given a network of queues that satisfy 1, 2, and 3 (above) then all local priority rules such that the distribution of processing times is the same for each priority class are equivalent with respect to mean system state and mean waiting time. When the distribution of processing times is different for different priority classes, the output of an exponential-exponential queue is not exponential, and Jackson's proof no longer applies.

It is interesting to note that the same condition—equal expected processing time for each priority class—implies both the equivalence of all priority assignments in the single-channel queue, and the independence of queues in the network configuration. Rules which are "different" in the single-channel queue (i.e., the expected processing time is not the same for each priority class) also cause the queues of a network to be nonindependent. Whether the magnitude of the difference is increased or decreased in the network configuration is not known.

4. AN EXPERIMENTAL INVESTIGATION

The single machine case has been quite extensively studied and is rather well understood in both the n job sequencing and the queuing models. In each case the shortest-operation discipline is known to be an important limiting discipline that is optimal with respect to certain measures of performance. In neither case are there comparable results available for an m machine network, and there is no basis for optimism about the early attainment of such results.

In order to explore the performance of the shortest-operation discipline in the inherently more interesting and important m machine case, we resorted to an experimental investigation of networks of queues by means of digital simulation. In the initial phase of this work, reported here, we were interested in the following questions:

1. Can it be shown statistically that the shortest-operation rule is

different from various other priority rules (with respect to aggregate measures of performance)?

2. What is the magnitude of this difference, and to what extent does it depend upon system parameters such as load ratio, number of centers, nature of the transition matrix?

3. What is the sensitivity of the shortest-operation rule to imperfect, or unprecise, a priori knowledge of processing times?

4. To what extent can the disadvantages of the shortest-operation rule be alleviated by modifying the rule or combining it with other disciplines?

5. Can it be established that the shortest-operation rule is the optimum local rule with respect to minimizing mean system state?

Questions 1 and 5 warrant some preliminary comment. Ordinarily tests of hypotheses are not particularly interesting or useful problem statements—when two "treatments" that are in fact physically distinct are being compared, one would expect there to be some difference in response, however small. Failure to reject the hypothesis that the two responses are equal really just means that the sample size was inadequate to establish the significance of that difference. In this case, which is still a theoretical rather than a physical investigation, the fact that many different priority rules have been shown to be completely equivalent in simple situations makes the formal test of the hypothesis of difference worthwhile.

The question of optimality raised in 5 is of more than academic interest. Optimality with respect to minimum system state and with respect to the set of local rules is hardly sufficient to justify immediate and widespread application. But it would nonetheless be important for its provision of a lower limit—an absolute standard against which other procedures could be compared. Other local procedures having certain desirable properties could be compared to this standard to determine the price exacted for these properties. Nonlocal procedures, which presumably entail greater information requirements, could be compared to the best local procedure to evaluate the benefit obtained from the additional information. However, the demonstration of optimality by experimental means is a very difficult task. One can, of course, demonstrate nonoptimality by the exhibition of a counterexample, but the failure to exhibit such a counterexample is, at best, inconclusive. By comparative tests, one can demonstrate the superiority of one particular procedure over all others tested, but the extension of these results to an assertion of optimality with respect to a set of procedures not all of whose members were tested is, in general, a difficult and hazardous undertaking.

The experimental investigation was carried out by means of a queue network simulation program for the Burroughs 220 [5]. Throughout the investigation the following conditions were maintained:

1. The distribution of processing times was the same for each machine in the network—in each case a discrete approximation to the exponential distribution with mean of ten time units.

2. The number of jobs in the shop at each point in time was held constant—when a job was released from the shop, another job was immediately released to the shop. Ordinarily one would fix the release rate and thus the shop utilization and observe the resulting distribution of number of jobs in the shop. The necessary sample sizes were reduced by inverting this process—fixing the number of jobs and observing the utilization and release rate.

Separate runs were made for the number of jobs equal to two, four, and six times the number of machines.

3. Two extreme types of transition matrix were employed. The *pure job shop* matrix had all equal entries (except for zeros on the principal diagonal), and the *pure flow shop* matrix had only zeros and ones in the matrix. A *pure job shop* is thus a shop in which a job leaving one machine is equally likely to go to any other machine in the shop (including an "exit" machine). A *pure flow shop* is a shop in which there is only one path that work can follow—each machine has a fixed predecessor and successor. In the case of job-shop runs, the number of operations/job was limited to nine for convenience in the program files; in the case of the flow shop runs the number of operations/job was equal to the number of machines in the shop.

4. Comparisons between rules were made on the same set of sample jobs. The sample size was at least 2000 jobs in each case. In several cases considerably longer runs were made, as indicated in the tables.

The dispatching rules considered are the following (abbreviations in parentheses are used in result tables):

Random Rule (R): jobs are selected for assignment at random from among those waiting. This rule was selected to represent the class of local rules that do not consider processing time—first come first served (FCFS), rank by value, select at random, etc.—which are assumed to be equivalent with respect to mean system measures.

Shortest-Operation Rule (S): job is selected for assignment that will take the least amount of processing time. Ties are resolved by first come, first served. It is assumed that the processing time for each operation is precisely known a priori.

Shortest-Operation Rule under Imperfect Prediction (S, X): same as Shortest-Operation Rule except that the processing times are not precisely known a priori. X is an index of the ability to predict the processing times. For a processing time S the errors of estimate were approximately normally distributed with mean 0 and standard deviation X_S. (Any negative estimates that resulted were taken to be zero.) Note that $S, 0 = S$ and $S, \infty = R$.

Two-Class Shortest-Operation Rule (2S, B): jobs are considered either short or long—preference being given to short jobs. A job is short if its processing time (which is precisely known a priori) is less than B.

Truncated Shortest-Operation Rule (TS, C): same as Shortest-Operation Rule except that an upper bound, C, is placed on the time that a job can spend in any one queue. When a job has waited for C time units it takes precedence in assignment regardless of its processing time. Note that TS, $0 = $ FCFS and TS, $\infty = S$.

Alternating Shortest-Operation and *First Come, First Served Rules (SF, P):* the Shortest-Operation and First Come, First Served Rules are used alternately for periods of fixed length. The cycle is 400 time units in each case (40 times the mean processing time), and P indicates the proportion of the cycle during which the Shortest-Operation Rule is used. Note that SF, $1 = S$ and SF, $0 = $ FCFS.

Subsequent-Operation Rule (A, K): (Not a local rule.) Dispatcher looks ahead to see where job would go after leaving machine in question. Preference is given to jobs that will go to a "critical" queue—being one with less than K time units of work waiting. Among jobs that will go on to critical queues, selection is by the Shortest-Operation Rule.

It can easily be shown that for an unsaturated job shop the following relation holds, regardless of priority discipline [11]:

$$C = (XN) \cdot Y$$

where C is the mean flow-time, Y is the mean time between arrivals, and XN is the mean number of jobs in the shop.

For a shop in equilibrium this can be given as:

$$C = (XN) \frac{R}{N(1 - T)}$$

where N is the number of machines in the shop, T is the mean proportion of idle time, and R is the average work content of the arriving jobs. X, N, and R are set by the conditions of the experiment; C and T are the observed results. Attention was focused on the mean percentage of idle time as the principal measure of performance, since this appeared to be the more stable of the two statistics.

5. THE EFFECT OF SHOP CONDITIONS

The first portion of the experiment was designed to investigate the effect of changes in shop size, number of jobs in the shop, and prop-

Table 1 Mean percentage of idle machine time obtained in runs of 2000 jobs.

Shop size		Pure job shop			Pure flow shop		
		No. of jobs in shop			No. of jobs in shop		
N	Rule	$2N$	$4N$	$6N$	$2N$	$4N$	$6N$
2	S		13.11	3.95	2.28	11.43	1.42	0.82
2	R	(Exper.)	18.11	10.66	7.55	18.54	9.36	5.63
		(Theor.)	(20.00)	(11.11)	(7.69)			
3	S		15.80	5.36	2.84	15.18	2.80	0.65
3	R	(Exper.)	24.84	12.64	8.56	22.95	12.69	8.66
		(Theor.)	(25.00)	(14.29)	(10.00)			
6	S		21.26	6.89	2.69	18.49	5.06	1.98
6	R	(Exper.)	29.04	17.40	12.37	28.67	18.01	12.93
		(Theor.)	(29.41)	(17.24)	(12.19)			
9	S		21.17	8.63	4.66	19.48	5.17	1.88
9	R	(Exper.)	30.30	17.59	12.84	30.36	18.05	12.89
		(Theor.)	(30.77)	(18.18)	(12.90)			

erties of the transition matrix upon the mean percentage of idle time experienced under the random and shortest-operation discipline. A complete factorial experiment for the two rules (R and S), two types of shop (pure job shop and pure flow shop), four shop sizes (2, 3, 6, and 9 machines), and three levels of work-in-process (number of jobs in shop equal to 2, 4, and 6 times the number of machines) was executed. The results are given in Table 1. Under the special release mechanism, which was used in all of these experiments, and for the random rule and the pure job shop an analytical expression for the expected proportion of idle time can be obtained:[3]

$$\bar{T} = (N - 1)/(XN + N - 1).$$

The appropriate value of this expression is included in Table 1 for comparison.

These data have been plotted in Figs. 1, 2, and 3. A number of interesting observations can be drawn.

[3] Under the release mechanism used there are always XN jobs distributed in the shop of N machines. For consideration of idle time jobs may be considered indistinguishable and Bose-Einstein statistics are appropriate. The expression given is the ratio of the number of *distinguishable* arrangements of XN jobs on $N - 1$ machines to the number of *distinguishable* arrangements of XN jobs on N machines. See Feller, *Probability Theory and Its Applications,* 2nd ed., p. 38, Wiley, New York, 1957.

1. There is a difference between the performance of the shortest-operation rule and the random rule that is significant in both the statistical and the practical sense. Formal tests of the hypotheses that the performance figures for a particular set of conditions come

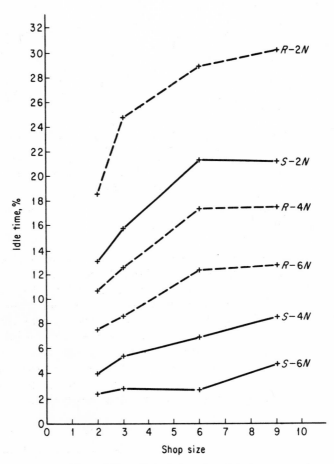

Figure 1 The effect of shop size—job shop.

from the same population leads to clear rejection. (The total time interval of the experiment was divided into equal, mutually exhaustive subintervals and the idle time was measured for each subinterval to give individual observations from which a measure of variability could be calculated. A '*t*' test of differences was performed as described on p. 105 of Dixon and Massey, *Introduction to Statistical Analysis*.)

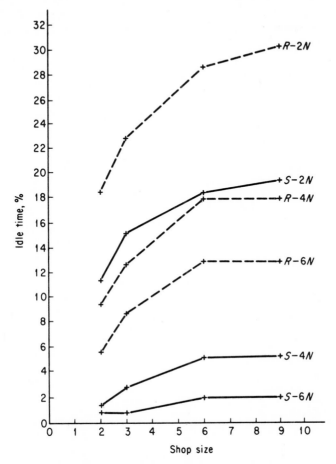

Figure 2 The effect of shop size—flow shop.

2. There is no indication that there exist conditions that would reverse this comparison—the shortest-operation rule is better for every condition tested, and there is no indication that extrapolation of conditions would be interesting. If anything, it is remarkable how little the difference between the two rules depends upon conditions. As the amount of work-in-process increases, one might expect Rule S to exhibit a constant proportion of the idle time exhibited by Rule R—in fact, it comes closer to retaining a constant absolute advantage (*see* Fig. 3).

3. There is reasonable agreement between the experimental and the theoretical results. The consistency in the direction of departure

is not surprising in view of the fact that the separate experimental runs are not independent—they are made with the same set of jobs.

4. There is surprisingly little difference between performance in the pure job shop and that in the pure flow shop. Since these are the extreme types of transition matrices, there is little evidence to support previous conjectures that the transition matrix is a principal determinant of priority rule performance.

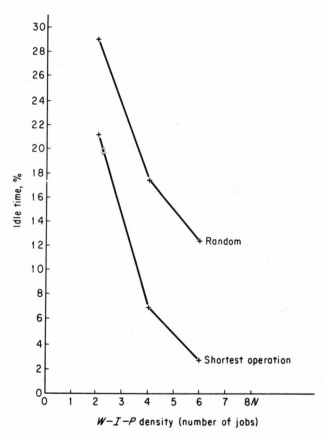

Figure 3 The effect of level of W-I-P inventory—job shop—6 machines.

 From this initial experiment a particular set of conditions was to be selected for continued investigation. The plot of performance against the size of the shop (Figs. 1 and 2) offered some justification for selecting a shop size of six machines for continuation. There was a very practical reason for selecting a small shop in that for a given sample size the computing time increased quite rapidly with the size of the shop. Subjectively, six machines seemed enough to exhibit some of the complexity and interaction of a large shop, and we convinced ourselves we could see some sort of a break in many of the performance curves at about that point—the difference in performance between six and nine machines did not seem worth the substantial increase in computing time that nine machines would require. The job-shop situation was considered to be of more interest than the flow shop, and the middle level of work-in-process $(4N)$ was arbitrarily selected.

6. SENSITIVITY OF THE SHORTEST-OPERATION RULE TO ERRORS IN ESTIMATING PROCESSING TIMES

A practical objection often raised to the use of the shortest-operation rule is the necessity of a priori knowledge of processing times. It is argued that often in practice only very crude estimates of proc-

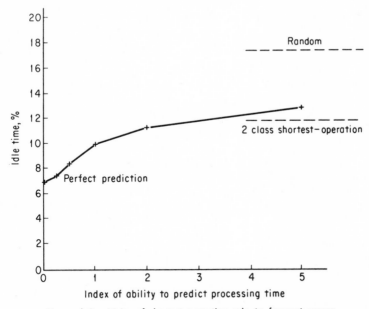

Figure 4 Sensitivity of shortest-operation rule to forecast errors.

essing times are available. Therefore, a series of experiments were executed in which priorities were assigned by the shortest-operation rule applied to an estimate of the processing time. The performance of the rule as a function of the quality of the estimates was the subject of study. The data are given in Table 2 and plotted in Fig. 4.

One can conclude from these results that errors of estimate do not present a serious problem and that the lack of accurate estimates of processing time is not a valid objection to the use of the shortest-operation discipline. Very crude estimates—a two-way classification, or estimates with a standard deviation of 2—still achieve fully half of the advantage of the shortest-operation rule over the random rule. There just is no question that experienced shop estimators can guess far better than that. The usual claims made for careful time study (± 10 percent) correspond to a value of X of the order of 0.03, for which value the performance is negligibly poorer than for the shortest-operation rule with perfect prediction. (The strength of the conclusion may to some extent depend upon the assumption of exponentially distributed processing times, and the tests might be repeated for some entirely different type of distribution.)

Table 2 Sensitivity of shortest-operation rule to errors of estimation.[a]

Rule (S, X)	Mean percentage of idle time
$S,$ $0 (= S)$	6.89
$S,$ 0.25	7.40
$S,$ 0.50	8.45
$S,$ 1.00	9.97
$S,$ 2.00	11.26
$S,$ 5.00	12.78
$S,$ $\infty (= R)$	17.40
Rule $(2S, B)$	
$2S,$ $0 (= S)$	6.89
$2S,$ 7	13.08
$2S,$ 10	11.76
$2S,$ 30	11.72
$S,$ $\infty (= R)$	17.40

a Transition matrix: pure job shop. Number of machines: 6. Number of jobs in shop: $4N$. Sample size: 2000 jobs.

7. DISADVANTAGE OF THE SHORTEST-OPERATION RULE[4]

The second objection to the use of the shortest-operation rule is less easily dismissed. This lies in the prohibitively long flow times that may be experienced by individual jobs, even though the mean flow time for all jobs is substantially reduced by this rule. Consider the following data obtained from a 2000-job run in the pure job shop of six machines with work-in-process of 36 jobs:

[4] In the discussion of these results the reader should bear in mind the conditions under which the tests were performed. Although we did not realize it at the time, this method of operation appears to discriminate very markedly against the shortest-operation discipline. In subsequent comparative tests, in which the release rate of jobs was held constant, the shortest-operation discipline shows up much more favorably in terms of variance of flow-time distribution than is indicated here.

Rule	Mean, distn. of time flow	Mean, distn. of flow time/operation	Variance, distn. of flow time	Variance, distn. of flow time/operation
FCFS	344.7	72.0	61,785	16,933
R	344.4	72.3	93,074	46,221
S	283.1	59.5	388,672	356,801

It would be highly desirable to find some variant of the shortest-operation rule that retained the advantage of the basic rule but without the disadvantage—a rule that would have a mean flow time close to that of the basic shortest-operation rule without the corresponding high variance. Two obvious methods of trying to accomplish this are:

1. Alternate the shortest-operation rule with a low variance rule periodically to "clean out the shop."

2. Forcibly truncate the shortest-operation rule by imposing a limit on the delay that individual jobs will tolerate.

Both of these modifications were explored. The shortest-operation rule was truncated by placing a limit, C, on the length of time a job would spend in any queue. When this limit is reached, a first

Table 3 Performance of the truncated shortest-operation rule.[a]

Rule	Mean idle time, %	Mean flow time	Mean flow time/opn.	Variance flow time	Variance flow time/opn.
TS, 0 (*FCFS*)	16.59	244.5	50.7	30,423	7,896
TS, 100	13.36	236.1	49.1	36,264	14,791
TS, 300	11.98	229.3	48.3	51,417	—
TS, 1000	7.60	220.4	45.9	75,984	24,557
TS, ∞ (*S*)	6.79	218.2	45.5	125,461	23,069

[a] Transition matrix: pure job shop. Number of machines: 6. No. of jobs in shop: 4N. Sample size: 20,000 jobs.

come, first served discipline is instituted until the delayed job is completed. The data for these experiments are given in Table 3 and plotted in Fig. 5.

As would be expected, the idle time and mean flow time are decreasing functions and the variances are increasing functions of the truncation number. The success of this type of modification must be evaluated in terms of the rate at which performance changes with the severity of truncation. One means of judging the severity of truncation is to compare the truncation number—which is approximately equal to the maximum waiting time in a single queue—for the shortest-operation rule under truncation, to the expected waiting per queue for the first come, first served rule. The mean flow time per operation under FCFS is given as 50.7 in Table 3. Since the mean processing time is ten time units, the mean waiting time per

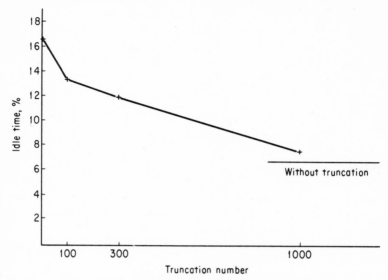

Figure 5 Sensitivity of shortest-operation rule to truncation.

queue is approximately 40 time units. (The mean waiting time for the basic shortest-operation rule is 35 time units.) A truncation number of 100 means that a job can at most wait about $2^1/_2$ times as long in a single queue as its *expected* waiting time would be under FCFS. Use of this truncated shortest-operation rule reduces idle time 3.23 points as compared to a reduction of 9.80 points for the untruncated rule. The variance is 1.19 times the FCFS variance. These comparisons can be summarized as follows:

Truncation number	Approximate ratio of max wtg. time under TS, C to expected wtg. time under FCFS	Fraction of advantage secured	Variance of TS, C/variance of FCFS
0	—	0	1.00
100	2.5	0.34	1.19
300	7.4	0.47	1.69
1000	25	0.92	2.50
∞	∞	1.00	4.13

One can find grounds for either optimism or pessimism in these results. On the pessimistic side, if the shortest-operation rule is subjected to "reasonable" truncation, say on the order of 300 time units, it loses half of its advantage. On the other side one could note that replacing the FCFS rule with a severely truncated shortest-operation (the maximum waiting time under TS, 100 would be the same order of magnitude as the *maximum* waiting time under FCFS) would yield one-third of the potential benefit without a prohibitive increase in variance. There are at least grounds to justify further inquiry, and there is no reason to conclude that variants of the shortest-operation discipline are completely impractical.

The second method of modifying the shortest-operation rule was to alternate its use with the first come, first served discipline. The

Table 4 Performance of alternating shortest-operation and first come, first served disciplines.[a]

Proportion of time using S	Mean idle time, %	Mean flow time	Mean flow time/opn.	Variance flow time	Variance flow time/opn.
0 (*FCFS*)	16.59	244.5	50.7	30,423	7,896
0.20	13.82	230.3	48.6	67,375	45,550
0.40	12.33	223.7	47.1	60,550	40,577
0.60	10.60	215.8	45.7	67,757	48,120
0.80	8.43	211.3	44.1	85,072	67,880
1.00 (*S*)	6.89	205.9	43.4	88,695	71,212

a Transition matrix: pure job shop. Number of machines: 6. Number of jobs in shop: 4N. Sample size: 2000 jobs, except 20,000 for FCFS.

intent was that during periods under FCFS jobs with large processing times could advance. (In operation, this would probably be very much like the alternate use of the shortest-operation and the longest-operation disciplines.) The cycle of alternation was held constant at 400 time units, equivalent to 40 times the mean processing times.

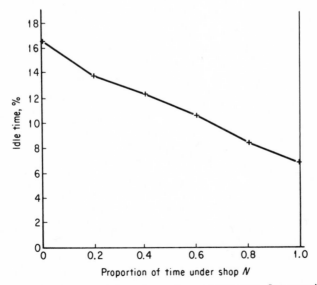

Figure 6 Alternating use of shortest-operation and first come, first served rules.

(This was intended to represent a 40-hour week for a shop in which the mean processing time was one hour.) The proportion of time under each of the rules was varied. The data are given in Table 4 and plotted in Fig. 6.

Figure 6 shows that the advantage secured by the use of the shortest-operation discipline is directly proportional to the fraction of time that discipline is used. The most surprising aspect of this performance is the tremendous increase in variance that occurs with the introduction of any use of the shortest-operation discipline. Apparently in introducing the shortest-operation discipline in this manner one secures the disadvantages more rapidly than the advantages.

The foregoing have been attempts to modify the shortest-operation rule in such a way as to preserve its advantages and reduce its disadvantages. An alternative approach is to seek a method of minimizing the harmful consequences of the high variance of the rule. It would seem likely that there are many cases where an unusually long flow time would not be particularly harmful, if it could be *predicted in advance* that this particular job would experience such an event. This predictive ability could be provided by a conditional distribution of flow times, if information is given about the job's processing times. It is not inconceivable that individual job flow times could be as precisely predicted under the shortest-operation rule as under random, or even first come, first served disciplines. This would appear to be a promising and practical avenue of investigation.

In considering the practicality of some form of shortest-operation discipline, we have been comparing it to first come, first served and random disciplines. We would note that many dispatching rules that are used in practice would come much closer to being classified as a longest-operation discipline. One reason for this is that in an attempt to serve a criterion that is weighted by some index of job importance people will often rank jobs by the index of importance alone. Since it is reasonable to expect some positive correlation between importance and processing time, this would tend to favor jobs with longer processing times. The longest-operation discipline is, of course, the antithesis of the shortest-operation discipline—it maximizes what the shortest-operation rule minimizes. Moreover, it is similar to the shortest-operation rule in having a high variance. In short, it possesses the disadvantages of the shortest-operation rule but not the advantages. The attractiveness of the shortest-operation rule (or the s/v ranking, where a weighted criterion is appropriate) is considerably enhanced by comparison with longest-operation disciplines.

8. ON THE OPTIMALITY OF THE SHORTEST-OPERATION RULE

Finally, a brief series of experiments was conducted in an attempt to demonstrate, by the exhibition of a counterexample, the nonoptimality in the general case, of the shortest-operation rule. We are inclined to believe that the shortest-operation rule is an optimum with respect to the set of local rules, although we cannot as yet prove this assertion, but we were also confident that by going outside of the set of local rules a superior rule would have a smaller mean system state; under the conditions employed here a superior rule would have a lower percentage of idle time.

A likely candidate for a nonlocal rule that could reduce idle time was the subsequent-operation rule—a rule that looked ahead one stage and gave preference to jobs that would move on to queues that were "very nearly empty." Among jobs destined for these critical queues, selection was made according to the shortest-operation discipline. The performance of this rule for different specifications of the meaning of "very nearly empty" is given in Table 5.

Table 5 Performance of the subsequent-operation rules[a].

K[b]	Mean idle time, %	Mean flow time	Mean flow time/opn.	Variance flow time	Variance flow time/opn.
0	9.07	215.1	47.3	68,284	43,593
10	8.88	217.3	41.8	64,937	39,454
20	8.91	217.7	47.5	66,692	42,423
$\infty\,(=S)$	6.89	205.9	43.4	88,695	71,212

a Transition matrix: pure job shop. Number of machines: 6. No. of jobs in shop: $4N$. Sample size: 2000 jobs.
b If the total work waiting in a queue is less than or equal to K time units, then the queue is considered "critical."

It is evident that whereas the subsequent-operation rule exhibited considerably better performance than the random rule it did not surpass the shortest-operation rule. This result greatly increased our respect for the ability of the shortest-operation discipline. Although we still believe that a superior (nonlocal) rule can be devised, it is not going to be an easy task and the rule may well have to be a very complex one.

9. SUMMARY

I. The following statements are made with regard to the *mean* value of the basic measures of system performance (waiting time, system state, utilization):

A. In simple n-job—one-machine sequencing problems it may be shown that:
 1. All rules that are independent of processing times are equivalent.
 2. The shortest-operation rule is optimal.
B. In simple queuing systems with exponentially distributed inter-arrival times it may be shown that:
 1. (Almost) all priority assignments such that the expected processing time is the same for each priority class are equivalent.
 2. The shortest-operation rule is optimal.
C. In a system consisting of a network of queues there is considerable support, both analytical and experimental, for conjectures that:
 1. All local priority rules such that the expected processing time is the same for each priority class are equivalent.
 2. The shortest-operation rule is optimal with respect to the set of all local priority rules.

II. The necessity of providing a priori information about the processing times of individual jobs does not present a serious practical problem in the implementation of the shortest-operation rule. The rule appears to be highly insensitive to errors of estimate.

III. There is reason to believe that the drawbacks inherent in the high variance of the shortest-operation rule can be overcome—either by modification of the rule, or by the development of a procedure that can better estimate the completion times of individual jobs.

We believe that the shortest-operation discipline is very deserving of further consideration and potentially is of great practical significance.

REFERENCE

1. Aczel, M. A., "The Effect of Introducing Priorities," *Opns. Res.* 8 (1960), 730-733.

2. Baker, C. T. and B. P. Dzielinski, "Simulation of a Simplified Job Shop," *Management Sci.* 6 (1960), 311-323.

3. Barry, J. Y., "A Priority Queuing Problem," *Opns. Res.* 4 (1956), 385.

4. Cobham, A., "Priority Assignment in Waiting Line Problems," *Opns. Res.* 2 (1954), 70-76.

5. Conway, R. W., B. M. Johnson, and W. L. Maxwell, "A Queue Network Simulator for the Burroughs 220," *Communications of the Assoc. for Computing Machinery* 2, 12 (1959), 20–23.

6. ———, "An Experimental Investigation of Priority Dispatching," *J. Indust. Eng.* 11 (1960), 221-230.

7. Jackson, J. R., "Networks of Waiting Lines," *Opns. Res.* **5** (1957), 518–521.

8. ———, "Some Problems in Queueing with Dynamic Priorities," *Naval Res. Log. Quart.* **7** (1960), 235–250.

9. ———, "Simulation of Queues with Dynamic Priorities," Research Report No. 71, Management Science Research Project, University of California, Los Angeles (March 20, 1961).

10. Kesten, H. and J. Th. Runnenburg, "Priority in Waiting Line Problems," *Koninkl. Nederl. Akademie Van Wetenschappen, Proceedings, Series A* **60**, 3 (1957).

11. Little, J. D. C., "A Proof for the Queueing Formula $L = \lambda W$," *Opns. Res.* **9** (1961), 383–387.

12. McNaughton, R., "Scheduling with Deadlines and Loss Functions," *Management Sci.* **6** (1959), 1–12.

13. Phipps, T. E., Jr., "Machine Repair as a Waiting-Line Problem," *Opns. Res.* **4** (1956), 76–85.

14. Smith, W. E., "Various Optimizers for Single-Stage Production," *Naval Res. Log. Quart.* **3** (1956), 59–66.

18

The Effect of Uncertainty in Job Times on Optimal Schedules

John F. Muth
CARNEGIE INSTITUTE OF TECHNOLOGY

The object of the study reported here has been to obtain a better understanding of the way the statistical properties of job times affect the time to process the jobs, especially under conditions of imperfect information. The main conclusion is that uncertainty about job operation time is of secondary importance in developing optimal scheduling procedures. (This is not to say, however, that accurate times are not needed elsewhere in plant operations, since accurate time data might be necessary for purposes of cost control and methods improvement.) Some of the effects are mitigated by having a large file of unfinished work. These conclusions were reached on the basis of simulation of a rather simple scheduling problem, namely, a two-stage production process. It is not known to what extent the results generalize to several stages.

A paper presented at the Factory Scheduling Conference, Carnegie Institute of Technology, May 10-12, 1961. This research was undertaken for the project, Planning and Control of Industrial Operations, at Carnegie Institute of Technology, under contract with the Office of Naval Research, Contract N-onr-760-(01), Project NR 047011. The author is indebted to P. R. Winters for his comments and suggestions.

It is usual in operations research studies to begin the analysis with a deterministic model, then to examine the sensitivity of the results to errors in the model, and finally to consider risk explicitly if necessary. When inventory control procedures are being analyzed, it usually is necessary to take risk into account. This study suggests, however, that risk is not crucial in factory scheduling.

The sensitivity of a model to unknown factors is important to understand if mathematical analysis is to be utilized in industrial scheduling systems. One thing common to scheduling problems is that the schedules are seldom adhered to exactly. The reasons for deviations are usually known—after the fact—and they frequently are very sensible ones. The point is that a variety of conditions are not allowed for at the present time in factory scheduling models. The sheer size of the analytical problem suggests that drastic oversimplifications will be studied for some time to come. Among the various sources of error are the following :

1. Job times.

2. Other job requirements (e.g., equipment and materials needed, particular human skills required).

3. Engineering changes.

4. What the job actually turns out to be (e.g., in repair work).

5. What the objectives of a scheduling system are.

6. The extent to which variables may actually be chosen by the decision maker.

The humble task of this paper is reflected in the fact that only the first of this rather long list is studied at all.

1. DESCRIPTION OF THE SIMULATION

Because a relatively large number of runs is necessary to get accurate information about the behavior of the scheduling process, it was decided to restrict attention to the simple problem which may be handled by the sequencing rule of S.M. Johnson [1]. This rule applies to the following problem : there is a fixed list of m jobs (m is called the file size), each of which is to be run on two machines in the same order. The objective is to minimize the length of time to process the entire list of jobs.

This situation can be illustrated with the list of jobs and the times for the two production stages given in Table 1. There is, of course, no upper limit to the length of time it would take to complete all of the jobs. Naturally, one restricts attention to so-called active schedules—that is, schedules in which no single operation can be made to start earlier. Johnson has further shown that it is sufficient to consider only those schedules in which the jobs are run in the same order through both machines. There remain, then, only six possible job sequences corresponding to the permutations of the three elements. These possible sequences are given in Table 2 together with their total schedule spans—that is, the length of time it would take to complete all of the jobs. The shortest of all these is the sequence 2, 1, 3 which takes 21 hours to complete. The average of all six schedules is 23.7 hours, which is about 13 percent longer than the optimum. One thing we would like to find out from the schedule simulations is the extent to which the average of all the possible schedules exceeds the minimum possible in order to get some idea of the benefits that may accrue through a scheduling procedure.

The second objective is to determine how close schedules based on expected times, not the same as the actual job times, would be to the true minimum. Suppose the scheduler did not know the time data appearing in Table 1, but instead used the expected times appearing in Table 3. He would still pick the sequence 2, 1, 3. Although he

Table 1 Illustrative job list—actual times.

Job	Stage 1	Stage 2
1	6 hours	5 hours
2	2	8
3	9	2

Table 2 Schedule spans for alternative job sequences.

Sequence	Schedule span
1, 2, 3	22 hours
1, 3, 2	25
2, 1, 3	21
2, 3, 1	22
3, 1, 2	28
3, 2, 1	24

Table 3 Illustrative job list—expected times.

Job	Stage 1	Stage 2
1	5 hours	6 hours
2	4	7
3	8	3

would expect the schedule span to be 22 hours, it would actually take 21 hours, according to the time data on Table 1. In this example incorrect expectations of job times make absolutely no difference in the performance of the scheduling procedure; the same sequence is chosen. However, it is not hard to find forecast errors to be such that a different sequence would be chosen with the result that the actual time could take as much as seven hours more than the optimal schedule. It is desirable to find out how much the schedule span would be altered by incorrect forecasts.

These problems were studied with the aid of a simulation model in which job times and forecasts of the job times were generated according to specified probability laws. The schedules drawn at random from the population of active schedules were compared with the schedules generated by Johnson's rule under perfect and imperfect information for various characteristics of the shop.

The times of the jobs were taken to be independent drawings from the bivariate log normal distribution. The variance of the actual job times ranged from one-half to twice the mean length of time on each of the two production stages. The variance represents the diversity of jobs performed in the shop, diversity in terms of the length of time required to complete the operations. For each job the times on the two machines were not always assumed to be statistically independent. They could, in principle, be either positively or negatively correlated. In the first case jobs would differ from one another primarily by a scale factor (a "big" job in Stage 1 would ordinarily take a long time on Stage 2 also). With negative correlation the two machines might be partial substitutes for one another.

The standard deviation of the forecast errors in the job times ranged from 20 percent to 80 percent in the average processed time. Remember that even the smallest of these figures, the 20 percent forecast error, is a substantial figure. The errors are normally distributed with a zero mean, so that only about 68 percent of the time would the actual processing time be within ±20 percent of the forecast.

The last characteristic to be varied in the simulation runs was the file size. The list of jobs performed was either 10, 35 or 100. (For the smallest file size 200 replications were obtained in the simulations; for the larger file sizes, however, computer time became a limiting factor, so the replications were reduced to 50 and 25 times each.)

2. PROPERTIES OF AVERAGE AND MINIMUM SCHEDULE SPANS

The effect of job diversity is shown in Table 4. Both the average and the minimum schedule spans are given for coefficients of variation in job times ranging from 0 to 200 percent. With a coefficient of 0 both the spans are at the minimum of 11 time units, if the average time to complete a single job in one stage is taken as the unit of time measurement. As the coefficient increases, both of the schedule spans tend to increase as well. What is surprising, however, is that the schedule spans, especially the minimum span, increase so little as the diversity of job times increases. When the standard deviation of the job times is twice as large as the average, the minimum schedule span is only about 10 percent larger than what it would be if all of the jobs were perfectly uniform in their time requirements.

Table 5 compares the schedule spans for various correlation ratios of the times for each job in the two stages. With a file size of ten jobs, it appears that both the average and the minimum spans are

Table 4 Effect of time variability on average and minimum schedule spans.[a]

Coefficient of variation	Average span	Minimum span
0 %	11.0	11.0
50 %	12.2	11.2
100 %	13.3	11.9
200 %	14.3	12.4

[a] Zero correlation of times for each job in the two stages, file size of ten jobs.

Table 5 Effect of job "structure" on average and minimum schedule spans.[a]

| Correlation ratio | File Size = 10 | | File Size = 35 | |
	Average span	Minimum span	Average span	Minimum span
−.4	13.6	12.2	43.0	39.6
.0	13.3	11.9	41.2	38.3
+.7	13.6	12.1	39.0	36.1

[a] Coefficient of variation of job times equals 100 percent in all cases.

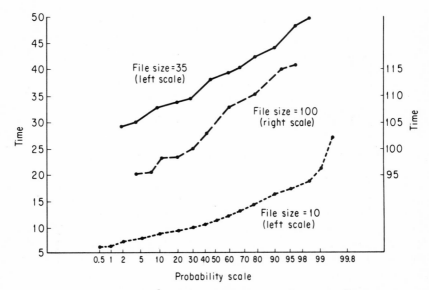

Figure 1 Probability distribution of schedule spans for various file sizes.

smallest when there is no statistical relationship between the times in the two stages. This effect is not very pronounced. When the file size is larger, however, the spans tend to decrease uniformly as the correlation ratio increases. In other words, there tend to be more opportunities for matching the various jobs when they differ from one another the same way in both stages. However, it does take a moderately large file size to take advantage of this matching.

The probability distribution of minimum schedule spans for various file sizes is given in Figure 1. The bottom curve is the cumulative distribution with file size of ten units. It appears here, and achi-square test suggests so as well, that the distribution has significant deviations from normality. However, the distributions for file sizes of 35 and 100 jobs tend to have a closer agreement with normality.[1]

3. "FAILURE" OF SCHEDULING PROCEDURE WITH IMPERFECT EXPECTED TIMES

The schedule span was also evaluated when the expected times were distributed around the actual job times according to the normal probability law with a standard deviation of the forecast running from 20 to 80 percent of the average time per stage. The results of these studies are summarized in Tables 6 and 7. The figures given in the

Table 6 "Failure" of schedule with incorrect expected times.[a]

Correlation coefficient	Standard deviation of forecast as percentage of the average time per stage		
	20 %	50 %	80 %
−.4	7.9	19.1	24.4
.0	8.6	23.9	31.7
+.7	13.1	39.2	54.4

[a] File size of ten jobs.

Table 7 "Failure" of schedule with incorrect expected times for various file sizes [a] (percent).

Correlation coefficient	Size of job file		
	10	35	100
−.4	7.9	4.4	3.3
.0	8.6	5.8	4.5
+.7	13.1	10.5	6.7

[a] Standard deviation of forecast error equals 20 percent of the average time per stage.

table are the "failure" measure of Theil [2]. Let T represent the length of the schedule span using Johnson's rule under imperfect information, T_{min} represent the minimum time possible with perfect

[1] Normality of the distribution of the schedule spans was conjectured by J. Heller of New York University.

information, and T_{avg} represent the average of all possible schedules. The failure measure is defined by the equation

$$F = \frac{T - T_{\min}}{T_{\mathrm{avg}} - T_{\min}}$$

This measure represents the amount of the differential between the minimum and average schedule span which is not obtained by the scheduling procedure under imperfect information. Thus the failure of the example in Tables 1 and 3 would be 0, because the schedule based on imperfect information would still be the optimal sequence.

What is striking about the statistics in Tables 6 and 7 is that they are so small. The failure with imperfect information, and often with a substantial degree of imperfect information, tends to be around 10 percent. In other words, 90 percent of the differential would be attributed to the scheduling procedure, whereas only the additional 10 percent or so could be attributed to improved knowledge of the process times. Table 6 shows that the failure increases at a fairly rapid rate as the standard deviation of the forecast errors increases from 20 percent to 80 percent. The failure also tends to increase as the correlation coefficient of the times for the two production stages for each job increases from $-.4$ to $+.7$. In other words, the scheduling procedure is most sensitive to forecast errors when the nature of the jobs is such that most of the variability in time is evenly divided between the two production stages.

Table 7 shows how the effects of incorrect expected times may be decreased somewhat by increasing the size of the job file. This is apparently possible because a large job file allows for cancellation of the effects of the errors in a way that is not possible with only ten jobs in the list. Note that it takes substantial increases in the file size in order to obtain any reduction in the failure statistic. Increasing the size of the job file by a factor of ten appears to cut the failure statistic in half.

4. CONCLUSIONS

The most important conclusion of the study seems to be that the schedule span is not very sensitive to moderately large errors in estimated job times. This conclusion is important in view of the difficulty one has in designing scheduling algorithms under certainty. Some of the effects of uncertainty in the job times may be reduced by increasing the size of the job file. However, this may be a very expensive way of meeting production commitments.

There is little in the results of these simulations to suggest that peculiarities in the statistical nature of the distribution of job times will be of much aid in constructing optimal schedules. For file sizes of moderate size the correlation ratio of the job times does not appear to affect either the average span or the minimum span much, unless there is a large file of jobs to be processed at any one time.

REFERENCES

1. Johnson, S. M., "Optimal Two- and Three-Stage Production Schedules with Set-up Time Included," *Naval Research Logistics Quarterly*, **1** (1954), 61–68. Reprinted as Chapter 2 of this volume.
2. Theil, H., *Economic Forecasts and Policy*, North-Holland, Amsterdam, 1958.

19

Queues with Dynamic Priority Discipline

James R. Jackson
UNIVERSITY OF CALIFORNIA, LOS ANGELES

1. INTRODUCTION

This paper is concerned with "dynamic-priority" queueing systems, in which each customer has a "scheduled start time," and if several customers are waiting in line when a server becomes free to serve a new customer, one is chosen with the earliest scheduled start time among those waiting. It is assumed that a customer's scheduled start time is the sum of his time of arrival in the system and a random "urgency number," drawn from a fixed probability distribution. If a customer's scheduled start time is interpreted as the latest desirable time for his service to begin, then his urgency number is the longest desirable time interval for him to wait in the queue for service. The details of these systems are spelled out in Section 2.

This paper was presented at the Factory Scheduling Conference, Carnegie Institute of Technology, May 10–12, 1961 and is reprinted from *Management Science* **8** (1961), 18–34. A preliminary version was presented to the Seventh International Meeting of the Institute of Management Sciences, New York City, October 20–22, 1960. This work was supported by the Office of Naval Research under Task 047–003, Management Sciences Research Project, UCLA. Reproduction in whole or in part is permitted for any purpose of the United States Government. The IBM 709 of the Western Data Processing Center, UCLA was used to make the computations.

Let u and v be urgency numbers with $u < v$. It seems plausible, when the queue is so long that any arriving customer is almost sure to wait a long time for service, that new arrivals with urgency number u will be in about the same statistical situation as customers with urgency number v who have already waited for $v - u$ units of time. Let the customers be classified by urgency number, into "urgency classes," and suppose an equilibrium waiting-time distribution is found for each class. The preceding remark suggests that the upper tails of the cumulative distribution curves will be similar in shape, but that the curve for urgency class v will be displaced from that for urgency class u by $v - u$ units of time in the direction of the positive time axis. This conjecture is formalized in Section 3, along with a stronger one which proposes a more complete description of the asymptotic behavior of the waiting-time distributions. Pertinent mathematical research, to be treated fully in a subsequent paper, is briefly taken up in Section 4. Section 5 is devoted to a general description of some computer simulations The results of these simulations are discussed in Section 6, with special reference to the conjectures just mentioned, and another conjecture is formulated. Section 7 briefly summarizes the conclusions of this paper from the point of view of potential applications, and gives some examples.

The conclusions are believed to be such as to provide practical working tools. The use of dynamic-priority rules to determine service order is widespread and natural in queueing systems where it is required that a large proportion of customers be served "on time." Thus, the upper tails of the waiting-time distributions tend to be of primary importance. It turns out, happily, that the experimentally observed convergence toward conjectured asymptotes is quite rapid in the cases of greatest interest—when the "load ratio" of demand for service to server capacity is close to unity.

2. DYNAMIC-PRIORITY QUEUEING SYSTEMS

This section outlines the general characteristics of the systems with which this paper is concerned.[1] In these systems, "customers" arrive from time to time at a facility consisting of one or several "servers." Each customer requires a "service," which will occupy the full attention of one server for an uninterrupted period of time, after which the customer will leave the system. If there is an unoccupied server at the time of a customer's arrival, then the new arrival's service starts at once. Otherwise, he joins a "queue" and waits for service.

[1] A detailed mathematical model of one class of these systems is presented in J. R. Jackson, "Some Problems in Queueing with Dynamic Priorities," *Naval Research Logistics Quarterly*, **7**, 3, (Sept. 1960), pp. 235–249.

Each customer has an "urgency number," and a "scheduled start time" which is defined as the sum,

Time of arrival in the system + urgency number.

Customers waiting in the queue are ordered according to increasing scheduled start time.[2] If customers are waiting when a service is completed, the server thus released begins at once to serve the customer who is then first in line.

The input of customers to the system is determined by three random processes, which are stationary, and which generate mutually independent sequences of mutually independent random numbers. The numbers needed for any given customer are (1) his urgency number, whose use was explained above; (2) the "interarrival interval" between his time of arrival in the system and that of the next-arriving customer; and (3) the "holding time" required to complete his service once it is started.

To determine an essentially unique dynamic-priority queueing system within the general limits set in the preceding two paragraphs, it is enough to specify (in addition to the number of servers) the probability distributions which govern the urgency numbers, the interarrival intervals, and the holding times. It is appropriate here to indicate the range of possibilities to which this paper has some relation, without yet being specific. Some notation and terminology will be introduced as this is done.

For reasons connected with the structure of practical problems and with the limitations of analytical methods and experimental techniques, this paper is restricted to systems whose urgency-number distributions attain only finitely many different values. The letters u and v will be reserved to stand for values of the urgency number which are actually attained. In a natural way, all customers having a given urgency number, say u, are thought of as forming an "urgency class," which will be referred to specifically as "urgency class u."

Let $p_u(i, n, w)$ be the probability that a customer, randomly chosen from among the first n in urgency class u to arrive after a moment when the configuration of the system is described by i, waits no longer than w units of time before his service is started. The systems of interest here are those such that

$$p_u(w) = \lim_{n \to \infty} p_u(i, n, w)$$

exists and is independent of i, and also that $p_u(w) < 1$ for finite w, while $p_u(w) \to 1$ as $w \to \infty$. In words, for each urgency class there

[2] If ties occur, they are ordered on increasing urgency number, further ties are ordered on increasing time of arrival, and ties still remaining are ordered randomly.

must be an "equilibrium" or "long-run" probability distribution of waiting time, and arbitrarily long waits must occur with positive frequencies.

It is evident from well-known queueing theory that a necessary condition for the fulfillment of the requirement of the preceding paragraph is that the interarrival-interval and holding-time distributions (which must in any case be nonnegative-valued) have positive means, and that the "load ratio,"

$$\rho = \frac{\text{(mean holding time)/(number of servers)}}{\text{mean interarrival interval}}$$

be less than unity. It seems clear, although it has not been proved, that a necessary and sufficient condition is that an equilibrium waiting-time distribution exist and that arbitrarily long waits occur with positive frequencies in the system which is identical to the dynamic-priority queueing system under consideration, except that in this new system service order is governed by the first come, first served rule. From the experimental viewpoint emphasized in this paper, the simulation outputs themselves provide evidence for the required waiting-time distributions for those dynamic-priority queueing systems which have been simulated.

3. TWO CONJECTURES

Consider a dynamic-priority queueing system satisfying the conditions specified in Section 2. Let $p_u(w)$ be the equilibrium probability that a customer in urgency class u will wait no longer than w units of time for service. For $0 \leq f < 1$, define

$$w_u(f) = \inf \{w \,|\, p_u(w) \geq f\}.$$

(This is the waiting time corresponding to fractile f in the cumulative waiting-time distribution for urgency class u.) Now consider a system identical to the original one, except that in it service order is governed by the first come, first served rule; let $p(w)$ be the equilibrium probability that a customer in this new system will wait no longer than w units of time for service; and, for $0 \leq f < 1$, define

$$w(f) = \inf \{w \,|\, p(w) \geq f\}.$$

Here are two conjectures.

Conjecture 1. In any dynamic-priority queueing system satisfying the conditions of Section 2, if u and v are urgency numbers which are actually attained, then

$$w_u(f) - w_v(f) \to u - v, \qquad \text{as } f \to 1.$$

Conjecture 2. For any dynamic-priority queueing system satisfying the conditions of Section 2, there exists a number u such that if u is any urgency number which is actually attained, then

$$w_u(f) - w(f) \to u - \bar{u}, \qquad \text{as } f \to 1.$$

Conjecture 1 formalizes the conclusion of the "plausible argument" in Section 1. It is evident that Conjecture 2 implies Conjecture 1, but both are stated because the simulation evidence is more straightforwardly consistent in its support of the weaker conjecture (see Section 6). The notation u in Conjecture 2 is suggestive of the fact that it will later be claimed that this number is approximately equal to the mean of the urgency-number distribution, within the range of systems which have been simulated, and perhaps exactly equal to it in certain cases.

Figure 1 illustrates the meaning of Conjecture 2 (specifically representating a single-server case with unit mean holding time, $\rho = .9$,

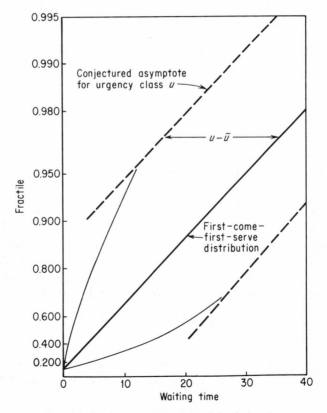

Figure 1 Graphical representation of Conjecture 2.

and exponentially distributed interarrival intervals and holding times). The choice of an inverted logarithmic vertical scale makes a straight line of the cumulative waiting-time distribution curve for a queueing system with exponentially distributed interarrival intervals and holding times, and with service order governed by the first come, first served rule.[3] The curved lines in the lower left-hand part of the figure roughly indicate the shapes of the dynamic-priority waiting-time distribution curves (estimated by simulation).

4. MATHEMATICAL RESULTS

Inquiries have, of course, been made as to the mathematical validity of the conjectures stated above—and with some success. This work is based upon an extension of the techniques used in an earlier paper[4] to answer a number of questions about mean waiting times in certain types of dynamic-priority queueing systems. The results obtained and their proofs will be treated fully in a subsequent paper, and the present section is intended merely to indicate the status of this research.

The basic tool used, which can be applied to a variety of dynamic-priority queueing systems with discrete time scales, is a technique for computing the probability distribution of number of customers in the system whose service will precede that of a randomly chosen customer, as a function of his urgency number and the length of time he has waited. Since the randomly chosen customer's service will start at the first moment after his arrival when the number of customers ahead of him is less than the number of servers, the technique leads to the equilibrium waiting-time probabilities for customers in each urgency class. More interestingly, at least from the viewpoint of the present paper, the technique also provides a way of reaching relatively general conclusions about the asymptotic behavior of the waiting-time probability distributions.

Conjecture 2 has been established as a theorem for a class of single-server dynamic-priority queueing systems with geometrically distributed interarrival intervals and holding times. It has been shown that $\bar{u}$ is slightly larger than the mean of the urgency-number distribution (the difference depending on the "coarseness" of the geometric distributions, viewed as approximations to exponential distributions). It appears that the method used to establish these results can be applied to cases with several servers and perhaps with other

---

[3] See P. M. Morse, *Queues, Inventories and Maintenance*, John Wiley & Sons, New York, 1958.

[4] See footnote 1.

distributions of interarrival intervals and holding times, but proofs have not been found.

The discrete-time models lend themselves to the application of formal limiting processes in which the time unit is shrunk toward zero while various system characteristics are preserved. These processes can be applied in such a way that the distributions of urgency numbers, interarrival intervals, holding times, and waiting times all tend toward limits; and it is reasonable to suspect that the continuous-time queueing systems with the limiting distributions of urgency numbers, interarrival intervals, and holding times will also have the limiting distributions of waiting time. These observations lead to support for Conjecture 2 in single-server systems with exponentially distributed interarrival intervals and holding times, but rigorous proofs based upon them have not yet been found. The value of u does indeed approach the mean of the urgency-number distribution, as the time unit is shrunk toward zero; whence the nonrigorous limiting argument supports the proposition that $\bar{u}$ is equal to this mean in single-server systems with exponentially distributed interarrival interval and holding times.

5. THE SIMULATIONS

In this section, the simulations which were run to study the behavior of dynamic-priority queueing systems are described. The codes were written in FORTRAN II programming language.

Preliminary. It was convenient throughout the simulations to use the mean holding time, for whatever system was under consideration, as the unit of time. The experimental variables which could be expected to influence the equilibrium statistical behavior of a dynamic-priority queueing system satisfying the conditions of Section 2 can be considered to be the following.

1. The number of servers.
2. The form of the interarrival-interval distribution.
3. The form of the holding-time distribution.
4. The load ratio ρ.
5. The urgency-number distribution.

Simulation runs were actually made with one, two, three, four, six, and eight servers. Constant and exponentially distributed interarrival intervals were used; so were constant and exponentially distributed times. (No runs were made, of course, with both constant interarrival intervals and constant holding times.) The following values of ρ were included in in the experimentation: .4, .6, .8, .9, .95, .98.

The behavior of a dynamic-priority queueing system is not changed if the same number is added to all the urgency numbers, so there was no loss of generality in restricting the experiments to urgency-number distributions with mean zero. A number of different kinds of urgency-number distributions were used, including uniform distributions with varying numbers of distinct values, binomial distributions, highly skewed distributions and multi-valued bimodal distributions. The interval between successive numerical values actually attained by the urgency number was treated as a separate variable, and allowed to vary from zero (first come, first served rule) to infinity (service order governed by "rigid priorities"). The emphasis was, of course, on intermediate values (dynamic priorities). For most runs, the difference between the largest and smallest values attained by the urgency number was between one and twenty times the equilibrium mean waiting time for the system simulated.

It was necessary to decide upon run lengths and initialization procedures. The choices made were necessarily compromises, limited by considerations relating to ease and efficiency in computing, but also guided by the known theory which is of special relevance to queue sampling,[5] and by the consistency and agreement of output with established theory, when applicable. For most runs, the queue was preinitialized by placing in it approximately the equilibrium mean number of customers in the system concerned. The first 500 additional customers to arrive provided further initialization, and did not contribute to the statistical output, which was based entirely upon the records of the next 7500 arrivals. To guard against end effects, new customers continued to enter the system until all of these 7500 customers had started their service. Over the entire range of experimentation, these choices did result in reasonably consistent outputs when the same statistical conditions were replicated, and in good agreement with established equilibrium theory—except that, as had been qualitatively predicted on theoretical grounds, the waiting times corresponding to the higher fractiles in the waiting-time distributions for systems with large load ratios were usually underestimated.

Except in a few preliminary runs, the computational outputs included the waiting times corresponding to the following fractiles of the sample waiting-time distribution for each urgency class: .2, .4, .6, .8, .9, .95, .98, .99, .995, .998. The means and standard deviations of these sample distributions were also output. In addition, the same collection of data was output for the sample waiting-time distribution for all customers (lumped together, without regard for urgency class).

[5] See, for instance, J. R. Jackson, "Some Expected Transition Times in Simple Queues," *Operations Research*, Vol. 9, No. 2, (Mar.–Apr. 1961) pp. 277–279.

These last data facilitated estimating the $w(f)$ of Conjecture 2, by making runs with all urgency numbers set equal to zero, in which case the dynamic-priority rule governing service order reduces to the first come, first served rule.

The experimentation. To start the experimentation proper, 30 or 40 runs were made with various arrangements of the experimental variables. The results were graphed in several ways. The graphs of cumulative waiting-time distributions on inverted semilogarithmic paper (such as that used for Figure 1) showed striking regularities, which led to the conjectures stated in Section 3. Further experimentation was planned primarily to develop these conjectures and explore their validity. About 500 runs were made in all, using about twenty hours on the Western Data Processing Center's IBM 709 computer. The purpose of these runs was to study the general behavior of the systems simulated, rather than to test clear-cut hypotheses, and the use of a formal "statistical design" seemed neither feasible nor desirable.

Of the 500 runs, 270 constituted a "main experiment," limited to single-server systems, with exponentially distributed interarrival intervals and holding times, and with three equally spaced and equally probable values of the urgency number. Two parameters were varied: the load ratio ρ; and the ratio

$$K = \frac{\text{(largest urgency number)} - \text{(smallest urgency number)}}{\text{over-all mean waiting time for the system concerned}}$$

The experiment covered all combinations of the following values of ρ and K:

$$\rho \quad .4 \quad .6 \quad .8 \quad .9 \quad .95$$
$$K \quad 0 \quad 1 \quad 2 \quad 4 \quad 6 \quad 8 \quad 12 \quad 20 \quad \infty$$

Six runs of 7500 customers were made for each combination, so the aggregate statistics are based upon the records of 45,000 customers. Only six distinct loads of customers were actually generated, and each of these was modified by parameter changes to provide a run for each combination of values of ρ and K. This practice saved greatly on the most time-consuming parts of the computations (generating pseudorandom numbers and computing logarithms to convert them to exponential distributions), and also reduced the effects of sample error upon comparisons of output data corresponding to different parameter values.

The remaining 230 runs provided a well-scattered (although not systematic) sampling of system behavior under various arrangements of the experimental variables. In most cases, one or two of the following changes were made in the general model of the "main experiment": increasing the number of servers; substituting constant interarrival intervals for exponentially distributed ones; substituting constant holding times for exponentially distributed ones; using different urgency-number distributions. As in the "main experiment," a load of customers, once generated, was usually used for several runs—with different load ratios and different intervals between successive values attained by the urgency number. In most cases, a run was made with all urgency numbers set equal to zero, to obtain a sample estimate of the $w(f)$ of Conjecture 2, as explained above.

6. SIMULATION RESULTS

This section summarizes the outcomes of the simulations run to study the behavior of dynamic-priority queueing systems. The general approach—which reflects the point of view taken in planning and running the simulations—is descriptive, rather than formally statistical.

Support for Conjecture 1. The simulation results are all consistent with Conjecture 1, and, with certain exceptions to be noted and explained below, they generally provide affirmative support for the conjecture. Figure 2, based upon the six "main experiment" runs with $\rho = .8$ and $K = 2$, is typical. Ignore the broken lines in the figure for the moment. The solid, polygonal curves join observed points in the sample cumulative distributions of waiting time for the three urgency classes (labelled with their urgency numbers at the top of the graph). The content of Conjecture 1, interpreted graphically, is that the upper parts of these curves should be similar in shape, but displaced from one another by directed horizontal distances equal to the algebraically signed differences in their urgency numbers. The moderate deviations from this condition are, in the main, small compared with the variation from one run to another among the six runs whose aggregate output is summarized in Figure 2, in the location of the sample waiting-time distribution curves.

Figures 3 and 4 are similar to Figure 2, but Figure 3 is based upon the "main experiment" runs with $\rho = .8$ and $K = 4$, and Figure 4 upon the runs with $\rho = .8$ and $K = 6$. Again in these cases, the deviations from Conjecture 1 seen in the upper parts of the curves are small compared with the run-to-run variation in the locations of these curves. The simulation results, in general, are as supportive of Conjecture 1 as are those graphed in Figures 2, 3, and 4, except as noted in the following paragraph. (But, as would be expected, the sample waiting-time distribution curves based upon one or two simulation runs are slightly less regular than those from the "main experiment," each based upon six runs.)

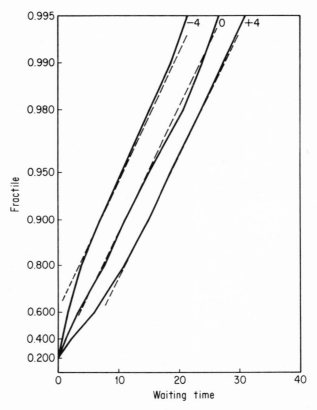

Figure 2 "Main experiment," $\rho = 0.8$, $K = 2$.

The sequence of Figures 2, 3, and 4 indicates why it was necessary to admit "certain exceptions" to the statement that the simulations provide "affirmative support" for Conjecture 1. If the tops of these figures were cut off at fractile .950, then the remainder of Figure 4 would no longer show how the upper parts of the sample curves approximate the limiting behavior predicted by the conjecture. In some of the runs, such behavior was not exhibited up to the highest output fractile, .998; but in all cases the form of the curves is consistent with the assumption that such behavior would appear if only the curves were extended up to sufficiently high fractiles. This assumption is given credibility by the fact that these "questionable" results consistently fit into patterns with the results of other, related

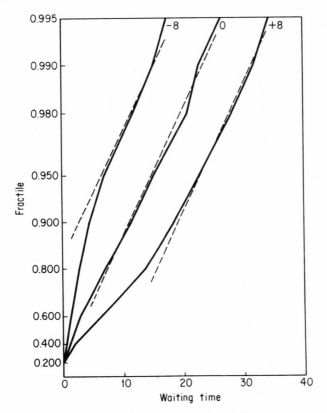

Figure 3 "Main experiment," $\rho = 0.8$, $K = 4$.

simulation runs—comparable to the pattern which the reader can see for himself in the progression from Figure 2 to Figure 3 and then to Figure 4.

Support for Conjecture 2. Two approaches can be taken in testing Conjecture 2. On the one hand, if sample estimates of the values of $w(f)$ are obtained, as explained in Section 5, these can be used to interpret the conjecture. On the other hand, in some cases the mathematically correct values of $w(f)$ can be calculated, and these can be used. The results of these two approaches can differ, of course, only insofar as the sample values of $w(f)$ differ from the mathematically correct ones. In fact, the simulation runs were not long enough to locate accurately the highest output fractiles of the waiting-time distributions for systems with $\rho \geq .8$. The results for $\rho = .8$, when compared with established equilibrium theory, are seen to be fairly accurate up to fractile .990; but the limit of reasonable accuracy with $\rho = .9$ appears to be close to fractile .950; the limit with $\rho = .95$ is near fractile .900; and that with $\rho = .98$ is near fractile .800.

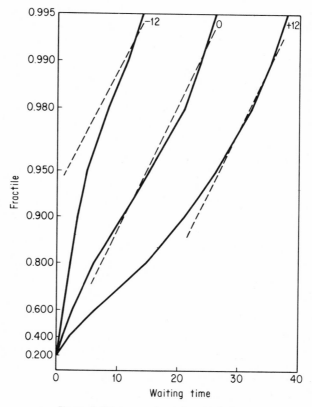

Figure 4 "Main experiment," $\rho = 0.8$, $K = 6$.

Up to the limits just mentioned, and up to the highest output fractiles in cases with $\rho = .4$ or .6, the simulation results all show striking agreement with Conjecture 2, regardless of which of the (almost equal) values of $w(f)$ are used—excepting cases which can be explained, as in the discussion of evidence favoring Conjecture 1, by the assumption that the fractiles used simply do not reach high enough to demonstrate behavior approximating the limiting behavior predicted by Conjecture 2. As before, this assumption is made credible by the way the "questionable" results fit into patterns with "more satisfying" results of other, related simulation runs.

Above these limits, the simulation results still agree consistently with Conjecture 2, if the sample values of $w(f)$ are used in interpreting the conjecture.   But in almost all cases where the mathematically correct graph of $w(f)$ has been plotted, the graph based on sample values sweeps upward more rapidly than the equilibrium theory predicts, and the whole system of sample waiting-time distribution curves sweeps upward with it.   This phenomenon reflects sample values which underestimate the waiting times corresponding to these higher fractiles in the equilibrium waiting-time distributions.

The central one of the three broken lines in each of Figures 2, 3, and 4 is the mathematically correct equilibrium waiting-time distribution curve for a system exactly like the dynamic-priority system to which the figure relates, except with service order governed by the first come, first served rule.   The other two broken lines are parallel to the central one, and displaced from it by directed horizontal distances equal to the nonzero urgency numbers which are attained in the dynamic-priority system.   The meaning of Conjecture 2, graphically interpreted, is that the dynamic-priority waiting-time distribution curves should have asymptotes parallel to the broken lines, and displaced from them in the same direction by the same distance.   The simulation results are generally as supportive of Conjecture 2 as are those graphed in Figures 2, 3, and 4, with the interpretations and qualifications previously noted.   The uppermost parts of these figures provide a mild illustration of the sample-error phenomenon mentioned in the preceding paragraph.

Estimates of $\bar{u}$. The simulation results are all consistent with the assumption that, in any given dynamic-priority queueing system, the value of $\bar{u}$ does not differ from the mean of the urgency-number distribution by more than a few percent of the difference between the largest and the smallest urgency numbers attained in the system. The simulation outputs for systems with constant interarrival intervals and exponentially distributed holding times, or with exponentially distributed interarrival intervals and constant holding times, suggest that $\bar{u}$ may typically be slightly larger than the mean urgency number in such cases.   This observation seems to fit with the mathematical fact that the same thing is true in certain systems whose time scales are discrete (see Section 4).

On the basis of the pertinent simulation outputs, along with the nonrigorous argument based upon mathematical results which is mentioned at the end of Section 4, the following, sharpened version of Conjecture 2, limited in scope to a special class of systems, is set forth.

Conjecture 3. Conjecture 2 holds with $\bar{u}$ equal to the mean of the urgency-number distribution, for systems with exponentially distributed interarrival intervals and holding times.

Note that the above statement is conjectured to hold for multiserver systems with exponentially distributed interarrival intervals and holding times, as well as for single-server systems.

Interpreted graphically, Conjecture 3 proposes that the broken lines in Figures 2, 3, and 4 are themselves asymptotes of the dynamic-priority waiting-time distribution curves. These figures are typical of the agreement of pertinent simulation outputs with Conjecture 3, subject to interpretations and qualifications parallel to those previously noted in connection with evidence favoring Conjecture 2. The more general conclusion suggested above, that for a wide variety of dynamic-priority queueing systems the value of $\bar{u}$ is not much different from the mean of the urgency-number distribution, has the graphical interpretation that the waiting-time distribution curves for these systems should be asymptotic to curves which are "close" to curves constructed in the same way as the broken lines in Figures 2, 3, and 4.

Convergence toward the asymptotes. The remainder of the present section starts from the assumption that Conjectures 2 and 3 hold, and consists of remarks about the shapes of the lower parts of the sample dynamic-priority waiting-time distribution curves, and about the way in which these curves are observed to converge toward their conjectured asymptotes. The "asymptotes" referred to below are generally those located using the sample values $w(f)$. In cases outside the scope of Conjecture 3, the horizontal location of the whole set of conjectured asymptotes was selected visually to insure the best possible agreement (subjectively judged) with Conjecture 2. There was no instance, however, in which the location chosen was inconsistent with the assumption that $\bar{u}$ differed from the mean of the urgency-number distribution for the system concerned by at most a few percent of the difference between the largest and the smallest urgency numbers attained in the system.

The curves shown in Figures 1 through 4 typify the general appearance of the sample waiting-time distribution curves. Except for small discrepancies which can reasonably be attributed to sample error, the whole set of curves for any given system is always seen to lie between the asymptotes corresponding to the smallest and the largest urgency numbers attained in the system; and the waiting times corresponding to a given fractile, for different urgency classes, are always ordered according to increasing urgency number. The curves for the smallest and the largest urgency numbers are always seen to "fan out" fairly smoothly toward their asymptotes. Those for intermediate urgency classes are generally more complicated in appearance, and they tend to go upward rather sharply when they first break away from the vertical axis, as compared with smoothly concave or convex curves starting at the same points on the vertical axis and having the same asymptotes. Attempts to "fit" the lower parts of the dynamic-priority waiting-time distribution curves with parametrized mathematical formulae have led only to unsatisfactory results.

Generally speaking, the sample waiting-time distribution curve for the smallest urgency number is seen to converge toward its asymptote most slowly; that is the curves for larger urgency numbers settle down to within any given small horizontal distance from their asymptotes at lower fractiles than it does. However, the difference in the rates of convergence for the different curves relating to any one system is not large, and it seems suitable to limit further remarks on this subject to the curve for the smallest urgency number. As a rough, empirically discovered means for describing the convergence of this curve, it is useful to define

$$L = \frac{\text{(mean urgency number)} - \text{(smallest urgency number)}}{\text{over-all mean waiting time}}$$

for any dynamic-priority queueing system, and to set

$$M = \rho^2 e^{-L}.$$

Note that the over-all mean waiting time for a dynamic-priority system is the same as that for the queueing system which is identical with it, except with service order governed by the first come, first served rule; so L and M can easily be calculated for a wide variety of cases, by using well-known mathematical results.

It turned out in the simulations that the horizontal distance, at fractile $1 - M$, between the sample waiting-time distribution curve for the smallest urgency number and the conjectured asymptote for this curve is always *roughly* one-half of the over-all mean waiting time for the system. In symbols,

$$w(1 - M) - w_u(1 - M) \cong \bar{u} - u - \frac{\overline{w}}{2}$$

where $\bar{u}$ is the smallest urgency number attained in the system, and $\overline{w}$ is the over-all mean waiting time for the system. In most cases, the difference at fractile $1 - M/2$ is too small to estimated with any significance if the simulation data is used. Table 1 gives a few approximate values of $1 - M$.

The value of L for the system to which Figure 2 relates is unity, and $\rho = .8$ From the table, $1 - M = .77$.   Thus, the intent of the immediately preceding paragraphs, interpreted for Figure 2, is that the broken lines are "reasonable" approximations to the sample waiting-time distribution curves from fractile .77 upward.   The corresponding fractiles for Figures 3 and 4 are .91 and .97, respectively.

7. CONCLUSION; EXAMPLES

It is believed that the evidence presented in this paper provides sufficient support for the following statements to make them worthwhile as working hypotheses:

1. Conjecture 2 is true for a wide variety of dynamic-priority queueing systems, as an approximation accurate enough for most practical purposes.

2. Further, for most practical purposes, the mean of the urgency-number distribution can be used in place of the $\bar{u}$ of Conjecture 2.

3. Finally, at fractiles not lower than fractile $1 - M$ (as defined near the end of Section 6), the hypothetical approximate asymptotes determined by applying the two preceding statements are sufficiently close approximations, for most practical purposes, to the waiting-time distribution curves themselves.

In a more conservative mood, the writer might have substituted "fractile $1 - M/2$" "fractile $1 - M$" in the third of the above statements.   Whichever formulation is used, it will be seen that the dynamic-priority queueing systems for which the results of this paper are most satisfactory are those with load ratios close to unity, with moderate differences between the mean of the urgency-number distribution and the smallest urgency number attained, and in which interest is focused upon the higher fractiles of the waiting-time distributions.

Examples. The remaining paragraphs provide hypothetical applications of Conjecture 3.   Each case is concerned with a single-server queueing system, with exponentially distributed interarrival intervals and holding times, mean holding time one, and load ratio $\rho = .9$. In such cases, Figure 1 provides an appropriate basis for interpreting the conjecture; the over-all mean waiting time, needed to calculate L for use in connection with Table 1, is $\rho/(1 - \rho) = 9$.

In the first example, customers will fall into three classes—comprising 10, 25, and 65 percent of all customers, respectively, and scheduled to start service 20, 30, and 50 units of time after arriving in the system.   It is desired to predict the percentage of customers who will start service "on time" if the queue is sequenced according to scheduled start time. If we take 20, 30, and 50 as the urgency numbers, the expected urgency number is 42. This is the $\bar{u}$ of Conjecture 3. The proposed asymptotes are parallel to the "first-come, first-served distribution" shown in Figure 1, and displaced from it by directed horizontal distances -22, -12, and $+8$ (the three values of $u - \bar{u}$). These lines are seen to cross the "on-time" waiting-time limits (20, 30, and 50 units) close to fractile .980. Since $L = (42 - 20)/9 = 2.4$, Table 1 shows that $1 - M$ is less than .95. It can thus be assumed that the actual waiting-time distribution curves are close to their asymptotes at fractile .980. The conclusion is that about 98 percent of the customers in each class will start service "on time."

Table 1. Values of $1 - M$. The definitions and significance of these numbers are explained in the last part of Section 6.

L	ρ .4	.6	.8	.9	.95
1	.94	.87	.77	.71	.68
2	.98	.95	.91	.89	.88
3	.992	.98	.97	.96	.95
4	.997	.993	.988	.985	.984

If, in the preceding example, the same classes of customers were scheduled to start service 5, 15, and 35 units of time after arrival, the fractile located on the proposed asymptotes, using Figure 1, would be about .920. Since this is close to $1 - M$, the conclusion that 92 percent of the customers would start service "on time" would be a comparatively rough approximation. One would, in fact, expect a slightly lower percentage of customers in the "most-urgent class" to start service "on time."

In a third and final example, all customers fall into two classes, say classes A and B, comprising 40 percent and 60 percent of all customers, respectively. It is desired to design a two-class, dynamic-priority rule under which at least 95 percent of the class A customers will start service within 15 time units of arriving in the system, and which will (within this limitation) yield the best possible service for class B. The second requirement is interpreted to mean, using a natural notation, that $u_B - u_A$ is to be minimized. If we tentatively assume that the pertinent parts of the waiting-time distribution curves are "close enough" to their asymptotes, the requirement for class A is that the asymptote for class A must pass through or above the point (15, .950) in Figure 1. Since the "first come, first served distribution" passes through (30, .950), this demand is expressed by the inequality, $u_A - u \le 15 - 30 = -15$. Since $\bar{u} = .4u_A + .6u_B$, this inequality can be re-expressed as the requirement that $u_B - u_A \ge$

25, after simple manipulations. The required minimum is obviously achieved if $u_B = u_A + 25$. Now the preceding tentative assumption can be tested. The L of Table 1 turns out to be about 1.7, and $1 - M$ is less than .89, whence a close fit of the waiting-time distribution curves to their asymptotes can indeed be assured at fractile .950, and the original problem will indeed be solved by setting $u_B = u_A + 25$. One specific solution would be to determine scheduled starting times as follows: for customers in class A, time of arrival plus 15; for customers in class B, time of arrival plus 40.

V

Scheduling
Complex Activities

Since its formal introduction in 1959 by James E. Kelley and Morgan R. Walker [1] *critical-path method* has found immediate acceptance as a theoretical discipline and application as a practical tool. A related technique, called PERT, has been described by Malcolm and others [2]. The methods have since been applied in a variety of ways, and recently a number of computer firms have advertised programs for making critical-path calculations as a part of their "software" service to customers.

Since it is basically a simple graphical method of presenting the work to be done in order to complete a project, and involves only elementary arithmetical operations (finding the maxima and minima of finite sets of numbers), it is remarkable that the idea was so long in forthcoming. The immediate and widespread acceptance of the critical-path method is the best evaluation of its importance.

Levy, Thompson, and Wiest in their "Introduction to the Critical-Path Method" (Chapter 20) give an elementary exposition of the theory of the method, illustrating it with simple examples. Their exposition is nontechnical and is directed at the general reader who wants an easy entry to the theory.   By representing jobs as boxes rather than arrows (as Kelley and Walker do) they are able to avoid the technical and expositional difficulty of introducing dummy jobs—a necessity in the "arrow diagram" of Kelley and Walker. Mathematically, the two descriptions are equivalent, but questions of taste may make one method preferable to the other.   The Levy, Thompson, Wiest paper is a clear and technically accurate description of one version of the theory.

Although statements are made in the critical-path literature that the critical jobs (those with minimum slack) are the important ones to monitor in following a project, this is strictly true only if unlimited resources are available to the firm involved in carrying out the project. If there are machine or manpower limitations, then it can easily happen that noncritical jobs can delay the project simply because there are no resources available to finish them.   In Chapter 21, "The Critical-Path Method: Resources Planning and Scheduling," Kelley addresses himself to this problem.   After a brief description of the arrow-diagram version of the critical-path method, Kelley discusses various models that could be used to schedule men and machines to jobs in a project while taking into account limitations on these resources. Such models involve corresponding computer programs actually to carry out the allocation of resources to jobs.   And, according to Kelley, a considerable amount of "art" is involved in evaluating various versions of these models.   This paper will undoubtedly be important in stimulating further work on various models using the critical-path method.   Such developments are crucial to furthering the usefulness of the critical-path method.

The precedence requirements that exist among jobs in a project lead to what mathematicians call a "relation."   At the basis of the critical-path method is the predecessor relation that exists between some pairs of jobs. In "Mathematical Basis of the Critical-Path Method" (Chapter 22), Levy, Thompson, and Wiest study the mathematical properties of this relation. Curiously, the immediate predecessor relation should be irreflexive and k-intransitive (terms defined in the paper), which are unusual properties for mathematical relations.   The present paper is a more advanced version of the earlier introductory paper by the same authors.   They develop algorithms for insuring that the job data of the project leads to immediate predecessor relations that have the desired properties.   Actually, two versions of each algorithm are given, one version dependent upon matrix algebra methods of analysis [which bear close relationships to the results in the paper by Giffler (Chapter 4)], and a second version of the algorithm which is graph-theoretic in nature.   The latter version is perhaps the most economical of computer memory space.

The three papers presented in this section thus report on the current status and indicate some likely trends in an important current topic of the scheduling literature.

REFFERENCES

1. Kelley, M. E., Jr. and M. R. Walker, "Critical-Path Planning and Scheduling," *Proc. Eastern Joint Computer Conference*, pp. 160–173, Boston (Dec. 1–3, 1959).

2. Malcolm, D. G., J. H. Roseboom, C. E. Clark, and W. Fazar: "Application of a Technique for Research and Development Program Evaluation," *Operations Research*, **7** (1959), 646–669.

20

Introduction to the Critical=path Method

F. K. Levy, G. L. Thompson, J. D. Wiest
CARNEGIE INSTITUTE OF TECHNOLOGY

Recently added to the growing assortment of quantitative aids to business decision-making is the critical-path method—a powerful but basically simple technique for analyzing, planning, and scheduling large, complex projects. In essence, the method provides a means of determining (1) which jobs or activities, of the many which comprise a project, are "critical" in their effect upon total project time, and (2) how best to schedule all jobs in the project in order to meet a target date at minimum cost. Widely diverse kinds of projects lend themselves to analysis, as is suggested in the following list of applications:

1. The construction of a building (or a highway, or a new plant).
2. Planning and launching a new product.
3. A turn-around in an oil refinery (or other maintenance projects).
4. Installing and debugging a computer system.

The preparation of this paper was supported by the Office of Naval Research and the Bureau of Ships through grants to the Graduate School of Industrial Administration, Carnegie Institute of Technology.

5. Research and engineering design projects.

6. Scheduling ship construction and repairs.

7. The manufacture and assembly of a large generator (or other job-lot operations).

8. Missile countdown procedures.

1. REQUIRED CHARACTERISTICS FOR CRITICAL-PATH ANALYSIS

Each of these projects has several characteristics that are essential for analysis by the critical-path method:

1. The project consists of a well-defined collection of jobs (or activities) which, when completed, mark the end of the project.

2. The jobs may be started and stopped independently of each other, within a given sequence. (This requirement eliminates continuous-flow process activities, such as oil-refining, where "jobs" or operations necessarily follow one after another with essentially no slack.)

3. The jobs are ordered—that is, they must be performed in a given sequence. (For example, the foundation of a house must be constructed before the walls are erected.)

2. THE METHOD

The concept of the critical-path method is quite simple and may best be illustrated in terms of a project graph. The graph is not an essential part of the analysis; computer programs have been written which permit necessary calculations to be made without reference to a graph. Nevertheless, the project graph is valuable as a means of depicting, visually and clearly, the complex of jobs in a project and their interrelations. First of all, each job necessary for the completion of a project is listed with a unique identification (usually a number), the time required to complete the job, and its immediate prerequisite jobs.[1] Then each job is drawn on the graph as a circle, with its number and time appearing within the circle. Sequence relationships are indicated by arrows connecting each circle (job) with its immediate successors, with the arrows pointing to the latter. For convenience, all circles with no predecessors are connected to a circle marked "Start"; likewise, all circles with no successors are connected to a circle marked "finish."[2] Typically, the graph then depicts a

[1] For convenience in graphing, and as a check on certain kinds of data errors, the jobs may be arranged in "technological order," which means that no job appears on the list until all of its immediate predecessors (and hence all of its predecessors) have already been listed. Technological ordering is impossible if a cycle error exists in the job data (e. g., job A precedes B, B precedes C, and C precedes A).

[2] The "start" and "finish" circles may be considered to be pseudo-jobs of zero time length.

number of different "arrow paths" from start to finish. The time required to traverse each path is the sum of the times associated with all jobs on the path. The critical path (or paths) is the longest path (in time) from start to finish; it indicates the minimum time necessary to complete the entire project.[3]

In essence, the critical path is the bottleneck route. Only by finding ways to shorten jobs along the critical path can the over-all project time be reduced; the time required to perform non-critical jobs is irrelevant from the viewpoint of total project time. The frequent (and costly) practice of "crashing" *all* jobs in a project in order to reduce total project time is thus unnecessary. Typically, about ten percent of the jobs in large projects are critical. (This figure will naturally vary from project to project.) Of course, if some way is found to shorten one or more of the critical jobs, then not only will the project time be shortened, but the critical path itself may shift and some previously noncritical jobs may become critical.

3. AN EXAMPLE: BUILDING A HOUSE

A simple and familiar example should help to clarify the notion of critical-path scheduling and the process of constructing a graph. The project of building a house is readily analyzed by the critical-path technique and is typical of a large class of similar applications. Although a contractor might want a more detailed analysis, we shall

---

[3] The above method of depicting a project graph differs in some respects from the representation used by James E. Kelley, Jr. and Morgan R. Walker, who, perhaps more than anyone alse, were responsible for the initial development of critical-path scheduling. (For an interesting account of its early history, see their paper, Critical-Path Planning and Scheduling," reported in *Proceedings of the Eastern Joint Computer Conference*, Boston, December 1–3, 1959.)

In the widely used Kelley-Walker form, a project graph is just the opposite of that described above: jobs are shown as arrows, and the arrows are connected by means of circles (or dots) that indicate sequence relationships. Thus all immediate predecessors of a given job connect to a circle at the tail of the job arrow, and all immediate successor jobs emanate from the circle at the head of the job arrow. In essence, then, a circle marks an event: the completion of all jobs leading into the circle. Since these jobs are the immediate prerequisites for all jobs leading out of the circle, they must all be completed before *any* of the succeeding jobs can begin.

In order to portray accurately all predecessor relationships, "dummy jobs" must often be added to the project graph in the Kelley-Walker form. [For a detailed explanation of dummy jobs, see James E. Kelley, Jr., "Critical-Path Planning and Scheduling: Mathematical Basis," *Operations Research*, pp. 301–302 (May–June, 1961)]. The method described above by the present authors avoids the necessity (and complexity) of dummy jobs, is easier to program for a computer, and seems more straightforward in explanation and application.

the following Should give you a good idea

be satisfied with the following list of major jobs (together with the estimated time and the immediate predecessors for each job).[4]

Job no.	Description	Immediate predecessors	Normal time (days)
a	Start		0
b	Excavate and pour footers	a	4/4
c	~~Pour concrete foundation~~ *lay Block*	b	2/3
d	Erect wooden frame, including rough roof	c	4/5
e	Lay brickwork	d	6
f	Install basement drains and plumbing	c	1
g	Pour basement floor	f	2
h	Install rough plumbing	f	3
i	Install rough wiring	d	2
j	Install heating and ventilating	d, g	4
k	Fasten plaster board and plaster (including drying)	i, j, h	10
l	Lay finish flooring	k	3
m	Install kitchen fixtures	l	1
n	Install finish plumbing	l	2
o	Finish carpentry	l	3
p	Finish roofing and flashing	e	2
q	Fasten gutters and downspouts	p	1
r	Lay storm drains for rain water	c	1
s	Sand and varnish flooring	o, t	2
t	Paint	m, n	3
u	Finish electrical work	t	1
v	Finish grading	q, r	2
w	Pour walks and complete landscaping	v	5
x	Finish	s, u, w	0

The column "Immediate Predecessors" determines the sequence relationships of the jobs and enables us to draw the project graph (Figure 1). In each circle the job identification (letter) appears before the comma, and the job time appears after the comma.

Following the rule that a "legal" path must always move in the direction of the arrows, we could enumerate 22 unique paths from start to finish, with associated times ranging from a minimum of 14 days (path a–b–c–r–v–w–x) to a maximum of 34 days (path a–b–c–d–j–k–l–n–t–s–x). The latter is the critical path; it determines the over-all project time and tells us which jobs are critical in their effect on this time. If the contractor wishes to complete the house in less than 34 days, it would be useless to shorten jobs not on the critical path. It may seem to him, for example, that the brickwork (e) delays progress, since work on a whole series of jobs (p–q–v–w) must wait until it is completed. But it would be fruitless to rush

[4] The job list and project graph for the house-building example were developed by Peter R. Winters.

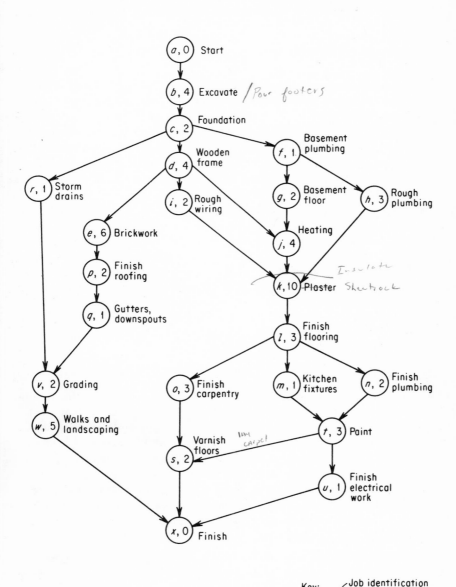

Figure 1 Building a house: project graph.

the completion of the brickwork, as it is not on the critical path and therefore is irrelevant in determining total project time.

4. SHORTENING THE CRITICAL PATH

If the contractor were to use these techniques, he would examine the critical path for possible improvements. Perhaps he could assign more carpenters to job d (framing), reducing it from four to two days. Then the critical path would change slightly, passing through jobs f and g instead of d. Notice that total project time would be reduced only one day, even though two days had been shaved off job d. Thus the contractor must watch for possible shifting of the critical path as he effects changes in critical jobs.

Shortening the critical path requires a consideration of both engineering problems and economic questions. Is it physically possible to shorten the time required by critical jobs (by assigning more men to the job, working overtime, using different equipment, etc.)? If so, would the costs of speed-up be less than the savings resulting from the reduction in over-all project time? The critical-path method is useful because it quickly focuses attention on those jobs that are critical to the project time, it provides an easy way to determine the effects of shortening various jobs in the project, and it enables the user to evaluate the costs of a "crash" program.

Two important applications of these features come to mind:

DuPont, a pioneer in the application of the critical-path method to construction and maintenance projects, was concerned with the amount of downtime for maintenance at its Louisville works, which produces an intermediate product in the neoprene process. Analyzing the maintenance schedule by the critical-path method, DuPont engineers were able to cut downtime for maintenance from 125 to 93 hours. Further refinements were expected to reduce total time to 78 hours. As a result, performance of the plant improved by about a million pounds in 1959, and the intermediate was no longer a bottleneck in the neoprene process.

PERT, a technique closely related to the critical-path method, is widely credited with helping to shorten by two years the time originally estimated for completion of the engineering and development program for the Navy's Polaris missile. By pinpointing the longest paths through the vast maze of jobs necessary for completion of the missile design, PERT enabled the program managers to concentrate their efforts on those activities that vitally affected total project time.

Even with our small house-building project, however, the process of enumerating and measuring the length of every path through the maze of jobs is tedious. A simple method of finding the critical path and, at the same time, developing useful information about each job is next described.

5. THE CRITICAL-PATH ALGORITHM

If the start time or date for the project is given (we denote it by S), then there exists for each job an earliest starting time ES which is the earliest possible time that a job can begin, if it is given that all its predecessors are also started at their ES. And if the time to complete the job is t we can define, analogously, its early finish time EF to be $ES + t$, that is, the early start time plus the time it takes to do the job.

There is a simple way of computing ES and EF times by using the project graph. It proceeds as follows: (1) mark the value of S to the left and to the right of Start; (2) consider any new unmarked job *all of whose predecessors have been marked*, and mark to the left of the new job the *largest* number marked to the right of any of its immediate predecessors (this is its early start time); (3) add to this number the job time and mark the result to the right of the job (early finish time); (4) continue until Finish has been reached, then stop. Thus at the conclusion of this calculation the ES time for each job will appear to the left of the circle which identifies it, and the EF time will appear to the right of the circle. The number which appears to the right of the last job, Finish, is the early finish time F for the entire project.

6. AN ILLUSTRATION

To illustrate these calculations we consider the following simple production process. An assembly is to be made from two parts A and B. Both parts must be turned on the lathe, and B must be polished, whereas A need not be. The list of jobs to be performed, together with the predecessors of each job and the time in minutes

Job no.	Description	Immediate predecessors	Time
a	Start		0
b	Get materials for A	a	10
c	Get materials for B	a	20
d	Turn A on lathe	b, c	30
e	Turn B on lathe	b, c	20
f	Polish B	e	40
g	Assemble A and B	d, f	20
h	Finish	g	0

Figure 2

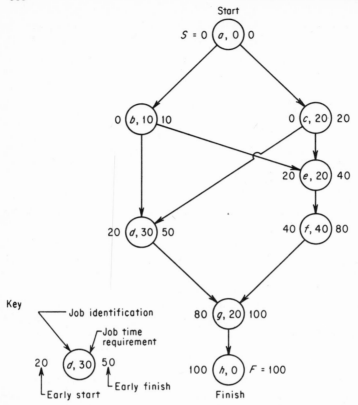

Figure 3 Calculation of early start and early finish times for each job.

to perform each job, is given in Figure 2. The graph for this project is shown in Figure 3. As before, the number of each job appears before the comma, and its job time after the comma. Also
shown on the graph are the *ES* and *EF* times for each job, if it is
assumed that the start time *S* is 0. The *ES* time appears to the
left of the circle representing a job and the *EF* time appears to the
right of the circle. Note that $F = 100$.

7. LATEST START AND FINISH TIMES

Suppose now that we have a target time T for completing the project. In order to be feasible it is clear that T must be greater than
or equal to F, the early finish time for the project. Assuming that
T is greater than or equal to F, we can define the concept of late
finish LF, or the latest time that a job can be finished without delaying the total project beyond its target time T. Similarly, late
start LS is defined to be $LF - t$, where t is the job time.

These numbers are determined for each job in a manner similar to the previous calculations, except that we work from the end of the project to its beginning. We proceed as follows: (1) mark the value of T to the right and left of Finish; (2) consider any new unmarked job *all of whose successors have been marked*, and mark to the right of the new job the *smallest* number marked to the left of any of its immediate successors; (3) subtract from this number the job time and mark the result to the left of the job; (4) continue until Start has been reached, then stop. At the conclusion of this calculation the *LF* time for a job will appear to the right of the circle which identifies it, and the *LS* time for the job will appear to the left of the circle. The number which appears to the right of Start is the latest time that the entire project can be started and still finish at the target time T.

In Figure 4 we carry out these calculations for the example of Figure 2. Here $T = F = 100$, and we separate early start and finish

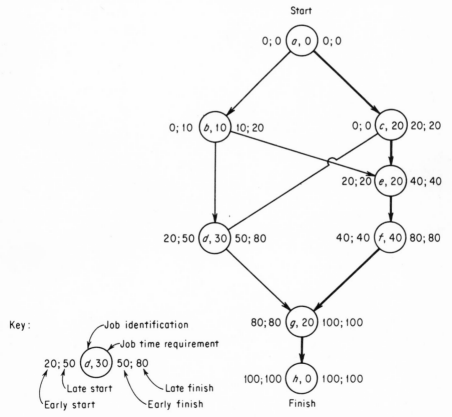

Figure 4 Calculation of late start and late finish times for each job.

and late start and finish times by semicolons so that ES; LS appears to the left of the job and EF; LF to the right.

8. THE CONCEPT OF SLACK

Examination of Figure 4 shows that some jobs have their early start equal to late start, while others do not. The difference between a job's early start and its late start (or between early finish and late finish) is called *total slack* (TS). Total slack represents the maximum amount of time a job may be delayed beyond its early start without necessarily delaying the project completion time.

We earlier defined critical jobs as those on the longest path through the project. That is, critical jobs *directly* affect the total project time. We can now relate the critical path to the concept of slack.

9. FINDING THE CRITICAL PATH

If the target date T equals the early finish date for the whole project F, then all critical jobs will have *zero* total slack. There will be at least one path going from Start to Finish that includes critical jobs only, i.e. the *critical* path.

If T is greater than F, then the critical jobs will have total slack equal to $(T - F)$. This is a minimum value; all noncritical jobs will have *greater* total slack. The critical path, once again, includes only critical jobs, and hence those with minimum TS.

In Figure 4, the critical path is shown by darkening the arrows connecting critical jobs. In this case there is just one critical path, and all critical jobs lie on it. (In other cases there may be more than one critical path.) Note that $T = F$; thus the critical jobs have zero total slack. Job b has $TS = 10$, and job d has $TS = 30$; either or both of these jobs could be delayed by these amounts without delaying the project.

10. FREE SLACK

Another kind of slack is worth mentioning. Free slack (FS) is the amount a job can be delayed without delaying the early start of any other job. A job with positive total slack may or may not also have free slack, but the latter never exceeds the former. For purposes of computation, the free slack of a job is defined as the difference between the job's early finish time and the *earliest* of the early start times of all its immediate successors. Thus in Figure 4, job b has $FS = 10$, and job d has $FS = 30$. All other jobs in Figure 4 have zero free slack.

11. THE SIGNIFICANCE OF SLACK

When a job has zero total slack, its scheduled start time is automatically fixed (early start equals late start); to delay the calculated start time is to delay the whole project. Jobs with slack, however, allow the scheduler some discretion in setting their start times. This

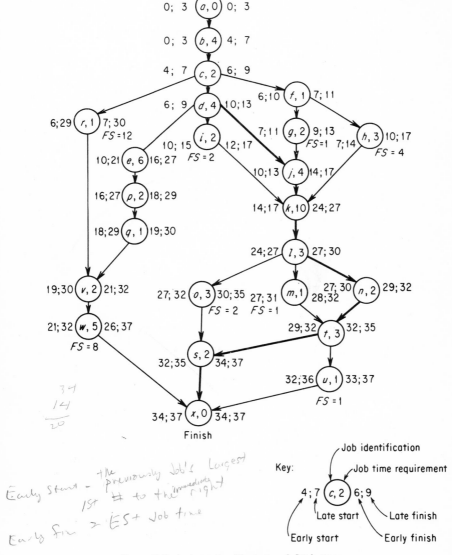

Figure 5 Project graph with start and finish times.

flexibility can usefully be applied to smoothing work schedules. Peak loads that develop in a particular shop (or on a machine, or within an engineering design group, to cite other examples) may be relieved by shifting jobs on the peak days to their late starts. Slack allows this kind of juggling without affecting project time.[5]

Free slack can be used effectively at the operating level. For example, if a job has free slack, the foreman may be given some flexibility in deciding when to start the job. Even if he delays the start by an amount equal to (or less than) the free slack, the delay will not affect the start times or slack of succeeding jobs (which is not true of jobs that have no free slack). For an illustration of these notions, we return to our house-building example.

12. BACK TO THE CONTRACTOR

In Figure 5 we reproduce the diagram of house-building jobs, marking ES; LS to the left and EF; LF to the right of each job. We assume that construction begins on day zero and must be completed by day 37. Total slack for each job is not marked, since it is evident as the difference between the pairs of numbers ES-LS or EF-LF. However, jobs that have positive free slack are so marked. There is one critical path, which is shown darkened in the diagram. All critical jobs on this path have three days total slack.

Several observations can be drawn immediately from the diagram.

1. The contractor could delay starting the house three days and still complete it on schedule (barring unforeseen difficulties). This delay would reduce the total slack of all jobs by three days, and hence reduce TS for critical jobs to zero.

2. Several jobs have free slack. Thus the contractor could delay the completion of rough wiring by two days, the basement floor by one day, rough plumbing by four days, the storm drains by 12 days, and so on—without affecting succeeding jobs.

3. The series of jobs e (brickwork), p (roofing), q (gutters), v (grading), and w (landscaping) have a comfortable amount of total slack (eleven days). The contractor can use these (and other slack jobs) as "fill-in" jobs for workers who become available when their skills are not needed for currently critical jobs. This is a simple application of work-load smoothing: juggling the jobs with slack in order to reduce peak demands for certain skilled workers or machines.

---

[5] A method for smoothing operations in a job shop, based on the critical-path method and the use of slack, is reported by the authors in "Multi-Ship, Multi-Shop Workload Smoothing Program," *Naval Logistics Research Quarterly*, **9**, March 1962, pp. 37–44.

If the contractor were to effect changes in one or more of the critical jobs, the calculations would have to be performed again. This he can easily do; but in large projects with complex sequence relationships, hand calculations are considerably more difficult and liable to error. Computer programs have been developed, however, for calculating *ES*, *LS*, *EF*, *LF*, *TS*, and *FS* for each job in a project, if the set of immediate prerequisites and the job times for each job are given.[6]

13. DATA-COLLECTION PROBLEMS

Information concerning job times and predecessor relationships is gathered, typically, by shop foremen, scheduling clerks, or others closely associated with a project. It is conceivable that several kinds of errors may occur in such job data:

1. The estimated job times may be in error.

2. The predecessor relationship may contain cycles; e.g., job *A* is a predecessor for *B*, *B* is a predecessor for *C*, and *C* is a predecessor for *A*.

3. The list of prerequisites for a job may include more than the immediate prerequisites; e.g., job *A* is a predecessor of *B*, *B* is a predecessor of *C*, and *A* and *B* are predecessors of *C*.

4. Some predecessor relationships may be overlooked.

5. Some predecessor relationships may be listed that are spurious.

We first discuss errors of type 1. An accurate estimate of total project time depends, of course, upon accurate job-time data. The critical-path method eliminates the necessity (and expense) of careful time studies for *all* jobs, however. Instead, the following procedure can be used. Given rough time estimates, construct a graph of the project. Then those jobs that are on the critical path (together with jobs that have very small total slack, indicating that they are nearly critical) can be more closely checked, their times re-estimated, and another graph constructed with the refined data. If the critical path has changed to include jobs still having rough time estimates, then the process is repeated. In many projects studied, it has been found that only a small fraction of jobs are critical, so it is likely that refined time studies will be needed for relatively few jobs in a project in order to arrive at a reasonably accurate estimate of the total project time. The critical-path method thus can be used to reduce the problem of type 1 errors at a small total cost.

A computer algorithm[7] has been developed to check for errors of

---

[6] An algorithm upon which one such computer program is based is discussed in a paper by the authors, "Mathematical Basis for the Critical-Path Method," Chapter 22 of this volume.

[7] See "Mathematical Basis for the Critical-Path Method," Ibid.

types 2 and 3 above. The algorithm systematically examines the set of prerequisites for each job and cancels from the set all but immediate predecessor jobs. When an error of type 2 is present in the job data, the algorithm will signal a "cycle error" and print out the cycle in question.

Errors of type 4 and 5 cannot be discovered by computer routines. Instead, manual checking (perhaps by a committee) is necessary to see that prerequisites are accurately reported.

14. COST CALCULATIONS

The cost of carrying out a project can be readily calculated from the job data if the cost of doing each job is included in the data. If jobs are done by crews, and the speed with which the job is done depends on the crew size, then it is possible to shorten or lengthen the project time by adding or removing men from crews. Other means for compressing job times might also be found; but any speed-up is likely to carry a price tag. Suppose that we assign to each job a "normal time" and a "crash time" and also calculate the associated costs necessary to carry the job in each time. If we want to shorten the project, we can assign some of the critical jobs to their crash time, and compute the corresponding direct cost. In this way it is possible to calculate the cost of completing the project in various total times, with the direct costs increasing as the over-all time decreases.[8]

Added to direct costs are certain expenses which depend upon the total project time. The period—or "fixed"—costs of a project thus

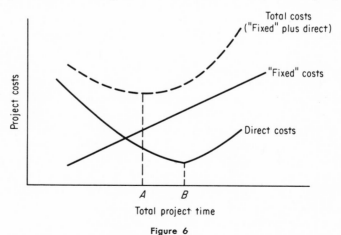

Figure 6

[8] Algorithms for carrying out these cost calculations are discussed by Kelley in "Critical-Path Planning and Scheduling," Ibid.

decrease as project time is shortened. A combination of "fixed" and direct costs as a function of total project time would probably appear as shown in Figure 6.

The minimum total cost (point A) would likely fall to the left of the minimum point on the direct cost curve (point B) indicating that the optimum project time is somewhat shorter than an analysis of direct costs only would indicate.

Other economic factors, of course, can be included in the analysis. For example:

A large chemical company starts to build a plant for producing a new chemical. After the construction schedule and completion date are established, an important potential customer indicates a willingness to pay a premium price for the new chemical if it can be made available earlier than scheduled. The chemical producer applies techniques of critical-path scheduling to its construction schedule and calculates the additional costs associated with "crash" completion of jobs on the critical path. With a plot of costs vs. total project time, the producer is able to select a new completion date such that the increased costs are met by the additional revenue offered by the customer.

15. CONCLUSION

Because of its characteristics—and especially its intuitive logic and graphic appeal—the critical-path method is a decision-making tool which can find wide appreciation at all levels of management.[9] Its use and an understanding of its operations are not limited to the skilled technician. The project graph helps the foreman to understand the sequencing of jobs and the necessity of pushing those that are critical. For the manager concerned with day-to-day operations in all departments, critical-path scheduling enables him to measure progress (or lack of it) against plans and to take appropriate action quickly when needed. The underlying simplicity of the critical-path method and its ability to focus attention on crucial problem areas of large projects make it an ideal tool for the top manager, on whose shoulders falls the ultimate responsibility for over-all planning and coordination of such projects in the light of company-wide objectives.

[9] A. Charnes and W. W. Cooper have given a network interpretation of the critical-path method, thus relating the technique to linear programming with its extensive literature and richly developed managerial applications and interpretations. See their paper, "A Network Interpretation and a Directed Sub-Dual Algorithm for Critical Path Scheduling," *Journal of Industrial Engineering* (1961), pp. 213–219.

21

The Critical=path Method:
Resources Planning
and Scheduling

J. E. Kelley, Jr.
MAUCHLY ASSOCIATES, INC.

1. INTRODUCTION

Previously published work on the critical-path method [5,6] has dealt with project planning and scheduling primarily from the viewpoint of the methods for accomplishing the work. Considerations of the availability of limited resources have not been made explicit except in a few minor ways. Even so, the hundreds of people who currently are applying the technique [1, 2, 3, 4, 7, 8] have obtained significant improvements in project work. The main reasons for this success are that the technique is simple in concept and execution, and that it enforces a discipline requiring far more objectivity than heretofore possible. The method has provided a new way of thinking about projects. As a by-product, many of the difficulties involving limited resources have been resolved.

A paper presented at the Factory Scheduling Conference, Carnegie Institute of Technology, May 10–12, 1961. Reprinted by permission of Mauchly Associates, Inc.

However, this is not to imply that more explicit consideration of limited resources is not required. Although the basic critical-path method provides plans and schedules that are technologically feasible, they may not always be practical from other points of view. The equipment and manpower requirements for a particular schedule may exceed availability or fluctuate violently over the course of the project life. Similarly, a schedule may require that money be spent faster than it can be raised or may tie up funds that could be used profitably elsewhere. Thus some means is required for planning and scheduling a project that accounts for not only the work methods employed but also the availability of resources.

A study of the situation reveals two major sources of difficulty— how should the problem of resource loading be formulated, and how can it be solved?

Formulating the resource loading problem from a mathematical point of view is difficult because explicit criteria for obtaining the optimal use of resources are lacking. Critical examination of present management practices reveals that available levels of resources and also changes in level are established rather arbitrarily. This fact appears to be true regardless of the organization. At times various seemingly incompatible objectives are mixed together. The emphasis often swings from one objective to another as the project environment changes.

This situation stems partially from the fact that traditional estimating techniques can only approximate over-all requirements during the life of a project. The implications of shortages or surpluses cannot be adequately evaluated.

Company policy also adds to the difficulties, particularly the problem of labor management. Even in the construction industry, where the work is by nature temporary, it is desirable to have a reputation of being a consistent "project-life" employer—that at the very least an employee can be assured of several months' work. This condition is more critical in organizations employing many technical and professional engineering personnel. The employer is more acutely aware of the tangible costs of recruitment and layoff as well as the intangible costs of layoff to his over-all reputation and well-being. As a result, management carefully scrutinizes idle crafts and engineers or the need for additional personnel. This scrutiny may be considered commendable, but too often it is a myopic course of action out of focus with longer-range requirements.

Considerations of equipment, facilities and money are similar to those for labor in many respects. However, the problems to which they give rise do not appear to be quite so thorny.

Assuming that a mathematical model of the resource loading problem has been formulated, we run into another difficulty—mathematical techniques do not exist for obtaining solutions in a reasonable time. At least, the several models we have considered are completely intractable. However, the difficulty seems to be intrinsic to the problem. The way the restrictions on the sequence in which jobs may be performed interacts with resource requirements and availabilities forces a solution set which is unconnected. This property exists even if we assume that men and equipment are infinitely divisible.

Problems having unconnected solution sets are called combinatorial. Very few of them can be solved (in the mathematical sense) in a reasonable time. However, this does not imply that useful solutions cannot be obtained. *Ad hoc* intuitive methods, especially when used in conjunction with a computer to do the legwork, can be quite effective for obtaining satisfactory solutions.

In view of the difficulties involved, there does not appear to be any direct approach to formulating and solving the resource loading problem, but an indirect approach appears to yield useful results. What we have done is to formulate an idealization of our problem. (The particular one we have selected here is not the only possibility.) Our objective is to use this model to test the implications of various assumptions about the project. This is done in the following way:

The project analyst specifies such things as the methods to be used, the crew composition and duration of each job, assumed availabilities of labor by craft, equipment, money, and so forth. This information is given to a computer. The computer schedules the project by finding a solution to the model and determines the usage curve for each resource over the project life. The project analyst studies this output to determine if it is reasonable and desirable. If it is not, he modifies the input and performs another computer run. By this process of successive approximations, a solution can be obtained which satisfies all technological requirements and many of the undefinable or obscure desires of management. The fact that the model can be solved only approximately does not appear to detract from the approach either philosophically or practically.

In the following sections we treat in greater detail the various aspects of the problem and how we propose they be handled.

2. BASIC CONCEPTS

Fundamental to the critical-path method is the basic representation of a project. All projects are characterized by the fact that work must be performed in some specified order. Thus, in construction we obtain work sequences like: build forms, pour foundations, place footings, erect steel, and so forth; in maintenance we have the open-and-inspect operation followed by disassemble, repair, reassemble, test, and so forth. Similar work sequences are found in all project types. However, when all work to be performed is considered, many such sequences will occur for each project. These sequences interact with one another in complicated ways, some items of work being done in a serial manner, others being done in parallel with each other.

These relations of order can be shown graphically. Each job or work item is represented by an arrow showing the direction of time flow. Time flows from the tail to the head of the arrow. The arrows are interconnected to show graphically the sequence in which the jobs must be performed. (Some practical rules for constructing project diagrams are given in [5].)

The nodes of the project diagram, the points where arrows join, are called events. It is easy to see that the events of a project form a partially ordered set. There are two distinguished events in a project, origin and terminus, with the property that origin precedes and terminus follows every other event.

Each event is denoted by a nonnegative integer, its label. Events are labeled so that whenever event i precedes event j, then $i < j$. In particular, origin is labeled 0, and terminus is labeled n (there are $n + 1$ events in the project).

Associated with event j is a nonnegative number t_j, the occurrence time for the event. In particular, we let $t_0 = 0$.

If event i is at the tail of an arrow and event j is at its head, then the arrow (and the corresponding job) is designated by the number pair (i, j). Associated with each job (i, j) is a nonnegative number, y_{ij}, its duration. It is assumed that job (i, j) is performed between the occurrences of events i and j.

From this assumption it follows that relative to a fixed start time for a project P, each event has an earliest time of occurrence. Denoting the earliest occurrence of event i by $t_i^{(0)}$, we may compute the values of $t_j^{(0)}$ inductively as follows:

$$t_j^{(0)} = \begin{cases} 0, & j = 0 \\ \max_{(i,j) \in P}(t_i^{(0)} + y_{ij}), & 1 \le j \le n. \end{cases}$$

Similarly, relative to a stated project completion time, each event has a latest occurrence time. Let $t_i^{(1)}$ be the latest time for event i. If λ is the project completion time (where $\lambda \ge t_n^{(0)}$), then

$$t_i^{(1)} = \begin{cases} \lambda, & i = n \\ \min_{(i,j) \in P}(t_j^{(1)} - y_{ij}), & 0 \le i \le n. \end{cases}$$

We may now compute the following important quantities for each job (i, j) in the project:

$$\text{Earliest start time} \quad\quad = t_i^{(0)}$$
$$\text{Earliest finish time} \quad\quad = t_i^{(0)} + y_{ij}$$
$$\text{Latest start time} \quad\quad = t_j^{(1)} - y_{ij}$$
$$\text{Latest finish time} \quad\quad = t_j^{(1)}$$
$$\text{Maximum time available} = t_j^{(1)} - t_i^{(0)}.$$

Whenever the duration of a job equals the maximum time available for its performance, a delay in its completion will cause a comparable delay in completing the project. Such jobs are called critical. We may determine if a job is critical by computing its total float:

$$\text{Total float} = t_j^{(1)} - t_i^{(0)} - y_{ij}.$$

A job is critical if, and only if, its total float is zero.

A project contains critical jobs only if $\lambda = t_n^{(0)}$. In this case there exists at least one connected chain of critical jobs from origin to terminus called a critical path.

If a job's total float is positive, it is called a floater. Sometimes the start and finish times of floaters can be displaced to a certain extent without affecting the start or finish times of other jobs, or the completion of the project. Usually, however, any displacement in one floater will make it necessary to modify the start and finish times of a chain of floaters. Too great a displacement will affect completion of the project. The exact character of any floater can be found by referring to the project diagram.

At times it is useful to define several levels of criticalness. Thus, we might define jobs with total float of less than three days to be first-level critical; those with total float of between four and eight days to be second-level critical, and so forth. To some extent the breakdown into levels is arbitrary, subject to the project environment, the objective desired, and the time units used.

3. THE MODEL

At the heart of our approach to resources planning and scheduling is the following idealization of the resource loading problem. Schedule the jobs of a project so that

1. The work is performed by the method and in the sequence planned.

2. Resources do not exceed assumed availabilities.

3. The duration of the project is minimized.

In condition 1 we assume that the project has been planned and the data collected according to the basic critical-path method. The information for condition 2 will be considered below. Condition 3 requires us to find a schedule of shortest duration satisfying conditions 1 and 2. However, it is neither easy nor necessarily practical to satisfy condition 3 exactly, although it presents quite an interesting mathematical problem. We may, for most practical purposes, substitute the less exacting condition that the duration of the project be in a reasonable neighborhood of the minimum. We shall let the practitioner judge what is reasonable.

Two classes of algorithms (serial and parallel) have been developed to solve the above problem under the relaxed form of condition 3. Both are simple in concept, organized only to construct schedules that are feasible with respect to both sequence restrictions and assumed resource availabilities. However, during the process of schedule construction, each process applies intuitive rules which tend to yield short-duration schedules.

4. SERIAL METHODS[1]

The input to the serial methods is a list of all the jobs in the project in order of precedence. An order satisfying this rule is obtained by sorting the jobs in ascending sequence on the second coordinate of their (i, j) representations. Of course we are assuming that the events are labeled so that $i < j$. This is called the J-priority ordering.

Serial methods consist of scanning the list of jobs one at a time and scheduling each job as it is scanned. The scheduling is done by determining first the earliest time the job can be started. The start time for the first job on the list is time zero. In general, the earliest start time for a job is the latest time that any of its predecessors finished. Since the list is ordered so that all predecessors of a job will be scheduled by the time it is considered for scheduling, its earliest start time is readily computed by retaining the largest of the finish times of all arrows (jobs) entering an event. The earliest start time for job (i, j) is the time retained for the jobs entering event i.

Having the earliest start time for a job, we attempt to schedule it to start at that time. If the required resources are unavailable at that time, the start is delayed to the earliest feasible start time—the earliest time at which adequate resources are available.

[1] The basic idea is due to C. Bachman and M. R. Walker.

Some interpretation is required to determine when adequate resources are available to start a job. One alternative is that a job may start when sufficient resources are available to work the job, as planned, in a continuous manner. This interpretation places undesirable restrictions on the performance of work. In the first place, a large percentage of the jobs, by their nature, are not required to be worked in a continuous manner. Often it is quite advantageous to switch men back and forth between jobs. Some work, though necessary for the project's completion, may be regarded as fill-in work to keep men busy. It is a distinct advantage to be able to do such work a little at a time. Further, in practice it is almost impossible to work all jobs in a continuous manner and still complete the project in a reasonable way. Limitations on resources, changing conditions, and the general operating environment all contribute to this limitation.

Therefore, we shall assume, at least for the basic form of the serial methods, that jobs can be split arbitrarily into phases or parts that are an integral number of time units (say, days) long. It follows that the earliest feasible start time for a job is the first day after the completion of all its predecessors for which adequate resources are available to work the job for at least one day. We begin the job at its earliest start time and proceed to schedule it over the following days, splitting it when resources are not available and delaying the remainder of the job until the proper resources again become available. Of course, as a job is scheduled, the resources available to subsequent jobs in the list are reduced by the amount and type allocated to it.

Each job is treated in the same general way. The process of scheduling continues until the list is exhausted. As each job is scheduled, the start and stop times of each split portion are saved. Likewise, the usage of each resource over the project life is saved.

Of course, there are definite limitations to the practical use of the are above procedure. There are important contingencies which are not considered. However, the procedure provides a basic algorithm to which other rules can be added. We shall now consider some of these additions.

5. OTHER ORDERINGS

The serial methods require that the jobs of the project be listed in order of precedence. One way of obtaining such a list is to sort the jobs in ascending sequence on the second coordinate of their (i, j) representations. As is easily perceived, a list thus generated is not necessarily unique. For example, if (i, j) and (k, j) are in the list, it does not make any difference to the algorithm which of the two jobs precedes the other. Further, it is generally true that the events of a project can be labeled in many different ways and still retain the property that the event at the tail of an arrow is smaller than the event at the head. In this case the J-priority ordering will give a different list for each different labeling.

For a given labeling of the events of the project, we can obtain several variations of the J-priority ordering simply by sorting the job list on certain minor keys. Thus, we could sort the list on the first coordinate of the job (i, j) representations followed by a sort on the second coordinate—that is, a j-major, i-minor sort. For that matter, an i-major, j-minor sort would also be legitimate.

However, in view of the objectives of the algorithm, these orderings are not intuitively satisfying. It can be argued that the ordering used should reflect something with respect to the relative importance of the jobs in the project. For instance, critical jobs should be given precedence over noncritical jobs. Since total float is a measure of criticalness, we could let total float be one of the keys and sort the list in j-major, total-float-minor sequence. Of course, to do this type of sorting, an additional computation is required to obtain the values of total float.

Other priorities also might have intuitive justification. We might sort the list on the dollar value of each job, the number of men required, the duration of each job, some subjective measure of importance, and so forth. Even random ordering might be justified. Of course, all these keys are minor keys, j being the major key.

The main advantage of considering alternative orderings of the list of jobs is that one ordering might give rise to a shorter duration schedule than another. By performing the algorithm several times, using the same input data but different orderings, we have a better chance of obtaining the minimum duration schedule sought. Generally this procedure is practical only when the resource limitations are quite tight.

All the above orderings can be obtained by using a punched-card sorting device. If we define an ordering which is independent of the event labels, but which lists jobs in order of precedence, we require the services of an electronic computer to perform the sorting.

6. PARALLEL METHODS

Unlike serial methods, which schedule one job at a time, parallel methods schedule several jobs at a time. Parallel methods work along the following lines.

At time t in the life of the project certain jobs have been completed, or partially completed. Consider the set $P(t)$ of jobs that are in process or could start at time t because their predecessors are finished. Some subset $Q(t)$ of jobs in $P(t)$ can be scheduled to start at time t, the unselected jobs being delayed. The usage of resources by the jobs in $Q(t)$ cannot exceed availabilities during the time from t to $t+1$. It may happen that no job in $P(t)$ satisfies resource availabilities. In this case $Q(t)$ is empty, and all jobs in $P(t)$ must be delayed. However, generally $Q(t)$ can be selected in many different ways. Some decision rule is required to make the selection.

Once $Q(t)$ is determined, we attempt to schedule these jobs for successive days starting at time t. The scheduling proceeds until some resource becomes unavailable in the required amount or some job of $Q(t)$ is completed, whichever happens first. If we stop at time T, we must define sets $P(T)$ and $Q(T)$ and repeat the scheduling process. The process terminates when all jobs have been scheduled.

There are many possible decision rules for selecting $Q(t)$. The following rule gives priority to critical jobs : order the jobs of $P(t)$ in ascending sequence on total float. Now scan $P(t)$, thus ordered, one job at a time, selecting jobs for $Q(t)$. A job may be selected if, when added to $Q(t)$, resource restrictions are not violated. Scan $P(t)$ until all jobs have been examined.

There is no *a priori* reason to expect to get "better" results from parallel methods than from serial methods. Although it can be argued that since parallel methods take into account more information at each step than the serial methods they must give better results, the hope is illusory. In the first place, it is almost impossible to define "best" without becoming completely academic. Further, even if a definition is accepted, the nature of the processes belie always obtaining a better result from one method than the other. We will concede the possibility of one method having a statistical advantage over the other in this case. Some experimentation is required to determine if such an advantage exists.

At present, we feel that serial methods are more practical than parallel methods, particularly from the point of view of their intended use. Thus, we shall not give any further consideration to parallel methods here. Instead, we shall consider various factors that can be incorporated in the basic serial method.

7. NON-SPLIT JOBS

Sometimes it is impossible or very undesirable to split a job. It is not possible to split jobs that depend on chemical and some physical processes (for example, curing concrete). Jobs that tie up heavy equipment are undesirable to split. Generally, all critical and some semi-critical work should not be split.

To handle nonsplit jobs within the format of our algorithm, we proceed as follows: we attempt to schedule the job from its earliest start. If this is not possible because some required resource is not available sometime during the life of the job, we attempt to schedule it to start on the day after the last day for which the resource availability was exceeded. If resources now are available over the life of the job, we schedule it and proceed to the next job in the list. Otherwise, we delay the job until a feasible schedule for the job is found.

It is false to believe that all jobs fall into two categories—split and nonsplit. It is the nature of some jobs that if certain phases are not performed in a continuous manner, then the phases practically have to be started from the beginning.

We may handle this type of situation by representing the job in question by several arrows in series. Each arrow corresponds to a successive phase of the job. Any phase that cannot be split is treated like a nonsplit job. The other phases are handled like split jobs.

8. JOB START CONSTANT

The ability to select, within limitations, the start time for a job is sometimes quite useful. This may be accomplished by comparing the earliest start time with a desired start time. Whichever is larger is the time at which we begin to search for an earliest feasible start time.

9. CRAFT REQUIREMENTS THRESHOLDS

In the basic serial algorithm described above, it was assumed that the stated availability of manpower by craft could never be exceeded. This is a somewhat artificial assumption on two counts—exact availabilities are not generally known and often are set arbitrarily by management decision without the necessary regard for actual requirements. If we view the algorithm as a tool for evaluating the implications of the stated availabilities, then it is desirable to make the availabilities we use in the computation elastic. In this way we can help avoid a "poor" solution because of an artificial restriction.

One way to introduce elasticity into the availability limitations on manpower is to state an assumed limit plus a threshold. Thus, we might state that on project day 20 there will be 15 boilermakers. We allow the usage to mount to 18 boilermakers—the assumed availability plus the threshold. However, we do not allow the usage to exceed 18.

Having a threshold helps to avoid the situation where, for example, 16 boilermakers are needed but only 15 are available, with the result that some job must be delayed at the cost of delaying the project completion. The stated availability is not generally the true limitation but only an approximation to the maximum level of craft usage desired by management. The threshold may be interpreted as the limit of usage over the stated availability that management will accept without a good argument to the contrary, or, if you will, a reserve force.

Whenever the usage of a craft exceeds the stated availability, the jobs which first cause the overload should be indexed in some way. It may be possible to replan these jobs so an overload will not occur.

Of course, all jobs using the craft on the day in question contribute to the overload. Thus, we might ask why just mark those jobs which first cause the overload? In the first place, this is easier than going back over the jobs already scheduled to find all contributors. Further indexing all the jobs may give more information than can be assimilated, giving rise to some confusion. In many circumstances this may be sufficient justification. However, indexing all jobs contributing to an overload is not completely out of the question.

10. CREW REQUIREMENTS THRESHOLDS

As with craft availabilities, the planned assumptions on how many men in each craft will work a given job is to some extent arbitrary. Thus, it may be planned to use a crew of three carpenters and three laborers on a certain job. However, if at the time the job is to start there are only two carpenters or two laborers available, the chances are the foreman will start the job with what he has anyway. When additional men become available, they will be added to the crew. Therefore, we should try to approximate this course of action as the scheduling proceeds instead of delaying the start of a job when the exact number of men required is not available.

Again we may make use of a threshold. To avoid difficulties that arise from trying to determine how many men from each craft can form a crew for a job, we simply work on a percentage availability basis. For example, if a threshold of 80 percent is accepted and a job requires five riggers but only four are available, we would start the job. If only three riggers were available, we would delay the job. If the crew for a job consists of more than one craft, then at least 80 percent of the requirements in each craft must be available in order to start the job. If any craft availability does not satisfy this condition, the job is delayed.

Of course, this use of a threshold can be made more complicated by having a different threshold for each craft or for each job. Indeed, many decision rules could be adopted. However, as a general rule in this work, complications should be avoided unless they add significantly to the results obtained.

The question remains—if a job is not worked as originally planned, how can we determine when it will finish? If a job is planned so as to use three men for five days, but only two men are available, how long will the job take? Within our limitations, assuming that two men can do twice the work as one man in the same time is probably reasonable. Thus, the two men will take 7.5 days. It may be desirable to round the answer up to the nearest time unit being used to reflect a presumed inefficiency of not working the job as planned. An additional factor may be introduced to accomplish the same end.

If a crew for a job consists of more than one craft, there are two simple alternatives for determining the duration of the job with an incomplete crew. The easiest way is to add together the usage in all crafts and treat the job as if it is to be worked by only one craft as above. The other method depends on the notion of key craft. In most jobs requiring the services of several crafts, one of the crafts will do the majority of the work, or else the work will depend primarily on the services of that craft. We call the craft in question the key craft. The other crafts are present to help the key craft. Thus, we can make the duration of the job depend on how many men are available from the key craft. The simple rule above can usually be used if the threshold is not too small.

Finally, we must determine what to do if a job, or a split portion of it, is started with an incomplete crew but the job becomes split because of the lack of sufficient resources. At any particular time during the scheduling of a job, we know how many man-days (or similar work unit) have been expended either by the key craft or by the crew as a whole. We also know the total man-days required to perform the job along with the planned crew composition and planned job duration. Assume that all computations will be based on the manpower usage in the key craft or the crew as a whole. Let us say that $D(< M)$ man-days have been expended, and the average planned usage is T men per day. If we assume that whenever possible we will use the planned crew composition, the duration of the remaining portion of the job is $(M - D)/T$ days unless subsequent conditions warrant change. Again, it may be reasonable to round this time value up to the nearest time unit being used to reflect the presumed inefficiency that results from a split.

11. START DELAY THRESHOLD

It is conceivable that because of resource limitations the start of a job could be delayed indefinitely. This is likely to happen particularly with nonsplit jobs. Since the limitations are to some extent arbitrary, it seems reasonable to introduce a device for preventing too long a delay in starting the job. The results of using such a device can provide the necessary argument for obtaining more resources.

According to the previous rules given, if 80 percent of the planned craft usage exceeds the stated availability plus the craft threshold, the start of the job, or a split portion of it, must be delayed until the resource is available in the necessary amount. We introduce a threshold N, which tells how much we are willing to delay the start of a job. If we find that the start will be delayed more than N days, we schedule it over y_{ij} successive days from its earliest start time, regardless of how resource availabilities are exceeded. In case the job has been split already, we treat the remaining portion of the job like a complete job.

Of course, we want to know which jobs violated the start delay threshold, so we mark them accordingly.

The value of the delay threshold used is open to interpretation. It probably should not exceed by much one-tenth of the planned project duration.

There are alternative definitions of delay thresholds. Instead of making the delay threshold constant for the project, it could be a function of the job—say proportional to the value of total float. Further, instead of using the same delay threshold for each split portion of a job, it could be made to decrease as work on the job proceeded. Or the sum of the delays on all splits could be made not to exceed the delay threshold.

12. EQUIPMENT AND SPACE LIMITATIONS

It often happens that two or more jobs require the services of the same piece of equipment—say a crane. If some of these jobs can be done in parallel, then a conflict situation arises. Either another piece of equipment must be rented or purchased, or the start of some job must be delayed with the attendant possibility of delaying the completion of the project. Thus, it is required to take equipment availabilities into account when a project is being scheduled, particularly one which uses high-cost equipment.

We may handle equipment in the same manner as manpower. An equipment type is simply another craft. When the crew composition for a job is planned, we include any important equipment in the crew as a craft. In this case, one would hardly ever make use of a craft requirement threshold different from zero. However, one might include equipment in considerations of the crew requirements threshold.

Space limitations can also be handled like a craft. If two or more jobs that can be done in parallel must be performed in the same area, we must be careful that the crews do not get in each others' way. We may set limitations on some work areas so that, when we attempt to schedule a job, the job is delayed if previously scheduled jobs already make use of the available space.

13. BUDGET LIMITATIONS

A consideration of prime importance in almost all project work is the question of how to fund the project. In many situations it is not enough to know an estimate of the total cost of the project. How much money is required to support the project at various times during the project life is important information. With it, management can plan how to manage the capital so that funds are not needlessly tied up in one project and not available to another. It is also important to know early what steps must be taken to raise capital.

Many questions concerning capitalizing a project can be answered by incorporating costs into the algorithm we are discussing. All types of costs cannot be conveniently handled in this way, however. By and large, we restrict our considerations to the direct cost of labor. Cost of materials, equipment, and overhead are added in later to give the over-all picture.

To some extent we can view costs as just another craft. To treat them thus would give us the daily expenditure of project funds. However, usually the cumulative expenditure is what is needed. It is only from the cumulative that management can determine the budget for each phase of a project or regulate the rate at which money is spent.

Thus, when we attempt to schedule a job we ask if there are funds available to perform it. If not, we delay the job subject to the applicable rules already discussed. As jobs are scheduled, we accumulate their costs.

The dollar availability curve should have a threshold like the craft requirement threshold. By making the dollar availability curve increase by small steps, some control over the rate at which money is spent can be obtained.

14. TOTAL FORCE REQUIREMENTS

It is often desirable to know the total labor force requirements of a project independent of the individual crafts involved. This is important for anticipating the requirements for support facilities and organization. A project can absorb new personnel just so fast, so it is necessary to avoid too rapid build-up in force. Also, layoffs should not be processed en masse. Hence, some control over the rate at which the total force changes is necessary. Further, having high peaks in the total force curve can be undesirable. It is usually better to obtain a rather level force for the project's duration. A level force curve helps the company's reputation for being a consistent project-life employer.

Total force can be considered as a craft and treated accordingly during the scheduling process.

15. USE OF THE TECHNIQUES

Since the practical problem of resource loading is not well defined, we cannot expect any model of it to provide pat answers to be accepted without question. This is particularly true of all models which attempt to describe human activities. Here the subjective element is a major factor, quite difficult to cope with in the abstract.

The model of the resource loading problem we have proposed and the algorithm for "solving" it can be viewed only as tools to help project managers determine what they want to do. By helping them to evaluate various limitations that could be imposed on a project in terms of their implication, a service is provided which does not presently exist.

These remarks and the foregoing imply that a procedure along the following lines be followed at the planning stages of a project or when changing conditions require a revision of the plan.

First, a basic critical-path analysis is performed—a project diagram is drawn, job durations are collected, and fundamental schedule information is computed. Actually, this first step may require a few attempts—the schedule information indicating diagram and duration changes, and conversely—before an acceptable initial plan and schedule are obtained.

Now we want to get an idea of what this initial plan and schedule imply in terms of resource requirements. To do this, we apply our resource planning and scheduling algorithm to the project, assuming unlimited availabilities of all resources except any space limitations. The result of this calculation will be the daily usage of each resource over the life of the project, each job being started as early as possible.

Invariably, the results of this first computation will show some crafts or total force peaking in an undesirable manner. The manner in which these resources peak and the project environment suggest how the availability limitations on them should be restricted. Thus, the computed results might show a peak requirement for 150 boilermakers when there are only about 50 available in the area. Ten more boilermakers might be obtained, if needed, from other areas. We would change the availability of boilermakers to 50 with a threshold or reserve force of ten. This statement of availability could have been made initially. But if boilermakers peaked at 40 instead of 150, the restriction would not have been necessary. In practice it is better to determine first what is restrictive and what is not before any limitations are set.

An examination of the schedule requirements provided by the critical-path analysis may indicate that some floaters are scheduled to occur during some peak period. The start of these floaters sometimes can be delayed beyond the peak period with the result of reducing the peak. Imposing a start delay on floaters in conjunction with resource restrictions is usually quite an effective way to level peaks. In this way it is less likely that the completion of the project will be delayed than if resource restrictions alone are used. The delay can be accomplished by stating start constants for the jobs in question. Seldom should the start constant exceed the latest start time for a job. Otherwise, the project completion will surely be delayed.

After the input data modification is decided, a new schedule is computed. Presumably this schedule will be "better" than the first one computed. The resource usage curves should not peak as sharply. It is possible, though, because of the complex way the various factors interact, that an undesirable peak may develop in some craft usage curve, or the project completion may be pushed back too far, or some other problem may develop. It may be required to modify previous assumptions on any number of points—resource limitations, job methods and durations, crew compositions, and so forth—before we again try to schedule the project.

If the project completion is pushed back too badly, one may be able to improve it, using the same resource limitations, by ordering the jobs differently and making another computer run. We have already considered several ways to sort the jobs.

Several steps are usually required before an acceptable plan and schedule are obtained. No more than about five or six attempts should really be necessary if present experience can be extrapolated. After an individual gains some experience, this number could probably be reduced to three or four, particularly if the same type of project is always handled.

Although there are many possible factors that can enter an analysis of a project, a project is sensitive to only relatively few. These factors can generally be discovered and handled without much difficulty. Further, as we shall see below, the duration of projects seem to be fairly insensitive to large changes in the availabilities of most resources.

We have assumed all along that the scheduling algorithm is to be programmed for an electronic computer. It is too complicated to be performed manually. The iterative process of using the computer to prepare the schedule while the human analyzes it and modifies the input data for another run can be made quite efficient by allowing the project analyst to work at or near the computer and by providing a high-speed printing device. Until he has decided that a particular schedule is acceptable, the project analyst is not interested in all the detail about the project. A tabulation of the schedule and resource usage curves can tend to confuse the analysis rather than help it. What he really needs are the resource curves plotted together, so that he can see them all in relation to each other and the project as a whole. The detail can be used to help decide what course of action to take once an idea is generated from analyzing the curves.

Part of the output to the analyst is a high-speed printer plot of the resource usage curves, superimposed, if possible, when only a few resources are being considered. In this way the analyst can see within only a few minutes of computer processing just what his assumptions about the project imply.

16. STATISTICAL JUSTIFICATION

As with all methods based on intuition, we may well ask of our resource planning and scheduling method, "How good is it?" Really the only way to answer this question is to apply the method to some practical problems and see what happens. If the results are reasonable, there is some merit in the technique. Beyond this it is difficult to generalize, although some properties of the problem class may indicate, in some intuitive sense, that the technique should be useful for most problems in the class.

Some features of the resource planning and scheduling method have been programmed for the IBM 650 computer and applied to a number of real projects. Specifically, the code can handle only labor (or the equivalent) resources. Up to four crafts per job and nine crafts per project are allowed. A craft requirements threshold and start delay threshold can be used. However, the craft requirements threshold must be a constant for each craft. Likewise, the start delay threshold must be the same for each job. A job start constant can be specified for each job.

It would be desirable to give a case history of one of the projects actually planned by using this computer code. These have been several, and the resulting schedules have been reduced to practice. In this way the reader could appreciate better the practical value of the technique and what to expect from applying it. However, to do this in a meaningful way would require a separate paper. Here it suffices to say that present experience suggests that a reduction in peak total force of beween 35 percent and 50 percent from an un-limited available resource schedule can probably be expected. This reduction can probably be obtained with less than a 5 percent in-crease in the duration of the project. The project duration should rise sharply with any further reduction in peak total force.

There is another way to indicate the belief that the resource plan-ning and scheduling method should be generally successful, in the sense that for a given project duration there is a very large number of feasible schedules from which to select the "best." It is clear that the success of the method depends on the freedom with which the start and completion times for jobs can be changed. In turn, this freedom depends on the total float of the jobs. Thus, we could use the average total float per job as a measure of the freedom with which we can modify a project schedule. The larger this value, the greater the freedom. Of course, to make comparisons between proj-ects, this average should be normalized—say, expressed as a percent-age of the duration of the project.

However, the average is not so informative as the distribution of total float with respect to the jobs of the project. A project whose distribution is skewed right does not have the freedom of one whose distribution is skewed left, although their averages may be equal.

We have computed the total float distributions for ten projects that range from about 80 to 1000 jobs. A project distribution was deter-mined by partitioning its duration into a number of equal intervals. For each interval the number of jobs having a value of total float in the interval was counted. Then the cumulative distribution of jobs was formed.

To combine these cumulative distributions, we normalized them in the following way: Let $f_i(t)$ be the number of jobs in the ith project with total float not greater than t. Let D_i be the duration and J_i be the number of jobs in the ith project. Define the function

$$g_i(p) = \max\left[\frac{100t}{D_i}\middle| f_i(t) \leq pJ_i\right]$$

where $0 \leq p \leq 1$. This expression states that no more than $100p$ percent of the jobs in the ith project have a total float (expressed as a percentage of the project's duration) less than $g_i(p)$.

We have tabulated the average of the g_i over the ten sample projects and have bracketed the range by the maximum and minimum values. An examination of the table indicates that projects contain more float than one would normally expect. This gives some additional hope that our method should be generally successful. The tabulation is as follows:

$100p$	$\text{Min}_i g_i(p)$	$\text{Mean}_i g_i(p)$	$\text{Max}_i g_i(p)$
10	0+	6	35
20	1	12	45
30	2	20	56
40	7	26	63
50	15	37	68
60	23	38	73
70	26	43	75
80	33	51	84
90	42	61	87
100	66	94	100

REFFERENCES

1. Anonymous, "New Tool for Job Management—Perini Corp. Pioneers CPM," *Engineering News Record*, Jan. 26, 1961.

2. Anonymous, "Faster-Phased Plan Speeds Plant Building," *Chemical Week*, pp. 50-51, Aug. 26, 1961.

3. Astrachan, A., "Better Plans Come from Study of Anatomy of an Engineering Job," *Business Week*, pp. 60-66, March 21, 1959.

4. Christensen, B. M., "The Critical-Path Method," General Electric Computer Dept., Phoenix, Ariz., 1961.

5. Kelley, James E., Jr., "Critical-Path Planning and Scheduling: Mathematical Basis," *Operations Research*, Vol. **9**, pp. 296-320, 1961.

6. Kelley, James E., Jr. and Morgan R. Walker, "Crititical-Path Planning and Scheduling," *Proc. Eastern Joint Computer Conference*, pp. 160-173, Boston, Dec. 1-3, 1959.

7. Reeves, Eric, "Critical-Path Speeds Refinery Revamp," *Canadian Chemical Processing*, Oct. 1960.

8. Steben, Maj. E. S., "Critical-Path Method as Used in the Canadian Army," Mauchly Associates, Inc., Fort Washinfiton, Pa., May 12, 1961.

22

Mathematical Basis of the Critical=path Method

F. K. Levy, G. L. Thompson, J. D. Wiest

CARNEGIE INSTITUTE OF TECHNOLOGY

1. INTRODUCTION

The critical-path method for planning projects, introduced by J. E. Kelley, M. R. Walker, and others [3, 4], has recently found widespread application in industry. The formal mathematical properties of the method can be approached from several points of view [1, 2, 3, 5]. The purpose of this paper is to study it from the point of view of mathematical relations. It is interesting that the immediate precedence relation that is set up among jobs in a project should ideally be irreflexive and k-intransitive, in contrast to the properties usually possessed by mathematical relations (reflexivity and transitivity). This points up the need for more extensive study of the formal properties of mathematical relations by persons interested in management science. It is to this end that we have written the present paper.

The preparation of this paper was supported by the Office of Naval Research and the Bureau of Ships through grants to the Graduate School of Industrial Administration, Carnegie Institute of Technology.

In Section 2 we develop the properties of the relations "immediate predecessor" and "precedes" and the corresponding inverse relations, "immediate successor" and "succeeds." Next, in Section 3 we discuss the critical path analysis of a project. Section 4 develops algebraic characterizations, in terms of matrices, of the relations studied earlier. Finally, in Section 5 we describe algorithms for checking for irreflexivity and k-intransitivity.

2. THE IMMEDIATE PREDECESSOR, IMMEDIATE SUCCESSOR, AND PRECEDES RELATIONS

The purpose of this section is to study the mathematical properties of the immediate predecessor, immediate successor, and precedes relations defined on the set of jobs in a project.

Let $J = \{a, b, c, \ldots\}$ be a set of *jobs* that must be done to complete a project. Let $\ll$ denote a relation between two jobs a and b in J, such that $b \ll a$ is defined for some pairs of jobs a and b, and is read "b is an *immediate predecessor of a*" or, equivalently, "a is an *immediate successor* of b." The interpretation of the statement $b \ll a$ is that job b must be completed before job a can be started. Further, any given job can be started if and only if *all* its immediate predecessors have been completed. A *project* is the set J together with the relation $\ll$.

Assumption 1. The immediate predecessor relation, $\ll$, is irreflexive and k-intransitive for every k; that is,
  a. $a \ll a$ is false for all jobs a in J (irreflexivity).
  b. If $a = a_1 \ll a_2 \ll \ldots \ll a_k = b$, then it is false that $a \ll b$, for every pair of jobs a and b and every $k > 2$ (k-intransitivity).

Ordinary intransitivity corresponds to 3-intransitivity in the above definition. In Section 5 of this paper we shall develop tests for determining whether or not a given list of jobs satisfies Assumption 1.

Definition. The set $P_a = \{b \mid b \ll a\}$ is the *immediate predecessor* set of job a. Similarly, the set $S_a = \{b \mid a \ll b\}$ is the *immediate successor set* of job a.

Theorem 1. If Assumption 1 holds, then the set P_a is the smallest set of jobs in J that must be completed before a can be started. Similarly, S_a is the smallest subset of jobs in J that cannot be started until job a is completed.

Proof. Since $\ll$ is irreflexive, a is not an element of P_a. Hence, when all jobs in P_a have been completed, job a can be started.

Now suppose, contrary to the assertion, that job a can be started before some job x in P_a is known to be completed. Since $x \ll a$, this can happen only if the completion of job x is implied by the completion of some other job b in P_a. That is, there must be a relation of the form

$$x = b_1 \ll b_2 \ll \cdots \ll b_k = b \ll a$$

for some b in P_a. But since $x \ll a$, we have a contradiction of the assumption of k-intransitivity of $\ll$. This completes the proof of the first assertion. The proof of the other assertion is similar.

The *project graph* G of a project is a planar graph with points in the plane representing jobs, and a directed line segment connecting two jobs, a and b, if and only if $a \ll b$ holds. For examples of project graphs see [3, 5]. A *path* in G is a set of nodes a_1, a_2, . . . , a_n for which the immediate predecessor relation holds as follows:

$$a_1 \ll a_2 \ll \cdots \ll a_n.$$

A cycle in G is a closed path of the form

$$a_1 \ll a_2 \ll \cdots \ll a_{n-1} \ll a_n = a_1.$$

A project graph G is *acyclic* if and only if it has no cycles.

From the relation $\ll$ we can derive another relation $<$, as stated in the next definition.

Definition. $a < b$, read "a precedes b" (or, equivalently, "b succeeds a") if and only if there is a set of jobs $\{c_1, c_2, \ldots, c_n\}$, where $n > 2$, such that

$$a = c_1 \ll c_2 \ll \cdots \ll c_n = b.$$

In other words, a precedes b, if and only if there is a path from a to b in the project graph G. Note that k-intransitivity can be stated, "If $a < b$, then it is false that $a \ll b$."

Assumption 2. The precedes relation $<$ is asymmetric; that is, if $a < b$ then it is false that $b < a$, for all a and b in J.

Remark. Obviously, if G is acyclic, then $<$ is also irreflexive.

In Section 5 we shall develop effective tests for seeing whether a given set of jobs and an immediate predecessor relation define an asymmetric precedes relation.

Definition. A relation that is transitive and asymmetric is said to be a *preference relation*.

Theorem 2. If Assumption 2 holds, then the precedes relation $<$ is a preference relation, and the graph G is acyclic.

Proof. We prove first that $<$ is transitive. Suppose $a < b$ and $b < c$. Then there are paths

$$a = d_1 \ll d_2 \ll \cdots \ll d_k = b$$
$$b = e_1 \ll e_2 \ll \cdots \ll e_h = c.$$

But then it is clear that

$$a = d_1 \ll d_2 \ll \cdots \ll d_k = b = e_1 \ll e_2 \ll \cdots \ll e_h = c$$

is a path from a to c so that $a < c$.

Since $<$ is asymmetric (by assumption) and transitive (as just proved), then it is a preference relation. On the other hand, if "precedes" is a preference relation then, by definition, it is asymmetric.

Suppose that the project graph G contained a cycle of the form

$$a = b_1 \ll b_2 \ll \cdots \ll b_n = a$$

where $n > 2$. Hence, if we let $b = b_j$, where j is between 1 and n, we see that $a < b$ and $b < a$, which contradicts the asymmetry of the relation $<$. Therefore, G is acyclic.

Lemma 1. The graph G of a project is cyclic if and only if there is a subset Q of J such that $P_a \cap Q \neq \phi$ for all a in Q.

Proof. If G contains a cycle, let Q be the set of jobs that make up the cycle. Then it is obvious that Q satisfies the requirement of the lemma.

Conversely, let Q be a subset of J with the property stated. We shall show that G contains a cycle. Let a_1 be any element of Q; let a_2 be any element in $P_{a1} \cap Q$; let a_3 be any element of $P_{a2} \cap Q$, etc. Since J and hence Q have only a finite number of elements, we must eventually choose an element that has already been chosen before. We then have

$$a_1 \ll a_2 \ll \cdots \ll a_n$$

together with the fact that $a_n = a_j$ for some $j < n$. Hence G has a cycle.

Definition. An ordered *job list* $J^* = [a_1, a_2, \ldots, a_m]$ is obtained from a set of m jobs $J = \{a, b, \ldots\}$ by listing them in a definite order. An ordered job list J^* will be said to be in *technological order* if no job appears on the list until all of its predecessors have already appeared on the list.

Theorem 3. Assumption 2 holds if and only if it is possible to list the jobs in J in a technologically ordered job list J^*.

Proof. Let S_0 be the set of jobs in J that have no immediate predecessors. S_0 must be nonempty, or else at least one subset of J would have the property of Lemma 1 and G would be cyclic, contradicting Theorem 2. Let S_1 be the set of jobs in J whose immediate predecessors are all in S_0; let S_2 be the set of jobs in J whose immediate predecessors are in $S_0 \cup S_1$, etc.; in general, let S_k be the subset of jobs in J all of whose predecessors are in $S_0 \cup S_1 \cup \ldots \cup S_{k-1}$. Since J is a finite set, this process will stop, with, say, $k = n$.

Suppose now that there is a nonempty subset Q of J of elements that are not in any of the sets $S_0, \ldots, S_n$ so constructed. We shall show that Assumption 2 is violated. Every element a in Q must have the property that $P_a \cap Q \neq \phi$, since otherwise job a would have been a member of one of the sets S_k. But then Q has the property of Lemma 1, and G is cyclic. Since Theorem 2 says that Assumption 2 holds if and only if G is acyclic, it follows that Q must be empty and

$$J = S_0 \cup S_1 \cup \cdots \cup S_n.$$

We can now construct a technologically ordered listing J^* of J by first listing all the elements of S_0 in any order, then all the elements of S_1 in any order, etc., until we have listed all the elements in S_n, hence all the elements in J.

If, on the other hand, J can be listed as a technologically ordered job list J^*, and if the sets $S_0, S_1, \ldots, S_n$, and Q are then defined as before, it is obvious that Q is empty, so Assumption 2 holds.

3. JOB TIMES; CRITICAL JOBS; CRITICAL PATHS

Jobs take a certain amount of time to complete. Let t_a be the time to complete job a. For purposes of this article we assume that job times are known with certainty.

It is convenient (though not necessary) to introduce two fictitious jobs, Start and Finish, both of which have zero job times. The job Start is defined to be the unique predecessor of all jobs in J that do not have predecessors in J, and the job Finish is defined to be the unique successor of all jobs in J that do not have successors in J. These two jobs have the property of closing up the ends of the project graph. Start and Finish are added to the set J.

Suppose now that the project proceeds and every job in the project is started as soon as all of its immediate predecessors are finished. It is then possible to compute an early start ES for each job in the project, and also an early finish EF time for each job.

We describe an algorithm that will calculate $ES(a)$ and $EF(a)$ for each job a in J.

Algorithm C_1

1. Define ES and EF of Start both to be zero.[1]
2. Let a be any job such that the early finish EF times of all jobs in P_a have already been computed. Then compute

$$ES(a) = \underset{x \text{ in } P_a}{\text{Max}} EF(x)$$

and also

$$EF(a) = ES(a) + t_a.$$

3. Eventually, the early finish time F of Finish will be computed.

Theorem 4. If Assumption A_2 holds, then

a. Algorithm C_1 will assign unique early start and early finish times to all jobs in J.

b. For any job a in J the early finish time $EF(a)$ is the sum of the job times on the longest path from Start to and including a.

c. The earliest time that all jobs in the project can be finished is F.

Proof. Since Assumption A_2 holds, the jobs can be put in a technologically ordered list. We prove the first two parts of the theorem by induction on the kth element, a_k, of the list.

Proof of part a. The first job in the list is Start, which is always assigned early start and early finish times of 0. Suppose now that part a is true for $a_1, \ldots, a_{k-1}$. We want to show it true for a_k. Since the predecessors of a_k are already on the list and have unique early finish times, their maximum, which is the early start time assigned by the algorithm to a_k, is also unique. But then so is the early finish time of a_k, since it is obtained by adding the job time of a_k to the early start time of a_k.

Proof of part b. The statement is obviously true for the first job, Start. Suppose it is true for the first $k - 1$ jobs. Then, since the early start time of a_k is the maximum of the early finish times of its predecessors, there is a path whose length is equal to the early start time of a_k from Start up to a_k. Then, since it takes time t_{a_k} to complete a_k, it follows that there is a path of length $EF(a_k)$ from Start to the end of a_k, and this is the longest such path.

Proof of part c. Since Finish is a job on the list, statement b is true for Finish. Hence, Finish can be completed at time F. Since Finish has no successors, the entire project is also complete.

---

[1] Alternatively, any arbitrary start time (say S) can be used rather than 0 for the ES and EF of Start.

Projects usually have due dates or target dates T, by which they must be completed. The only achievable target dates satisfy $T \geq F$, since F is the earliest time at which all the jobs in the project can be completed. If we know a target date T, then, working backwards from the end of the project, we can compute the latest time at which each job in the project can be completed in order not to delay the entire project beyond the time T. We call this the latest finish LF time of the job. From this we can also deduce a late start LS time for each job. We next describe an algorithm to compute these times.

Algorithm C_2

1. Define the LF and LS of Finish both to be T.
2. Let a be any job such that the LS times of all jobs in S_a have already been computed. Then compute

$$LF(a) = \operatorname*{Min}_{x \text{ in } S_a} LS(x)$$

and also

$$LS(a) = LF(a) - t_a.$$

3. Eventually, the late start time L of Start will be computed. The quantity L will be shown to be the slack time of the project. (If S is not 0, then slack time of the project is $L - S$.)

Theorem 5. If Assumption A_2 holds, then Algorithm C_2 will assign unique late start and late finish times to all jobs in J.

Proof. The details are omitted, but the proof is similar to that for Theorem 4 (a).

Definition. For any job a, the quantity

$$SL(a) = LS(a) - ES(a) = LF(a) - EF(a)$$

is defined to be the *slack time* (or simply slack) of job a.

Intuitively, the slack of a job a is the maximum amount that the completion of a can be delayed without necessarily delaying the completion of the entire project.

Definition. By a *critical job* we shall mean a job having minimum slack time.

Obviously, every project has at least one critical job.

Lemma 2. If Assumption A_2 holds, then
a. Every critical job in J except Start and Finish has at least one

critical job as a predecessor and at least one critical job as a successor.

b. Finish and Start are critical jobs.

c. $L = T - F$ is the minimum slack time, i.e., the slack time of all critical jobs.

Proof a. Suppose, on the contrary, that there is a critical job a (other than Start) such that none of its predecessors x is critical. Then, since a is a successor of x, it is true that

$$LS(a) \geq LF(x). \tag{1}$$

Also, since a is critical while x is not, we have

$$LS(a) - ES(a) < LF(x) - EF(x). \tag{2}$$

Combining Equations (1) and (2), we have

$$LF(x) - ES(a) < LF(x) - EF(x)$$

which implies

$$ES(a) > EF(x) \tag{3}$$

for all predecessors x of a. However, since $ES(a)$ is defined to be the maximum of all the early finish times of its predecessors, we see that Equation (3) contradicts this definition. Hence, at least one predecessor of a is critical. The proof that at least one successor of a is critical follows similarly.

b. Let a be any critical job in J. It has at least one critical successor; pick one, say it is a_1. Now pick a critical successor of a_1, say it is a_2, etc. Eventually, Finish must be chosen as the critical successor of some job so that Finish is critical. Similarly, Start is critical.

c. Since Finish and Start are both critical, it follows that $L = T - F$ is the minimum slack time of all jobs in the project.

Theorem 6. If Assumption A_2 holds, then

a. There is at least one path, called a *critical path*, from Start to Finish such that every job on the path is critical.

b. Every critical job lies on such a path.

c. The sum of the job times on every critical path is F, which is at least as large as the sum of the job times on every other path from Start to Finish.

Proof. Let a be any critical job in J. Then, as in the proof of Theorem 5b, pick a critical successor a_1 and a critical predecessor b_1 of a; then pick a critical successor a_2 of a_1 and a critical predecessor b_2 of b_1; etc. Continue until Finish and Start are chosen. The result is a critical path from Start through a to Finish. This proves the first two statements. Statement c is simply a restatement of Theorem 4b for the job Finish.

4. PREDECESSOR AND SUCCESSOR MATRICES

In this section we shall develop some algebraic methods for studying the predecessor and precedes relations. We shall give algebraic characterizations of Assumptions 1 and 2 of Section 2.

In Section 2 we defined a path in the project graph G to be a set of k jobs satisfying $a_1 \ll a_2 \ll \ldots \ll a_k$. Two paths are different if they differ in the identity or order of jobs on the path. We shall say that the *length* of such a path is $k-1$.

Suppose now that our project consists of an ordered set $J = [a_1, a_2, \ldots, a_n]$ of n jobs, including Start, a_1, and Finish, a_n. We define a predecessor and a successor matrix for the project.

Definition. The *predecessor matrix* P for the project is the $n \times n$ matrix with components P_{ij} defined as follows:

$$p_{ij} = \begin{cases} 1, & \text{if } a_i \ll a_j \\ 0, & \text{otherwise.} \end{cases}$$

The successor matrix S for the project is defined to be the transpose of the matrix P.

Since $s_{ij} = p_{ji}$, it follows that

$$s_{ij} = \begin{cases} 1, & \text{if } a_j \ll a_i \\ 0, & \text{otherwise.} \end{cases}$$

By definition S and P are matrices having only 0 and 1 as entries. We shall concentrate our study on the matrix P, and at the end of the section make some remarks about the matrix S.

Since P is a square matrix, we can take powers of it, P^n. We denote the i,jth entry of P^n by $p_{ij}^{(n)}$.

Theorem 7. If $p_{ij}^{(k)} = m > 0$, then there exist m distinct paths of length k from a_i to a_j.

Proof. We prove the theorem by induction on k. The statement is true for $k = 0$ and 1. Suppose that it is true for the entries of P^{k-1}; we want to show that it is true for the entries of P^k. Since $P^k = P^{k-1} \cdot P$, we see that

$$p_{ij}^{(k)} = p_{i1}^{(k-1)} p_{1j} + p_{i2}^{(k-1)} p_{2j} + \cdots + p_{in}^{(k-1)} p_{nj}. \tag{4}$$

Since all of the terms in this sum are nonnegative, it follows that $p_{ij}^{(k)}$ is positive only if one or more of the terms $p_{ih}^{(k-1)} p^{hj}$ is positive. And the latter can happen only if $p_{ih}^{(k-1)} > 0$ and $p_{hj} > 0$. By the induction hypothesis, $p_{ih}^{(k-1)}$ gives the number of distinct paths of length $k-1$ from a_i to a_h, and since $p_{hj} = 1$, we can construct the same number of distinct paths of length k from a_i to a_j. Moreover, if

$p_{ih}^{(k-1)} > 0$ and $p_{im}^{(k-1)} > 0$, where $h \neq m$, the paths so constructed are distinct. Hence, the sum in Equation (4) counts exactly the number of distinct paths from a_i to a_j.

Corollary. If there is a longest path, i.e., a path containing the most nodes in the project graph G, and it is of length N, then $P^N \neq 0$ and $P^{N+1} = 0$.

Theorem 7 holds regardless of whether or not Assumptions 1 and 2 hold. In the remaining theorems we investigate the consequences of these assumptions.

Theorem 8. Assumption 1 can be characterized as follows:

a. The precedes relation $\ll$ is asymmetric if and only if $p_{ij} = 1$ implies $p_{ji} = 0$, or, equivalently, the maximum entry in $P + S$ is 1.

b. The precedes relation $\ll$ is k-intransitive for every k if and only if $p_{ij} = 1$ implies $p_{ij}^{(k)} = 0$ for all $k > 2$.

Proof a. If $\ll$ is asymmetric, then $a_i \ll a_j$ implies that it is false that $a_j \ll a_i$; hence $p_{ij} = 1$ and $p_{ji} = 0$, and conversely.

b. Since $p_{ij} = 1$ implies that there is a path of length 1 from a_i to a_j and $p_{ij}^{(k)} > 0$ implies that there is at least one path of length k from a_i to a_j, it follows that k-intransitivity implies that not both kinds of paths are permissible. The converse is also true.

The results of this theorem show that by examining P and its powers we can find out whether or not there are redundant predecessors in the project list.

Theorem 9. Assumption 2 holds if and only if $P^{N+1} = 0$ for some N.

Proof If Assumption 2 holds, then there are no cycles in the project graph. Hence, all paths must have finite length (since the number of jobs is finite) and, therefore, by the corollary to Theorem 7, $P^{N+1} = 0$ for some integer N. Conversely, if $P^{N+1} = 0$ for some N, there is no path longer than N; hence, there cannot be any cycles, and Assumption 2 holds.

Definition. If P is a square matrix, then the *Neumann inverse* of the matrix $I - P$ is defined to be

$$(I - P)^{-1} = I + P + P^2 + \cdots + P^n + \cdots \qquad (5)$$

when the series on the right converges.

Lemma 3. Let P be a matrix with integer entries; then the Neumann inverse of $I - P$ exists if and only if $P^{N+1} = 0$ for some $N > 0$.

Proof The infinite series in Equation (5) can converge only if $P^n \to 0$ with increasing n. However, since P and P^n have integer entries, this can happen only if $P^{N+1} = 0$ for some N, which proves the necessity of the condition.

To prove sufficiency, consider the following identity:

$$(I - P)(I + P + P^2 + \cdots + P^n) = I - P^{n+1} \qquad (6)$$

which can be established by induction. From Equation (6) it is clear that if $P^{N+1} = 0$, then $(I-P)^{-1}$ exists and

$$(I - P)^{-1} = I + P + P^2 + \cdots + P^N.$$

This completes the proof of the theorem.

Theorem 10. Assumption 2 holds if and only if the Neumann inverse Q exists and equals

$$Q = (I - P)^{-1} = I + P + P^2 + \cdots + P^N. \qquad (7)$$

That is, if and only if the project graph G has a longest path.

Proof. These statements are consequences of Theorems 7 and 9, and Lemma 3.

The entries of the matrix $Q = I + P + P^2 + \ldots + P^N$ have interesting interpretations. Clearly, q_{ij} is equal to the total number of paths, of all lengths, from a_i to a_j. This enables us to give still another characterization of Assumption 1.

Theorem 11. Assumption 1 holds if and only if $p_{ij} = 1$ implies $q_{ij} = 1$.

Proof. If both $p_{ij} = 1$ and $q_{ij} = 1$, then there is exactly one path, which is necessarily of length 1, from a_i to a_j. It follows that $\ll$ is both irreflexive and k-intransitive. The proof of the converse is similar.

There is a close connection between the results of this section and those of B. Giffler in his schedule algebra paper [2]. For if we put p_{ij} equal to the time of a_i when $a_i \ll a_j$, and redefine the matrix operations as Giffler does, then the entries of Q will be the maximum path from a_i to a_j. This technique can be used to make the critical-path calculations of Section 3.

5. REDUNDANT PREDECESSOR AND CYCLE CHECKS

The results of the preceding section can be immediately translated into algebraic checks for redundant predecessors and cycles in the project graph G. We state these as an algorithm. Assume that we are given a job list $J = \{a, b, \ldots\}$ and for each job a set of immediate predecessors P_a. We define an algorithm R_1 for cycle and redundant predecessor checking:

Algorithm R_1.

1. Set up the precedence matrix P.

2. Calculate $Q = (I - P)^{-1}$ if it exists. If it does not exist, then G has a cycle, and the original job data should be checked. (The Neumann inverse $(I - P)^{-1}$ may be computed by one of the standard matrix inversion routines, or else by various iterative schemes that quickly compute the partial sums $I + P + \ldots + P^k$.)

3. If for some i and j both $p_{ij} = 1$ and $q_{ij} > 1$, then job a_j has redundant predecessors, and the original job data should be checked. Computation of the powers P^k are useful in making this check.

Still another set of algorithms for checking for cycles and redundant predecessors can be derived from the results of Section 2. These algorithms are probably less wasteful of computer memory space than the matrix algorithms just described. We list the steps of the algorithm (R_2) below.

Algorithm R_2.

1. List the jobs in any order.

2. Pick the set P_0 of jobs with no predecessors (except Start).

3. For i going from 1 to N pick the set P_i of jobs all of whose predecessors are in P_{i-1}. Here N is the largest integer such that P_N is not empty.

4. If there are jobs in J that are not included in any of the sets $P_0, P_1, \ldots P_N$, then the original job data contains a cycle and should be checked. Otherwise, go to 5.

5. For k going from 2 to N, consider each job a in P_k. If a has a predecessor b in P_{k-1}, include in the predecessors of a all the predecessors of b. (At the conclusion of this step, each job will have a complete list of its predecessors, and hence there will be maximum redundancy in the predecessor lists. This redundancy is removed in step 6.)

6. For h going from 1 to N, consider a job a in P_h. If a is a predecessor of some job b in P_k (where $k > h$), then remove from P_b any prerequisites of a; i.e., replace P_b by $P_b - P_a$.

7. At the end of step 6, all jobs will have only immediate predecessors listed.

The proofs that Algorithm R_2 will check for cycles and will remove redundant predecessors are based on the material of Section 2.

REFFERENCES

1. Charnes, A., and W. W. Cooper, "A Network Interpretation and a Directed Sub-dual Algorithm for Critical-Path Scheduling," *Journal of Industrial Engineering* (1962), pp. 213-219.

2. Giffler, B., "Schedule Algebras and Their Use in Formulating General Systems Simulations," Chapter 4 of this volume.

3. Kelley, J. E., Jr., "Critical-Path Planning and Scheduling: Mathematical Basis," *Operations Research* **9** (1961), 296-320.

4. ———— and M. R. Walker, "Critical-Path Planning and Scheduling: an Introduction," *Proc. Eastern Joint Computer Conference* (1959), 160-173.

5. Levy, F. K., G. L. Thompson, and J. D. Wiest, "Introduction to the Critical-Path Method," Chapter 20 of this volume.

6. Levy, F. K., G. L. Thompson, and J. D. Wiest, "Multi-Ship, Multi-Shop Workload Smoothing Program," *Naval Research Logistics Quarterly* **8** (1962), pp. 37-44.

Bibliography

Selected References on Industrial Scheduling

Ackhoff, R. L., E. L. Arnoff, and C. W. Churchman, *Progress in Operations Research*, New York: John Wiley & Sons, Inc., 1961.

Aczel, M. A., "The Effect of Introducing Priorities," *Operations Research* 8 (1960), 730–733.

Akers, S. B. and J. Friedman, "A Non-Numerical Approach to Production Scheduling Problems," *Operations Research* 3 (1955), 429–442.

Allen, Morton, "The Efficient Utilization of Labor under Conditions of Fluctuating Demand," Chapter 16 of this volume.

Bachovzeff, C. and J. Corrigan, "Average Cost Method of Scheduling," Chapter 11 of this volume.

Baker, C. T. and B. P. Dzielinski, "Simulation of a Simplified Job Shop," *Management Science* 6 (1960), 311–323.

Barry, J. Y., "A Priority Queuing Problem," *Operations Research* 4 (1956), 385.

Bellman, R., *Dynamic Programming*, Princeton, N. J.: Princeton University Press, 1957.

————, "Some Mathematical Aspects of Scheduling Theory," *Journal of the Society of Industrial and Applied Mathematics* 4, 3 (Sept. 1956), 168–205.

———— and O. Gross, "Some Combinatorial Problems Arising in the Theory of Multi Stage Processes," *Journal of the Society of Industrial and Applied Mathematics* 2, 3 (Sept. 1954).

Bishop, G. T., "On the Problem of Production Scheduling," *Operations Research* 5, 1 (Feb. 1957).

Blake, K. R. and W. S. Stopakis, *Some Theoretical Results on the Job Shop Scheduling Problem*, Report M-1533-1, United Aircraft Corp. Research Dept., East Hartford, Conn. (July 1, 1959).

Bowman, E. H., "The Schedule-Sequencing Problem," *Operations Research* 7 (1959), 621–624.

————, "Production Scheduling by the Transportation Method of Linear Programming," *Operations Research* 4, 1 (Feb. 1956).

————, "A New Theory About Managerial Decision-Making," Chapter 7 of this volume.

Brown, R. G., *Statistical Forecasting for Inventory Control*, New York: McGraw-Hill Book Co., Inc., 1959.

Canning, R. G., "Electronic Scheduling Machine Requirements," Management Sciences Research Project, Research Report No. 29, University of California, Los Angeles (1955).

————, "Production Control through Electronic Data Processing," Management Sciences Research Project, Research Report No. 30, University of California, Los Angeles (1957).

Charnes, A. and W. W. Cooper, "A Network Interpretation and a Directed Sub-Dual Algorithm for Critical-Path Scheduling," *Journal of Industrial Engineering* (1962), 213-219.

————, *Management Models and Industrial Application of Linear Programming*, New York: John Wiley & Sons, Inc., 1961, 2 volumes.

Churchman, C. W., R. L. Ackoff, and E. L. Arnoff, *Introduction to Operations Research*, New York: John Wiley & Sons, 1957.

Clark, C. E., "The PERT Model for the Distribution of an Activity Time," *Operations Research* **10** (1962), 405-406.

Cobham, A., "Priority Assignment in Waiting Line Problems," *Operations Research*, **2** (1954), 70-76.

Conway, R. W., "An Experimental Investigation of Priority Dispatching," *Journal of Industrial Engineers* **11** (1960), 221-230.

————, "Some Problems of Digital Systems Simulation," *Management Science* **6** (1959), 92-110.

Conway, R. W., B. M. Johnson, and W. L. Maxwell, "A Queue Network Simulator for the Burroughs 220," *Communications of Associations for Computing Machinery* **2**, 12 (1959), 20-23.

Conway, R. W. and W. L. Maxwell, "Network Dispatching by the Shortest-operation Discipline," *Operations Research* **10** (1962), 57-73. Reprinted as Chapter 17 of this volume.

The Cornell Assembly Program (CAP) for the Burroughs 220, Department of Industrial and Engineering Administration, Cornell University, Ithaca, New York.

Dantzig, G. B., "A Machine Shop Scheduling Model," *Management Science* **6**, 2 (Jan. 1960), 191-196.

————, "On the Shortest Route through a Network," *Management Science* **6**, 2 (Jan. 1960), 187-190.

Doyle, V., *General Electric Simulation Test (Gest)*, General Electric Technical Information Series No. D 591S15, Schenectady, New York (Feb. 1959).

Dzielinski, B. P., C. T. Baker, and A. S. Manne, "Simulation Tests of Lot-Size Programming," Chapter 9 of this volume.

Fischer, H. and G. L. Thompson, "Probabilistic Learning Combinations of Local Job-Shop Scheduling Rules," Chapter 15 of this volume.

Forrester, J., *Industrial Dynamics*, New York: John Wiley & Sons, Inc., 1961.

Giffler, B., *Mathematical Solution of Production Planning and Scheduling Problems*, IBM ASDD Technical Report (Oct. 1960).

————, *Production Control Formalizations Suitable for Electronic Data Processing*, IBM Research Report RC-20 (May, 1957).

Giffler B., "Schedule Algebras and Their Use in Formulating General Systems Simulation," Chapter 4 of this volume.

———, *SIMPRO I: An IBM 704-7090 Simulation Program for Planning Scheduling and Monitoring Production Systems*, IBM ASDD Technical Report (Dec. 1961).

———, *Mathematical Solution of Explosion and Scheduling Problems*, IBM Research Report RC-118 (June 18, 1959), IBM Research Center, Business Systems Research, Yorktown Heights, N. Y.

Giffler, B. and G. L. Thompson, "Algorithms for Solving Production Scheduling Problems," *Operations Research* 8, 4 (Oct.-Dec., 1960), 487-503.

Giffler, B., G. L. Thompson, and V. Van Ness, "Numerical Experience with the Linear and Monte Carlo Algorithms for Solving Production Scheduling Problems," Chapter 3 of this volume.

Gomory, R. E., "An Algorithm for Integer Solutions to Linear Programs," Princeton-IBM Mathematics Research Project, Technical Report No. 1 (Nov. 17, 1958).

———, "All-Integer Integer Programming Algorithm," Chapter 13 of this volume.

———, "Mixed Integer Programming Algorithm," unpublished RAND memorandum.

———, "Outline of an Algorithm for Integer Solutions to Linear Programs," *Bulletin of the American Mathematics Society* 64 (1958), 275-278.

Healy, T. L., "Activity Subdivision and PERT Probability Statements" (with discussion), *Operations Research* 9 (1961), 341-350.

Held, M. and Richard M. Karp, "A Dynamic Programming Approach to Sequencing Problems," *Journal of the Society for Industrial and Applied Mathematics* 10 (1962), 196-210.

Heller, J. and G. Logemann, "An Algorithm for the Construction and Evaluation of Possible Schedules," *Management Science* 8 (1962), 168-183.

———, "Some Numerical Experiments for an $M \times J$ Flow Shop and Its Decision-Theoretical Aspects," *Operations Research* 8 (1960), 178-184.

———, *Combinatorial, Probabilistic and Statistical Aspects of an $M \times J$ Scheduling Problem*, Report NYO-2540, AEC Computing and Applied Mathematics Center, Institute of Mathematical Science, New York University, N. Y. (Feb. 1, 1959).

✳ Holt, C. C., "Priority Rules for Minimizing the Cost of Queues in Machine Scheduling," Chapter 6 of this volume.

✳ Holt, C. C., F. Modigliani, J. F. Muth, and H. A. Simon, *Planning Production, Inventries and Work Force*, Englewood Cliffs, N. J.: Prentice-Hall, Inc., 1960.

Howard, R. A., *Dynamic Programming and Markov Processes*, Cambridge, Mass.: Press of Massachusetts Institute of Technology, 1960.

Hu, T. C., "Parallel Sequencing and Assembly Line Problems," *Operations Research* **9** (1961), 841–848.

Hunt, G. C., "Sequential Arrays of Waiting Lines," *Operations Research* **4**, 6 (Dec. 1956).

Ishler, K. H., R. M. Sharp, and W. W. Staley, "Optimization of a Total Production and Distribution System," Chapter 10 of this volume.

Jackson, J. R., "An Extension of Johnson's Results on Job Lot Scheduling," *Naval Research Logistics Quarterly* **3** (1956), 201–203.

———, "Networks of Waiting Lines," *Operations Research* **5** (1957), 518–521.

———, "Simulation of Queues with Dynamic Priorities," Management Sciences Research Project, Research Report No. 71, University of California, Los Angeles, Mar. 20, 1961.

———, "Some Expected Transition Times in Simple Queues," *Operations Research* **9**, 2 (Mar.–Apr., 1961) 277–279.

———, "Some Problems in Queueing with Dynamic Priorities," *Naval Research Logistics Quarterly* **7** (1960), 235–250.

———, "Queues with Dynamic Priority Discipline," *Management Science* **8** (1961), 18–34. Reprinted as Chapter 19 of this volume.

———, *Some Problems in Queueing with Dynamic Priorities*, Management Sciences Research Project, Research Report No. 62, University of California, Los Angeles (Nov. 1959).

———, "Machine Shop Simulation Using SWAC: A Progress Report," Management Sciences Research Project, Discussion Paper No. 67, University of California, Los Angeles (Apr. 1958).

———, "Notes on Some Scheduling Problems," Management Sciences Research Project, Research Report No. 35, University of California, Los Angeles (Oct. 1954).

———, "Scheduling a Production Line to Minimize Maximum Tardiness," Management Sciences Research Project, Research Report No. 43, University of California, Los Angeles (1955).

———, "Simulation Research on Job Shop Production," *Naval Research Logistics Quarterly* **4**, 4 (Dec. 1957).

Jackson, J. R., and Y. Kuratani, "Production Scheduling Research: A Monte Carlo Approach," Management Sciences Research Project, Research Paper No. 61, University of California, Los Angeles (May 1957).

The Job Simulator: An IBM 704 Program, IBM Mathematics and Applications Department, International Business Machines Corporation, New York, N. Y. (1960).

Johnson, S. M., "Discussion," *Management Science* **5** (1959), 299-303.

——, "Optimal Two- and Three -Stage Production Schedules with Set-up Times Included," *Naval Research Logistics Quarterly* **1** (1954), 61-68. Reprinted as Chapter 2 of this volume.

Karush, W. and L. A. Moody, "Determination of Feasible Shipping Schedules for a Job Shop," *Operations Research* **6**, 1 (Feb. 1958).

Karush, W. and A. Vazsonyi, "Mathematical Programming and Service Scheduling," *Management Science* **3**, 2 (Jan. 1957).

Kelley, J. E., Jr., "Critical-Path Planning and Scheduling: Mathematical Basis," *Operations Research* **9** (1961), 296-320.

——, "The Critical-Path Method: Resources Planning and Scheduling," Chapter 21 of this volume.

Kelley, J. E., Jr. and M. R. Walker, "Critical-Path Planning and Scheduling," *Proceedings of the Eastern Joint Computer Conference*, Boston (Dec. 1-3, 1959), 160-173.

Kesten, H. and J. Th. Runnenburg, "Priority in Waiting Line Problems" *Koninkl Nederl Akademie Van Wetenschappen*, Proceedings, Series A, **60**, 3 (1957).

Koenigsberg, E., "Production Lines and Internal Storage: A Review," *Management Science* **5**, 4 (July 1959).

Kuratani, Yoshiro and R. T. Nelson, "A Pre-Computational Report on Job-Shop Simulation Research," Management Sciences Research Project, University of California, Los Angeles (Oct. 1959).

Kuratani, Y. and J. L. McKenney, "A Preliminary Report on Job Shop Simulations Research," Management Sciences Research Project, Research Report No. 65, University of California, Los Angeles (Mar. 1958).

Levitan, R. E., "A Note on Professor Manne's 'Dominance' Theorem," *Management Science* **5**, 3 (Apr. 1959), 332-334.

Levy, F. K., G. L. Thompson, and J. D. Weist, "Mathematical Basis for the Critical-Path Method," Chapter 22 of this volume.

——, "Introduction to the Critical-Path Method," Chapter 20 of this volume.

——, "Multi-Ship, Multi-Shop Workload Smoothing Program," *Naval Research Logistics Quarterly* **8** (1962), 37-44.

Little, J. D. C., "A Proof for the Queueing Formula $L = \lambda W$," *Operations Research* **9** (1961), 383-387.

Magee, J. F., *Production Planning and Inventory Control*, New York: McGraw-Hill Book Co., Inc., 1957.

Malcolm, D. G., "Bibliography on the Use of Simulation in Management Analysis," *Operations Research* **8**, 2 (Mar.-Apr. 1960).

Malcolm, D. G., *Report of System Simulation Symposium*, Baltimore, Md.: Waverly Press, 1957.

Malcolm, D. G., J. H. Roseboom, C. E. Clark, and W. Fazar, "Application of a Technique for Research and Development Program Evaluation," *Operations Research* **7** (1959), 646-669.

Manne, A. S., "On the Job-Shop Scheduling Problem," *Operations Research* **8**, 2 (Mar.-Apr., 1960), 219-223. Reprinted as Chapter 12 of this volume.

————, "Programming of Economic Lot Sizes," *Management Science* **4**, 2 (Jan. 1958), 115-135.

Maxwell, W. L., *Core II A Queue Network Simulator for the Burroughs 220*, Cornell Production Control Research Committee, Discussion Paper No. 17, Cornell University, Ithaca, New York (Nov. 1960).

McNaughton, R., "Scheduling with Deadlines and Loss Functions," *Management Science* **5** (1959), 1-12.

Mitten, L. G., "Sequencing *n* Jobs on Two Machines with Arbitrary Time Lags," *Management Science* **5** (1959), 293-298.

————, "A Scheduling Problem," *Journal of Industrial Engineering* **10** (1959), 131-134.

Morse, P. M., *Queues, Inventories, and Maintenance*, New York: John Wiley & Sons, Inc., 1958.

Muth, J. F., "The Effect of Uncertainty in Job Times on Optimal Schedules," Chapter 18 of this volume.

Nelson, R. T., "An Extension of Queueing Theory to a Series of Service Centers," Management Sciences Research Project, Research Report No. 68, University of California, Los Angeles. (Apr. 1958)

————, "An Empirical Study of Arrival, Service Time, and Waiting Time Distributions of a Job Shop Production Process," Management Sciences Research Project, Research Report No. 60, University of California, Los Angeles (1959).

————, "Priority Function Models for Job Shop Scheduling," Management Sciences Research Project, Research Report No. 51, University of California, Los Angeles (Feb. 1955).

Notes on Operations Research, Cambridge, Mass.: Technology Press of Massachusetts Institute of Technology, 1959.

Phipps, T. E., Jr., "Machine Repair as a Waiting-Line Problem," *Operations Research* **4** (1956), 76-85.

Pounds, W. F., "The Scheduling Environment," Chapter 1 of this volume.

The Production Simulator, Westinghouse Corporation, East Pittsburgh Division, Pittsburgh, Pa. (July 1960).

Reinfeld, N. V. and W. R. Vogel, *Mathematical Programming*, Englewood Cliffs, N. J.: Prentice-Hall, Inc., 1958.

Reinitz, R. C., *An Integrated Job Shop Scheduling Problem* (Ph. D. thesis, Case Institute of Technology, Cleveland, Ohio, 1961).

―――, *"On the Job-Shop Scheduling Problem,"* Chapter 5 of this volume.

Riley, V., "Bibliography of Queueing Theory," Appendix A, pp. 541-556, of McCloskey and Coppinger, *Operations Research for Management*, Vol. **2**, Baltimore, Md: John Hopkins Press, 1956.

Rowe, A. J., "Applicability of Standard Data to Production Scheduling," *Journal of Industrial Engineering* **6**, 6 (Nov. 1955).

―――, *Sequential Decision Rules in Production Scheduling*, General Electric Company (Oct. 1958).

―――, *Toward a Theory of Scheduling*, Report 3P-61, Systems Development Corp., Santa Monica, Cal. (Apr. 1, 1959).

Rowe, A. J. and J. R. Jackson, *Research Problems in Production Routing and Scheduling*, Research Report No. 46, University of California, Los Angeles (Oct. 1956).

Salveson, M. E., "On a Quantative Method in Production Planning and Scheduling," *Econometrica* **20**, 9 (Oct. 1952), 571-574.

―――, "A Problem in Optimal Machine Loading," *Management Science* **2**, 3 (Apr. 1956).

Sandeman, J., "Empirical Design of Priority Waiting Times for Jobbing Shop Control," *Operations Research* **9** (1961), 446-455.

Saaty, T. L., *Elements of Queueing Theory with Applications*, New York: McGraw-Hill Book Co., Inc., 1961.

Sasieni, M. W., A. Yaspan, and L. Friedman, *Operations Research: Methods and Problems*, New York: John Wiley & Sons, Inc., 1959.

Schild, A., "On Inventory, Production and Employment Scheduling," *Management Science* (Jan. 1959).

SCROL, *A Comprehensive Operating System for Linear Programming on the IBM 704*, C.E.I.R., Inc., 1200 Jefferson Davis Highway, Arlington2, Va.

Shubik, M., "Bibliography on Simulation, Gaming, Artificial Intelligence and Allied Topics," *Journal of American Statistical Association* **55**, 292 (Dec. 1960).

Sisson, R. L., "Machine Shop Simulation Using SWAC: Part II of a Proposal," Management Sciences Research Project, Research Paper No. 58 (May, 1956).

―――, "Method of Sequencing in Job-Shops—A Review," *Journal of the Operations Research Society of America* **7**, 1 (1959).

―――, "Sequencing Theory," Chapter 7 in *Progress in Operations Research*, R. L. Ackoff, ed., New York: John Wiley & Sons, Inc., 1961.

Smith, W. E., "Various Optimizers for Single-Stage Production," *Naval Research Logistics Quarterly* **3** (1956), 59-66.

Smith, W. E., "Applications of a Posteriori Probability," Management Science Research Project, Research Report No. 56. University of California, Los Angeles (Sept. 1958).

Solomon, M. J., "Use of Economic Lot Range in Scheduling Production," *Management Science* **5**, 4 (July 1959).

Story, A. E. and H. M. Wagner, "Computational Experience with Integer Programming for Job-Shop Scheduling," Chapter 14 of this volume.

Thompson, G. L., "Recent Developments in the Job Shop Scheduling Problem," *Naval Research Logistics Quarterly* **7** (1960), 585-589.

Tonge, F. M., "Summary of a Heuristic Line Balancing Problem," *Management Science* **7**, 1 (Oct. 1960), 21-39.

Vazsonyi, A., "Operations Research in Production Control: A Progress Report," *Operations Research* **4**, 1 (Jan. 1956).

———, *Scientific Programming in Business and Industry*, New York: John Wiley & Sons, Inc., 1958.

Voris, W., *Management of Production*, New York: The Ronald Press Co., 1960.

Wagner, H. M., "An Integer Linear-Programming Model for Machine Scheduling," *Naval Research Logistics Quarterly* **6**, 2 (June 1959).

Whitin, T., *The Theory of Inventory Control*, Princeton, N. J.: Princeton University Press, 1953.

Winters, P. R., "Inventory Control in a Multiple Warehouse System," Graduate School of Industrial Administration, Carnegie Institute of Technology (1958).

———, "Constrained Inventory Rules for Production Smoothing," *Management Science* **9** (1961), 470-481. Reprinted as Chapter 8 of this volume.